1/68

24

75 P.

3/5.

THE LIMITS OF MAN

HUGH NICOL

The Limits of Man

An enquiry into the scientific bases
of human population

CONSTABLE LONDON

Published by
Constable and Company Ltd
10-12 Orange Street
London WC2

© Hugh Nicol 1967

First published 1967

Printed in England by
Willmer Brothers Limited, Birkenhead

Contents

LEGEND TO FRONTISPIECE

South and East fronts of Herstmonceux Castle, built about 1440 by Sir Roger Fienes not far from Brighton on the south coast of England. This brick-built residence is one memorial to the first known fuel crisis in England. It is now occupied by the Royal Greenwich Observatory, and the photograph is reproduced with the permission of the Astronomer Royal.

See pages 156 and 176

...particular instances are studied, not for their own sake, or for the sake of profit, but for their part in promoting a general systematization of experience.

We may take it, then, that university knowledge has to be judged from two points of view: it has to be judged by its conformity with traditional university studies and by its internal consistency, that is, by its academic quality, on the one hand, and by its relevance to the current situation in society at large on the other hand.

We [academics] are supported on a scale which is only justifiable if the academic attitude has a valuable contribution to make to society. I believe that it has, and that the academic attitude, with its insistence on theory, and its critical and intellectual approach, is distinctive and important.

T. L. Cottrell, Inaugural Lecture on assuming the Chair of Chemistry in the University of Edinburgh; 20th November, 1959 (*Journal of the Royal Institute of Chemistry*, 1960, Vol. 84, 57-62)

It would appear that experimentation and even technological progress are insufficient by themselves to provide the basis for the establishment of what we should call a 'modern science'. Their results need to be related to an adequate intellectual framework which on the one hand embraces the observed data and on the other hand helps to decide at any moment the direction of the next enquiry.

Herbert Butterfield, 'The Origins of Modern Science: 1300-1800': London, Bell. 1957

The trouble with people is not that they don't know but that they know so much that ain't so.

Josh Billings (Henry Wheeler Shaw), 'Encyclopedia of Wit and Wisdom': 1874

Author's note: What the book is about

This book is about people; but, people can be kept alive only by means of food. Hence, the purpose of the book is to make known the severe restrictions, inherent in established scientific laws, that limit the supply of food henceforth. The actual size of the maximum possible population is not discussed; it depends on human choice, that being outwith the norms of scientific considerations, but the alternatives are made plain.

So far from there being grounds for the prevailing euphoria about indefinite progress in food-supply or with any other application of technology, it is shown that population of the world, as a whole and locally, must within foreseeable time undergo a decline, in company with every form of comfort and amenity. All forms of technology—including the provision of food—now depend on the availability of diminishing stocks of fossil fuel, for which there is, and can be, no substitute.

The book is written from first principles of natural science which are well known to physicists and chemists. For such as they, the premiss of the book could be set out in a paragraph, or at most a chapter, and the conclusions could be stated equally starkly if it were needful to state them at all. However, most non-biologists are unaware of the ways in which food is produced. Likewise, many biologists take little heed of the fundamental premises of Nature about work, energy, and substance; while other biologists have interests so specialized that they, too, know hardly anything that is to the point about the recent history of food-production.

A reader who is neither physicist nor biologist will, then, be no worse equipped for judging the future of Man as a population than are the majority of scientists.

The general reader—say, a complete layman in science—need not hang his head about his presumed ignorance of science. What he—and the majority of scientists—needs mostly is a *fresh start*.

There is a definite link that now exists to join not only the obvious matters of food and population: 'we must eat to live': but the subjects of fuel and food and population. That link is so simple and so much akin to everyday experience that it can readily be understood by everyone, once he or she is put in possession of the facts which have come to link food with fuel—and must continue to do so in the near future, for as long as fuel lasts.

General readers, and every sort of scientist, have the common ground of business and social experience that there is never, really, anything to be had for nothing. Whatever is taught or believed to the contrary must be a delusion: food does not come from sunlight, for example.

The book might be described as an introduction to energy of populations. In his book 'The concept of energy' (Spon: London, 1966) Dr D. W. Theobald wrote: 'This book has not been conceived as a textbook on energy, for this would mean nothing less than writing a comprehensive treatise on physics and chemistry.' If the practical difficulty of writing a book solely for thermodynamicists—in whom the sober basic facts and tenets of physics and chemistry can be assumed to be part of their mental equipment—is apparent, how much more difficult is it to be concise in writing about food, for people who already have been exposed for generations to so much misinformation about what ain't so?

This book assumes that readers have not entirely been mis-led by nutritional half-truths such as 'glucose for energy' put about by advertisers who want to sell glucose preparations. It may be more difficult—without at least referring the reader to books on biochemistry, nutrition, and agriculture (there being no 'comprehensive treatise' embracing those and many related subjects so as to deal with the whole theory and practice of food-production and -utilization)—to show in small compass that the Food and Agriculture Organization (for example) is even further from the truth than the exuberant advertisers are when it reckons sugar and cereals as 'food' without qualification.

Food is what sustains life and is capable of doing that throughout the whole of a normal life-span. The origins of the food-energy needed to keep a population alive can be presented in little more than illustrative form in any one book; but to give that outline is what this book attempts to do.

Though a researcher on particular points of the sciences from which this book borrows can cavil at points of detail (the dates may sometimes be a decade or so wide) or at emphasis (to the extent of leaving out something which he expects to see mentioned) the factual parts of this book can be quoted with confidence in chancelleries or canteens because the principal facts are not wrong, and the implications are science-based. The book is thus a source-book; and accurate information about all the principles of Nature whereby the future of Man is governed is something not hitherto assembled, with humane intent, within the covers of one book.

It is on universal truths that the book is built. That is for the necessary and sufficient reason that to give something in fair and appropriate exchange for some other thing—and on those business-like terms only—is the principle on which Nature operates in every major matter and minor detail: whether it be to yield food that people can eat, or for any other purpose that Man may select.

I

The great gamble

Of course the first thing to do was to make a grand survey of the
country she was going to travel through. 'It's something very like
learning geography', thought Alice.
—Lewis Carroll: *Through the Looking-glass*

About betting on racing there is a rule 'In all bets there must
be a possibility to win when the bet is made.'

Though the gamble of using fossil resources for purposes
connected with feeding the increasing population of countries like our own may have been looked upon at first as a
necessity rather than a speculation, and though applying fossil
fuel to win extra food has been written about (without dis-
crimination) as one of the many ingenious ways of 'harnessing
the forces of Nature to meet the needs of Man', there still
seems to be no effective realization how big a gamble it was
and remains. Nor has it been widely seen that there is no possibility of winning more than a temporary advantage during
the playing-out of the game thus casually embarked upon.

Very often, the subject of applying fossil fuel to satisfy
Man's increasing demands is seen as aspects of 'command
of' or 'mastery over' Nature. People who talk like that are
usually thinking about machinery, manufactures, and comfort; provision of food seldom enters in—that being, apparently, taken for granted as coming from an inexhaustible
shower of energy from sunlight. The general idea is, then,
that Man is seizing the reins of command and is deciding the
way the whole outfit shall go: as if he sapiently believed that

he is learning to lay down the rules—without having learnt that the rules which govern the course of human population were incorporated by Nature long, long, ago into the structure of the Universe.

Because the reserves of fossil fuel are fixed in quantity (modern accretions being negligibly small), every use of them for any purpose is a subtraction. Staking that capital of fossil fuel and other reserves against population brings temporary gain—as well as losses incurred through dispersal into the atmosphere, and scattering over the earth's surface, of products from what mining engineers call 'extractive processes': by which it is implied that the resources are limited and exhaustible.

Those acknowledged characteristics of the world's resources of fossil fuel have not been widely and cogently brought into relation with prospects for world population. The matter has not been discussed as seriously as it deserves.

It was recognized a century ago that reserves of coal were not illimitable, and that there might some day be a shortage of coal. Several factors—some real and substantial, others so imaginary as to be mythical—have distracted attention from the problem as it was seen by economists and engineers in 1865. One is the discovery of previously-unknown reserves in coal in various parts of the world, and of petroleum and other fossil fuels that can substitute for coal; therefore actual shortage of fuel is thought to be remote. Another factor is the discovery of 'atomic' energy. Mythical are the ideas that any new sources of energy—however well adapted to drive machines—can either produce food, or can themselves be produced without recourse to fossil fuel on an important scale.

The fallacious ideas about new sources of energy—such as electricity from nuclear energy—have been nursed largely in the belief that Man need concern himself only about power for machines.

Though the fact that sulphur, coal, and natural gas are burnt to produce fertilizers is fairly well known, the implications of that fact in relation to Man himself (as distinct from his machinery and the amenities derived from mechanical use of all sorts of energy) seem not to have been grasped by prophets who occupy themselves with guesses about the sizes and state of future population. The myths about what is expected from nuclear power (for example) seem thus to be expressions of the sort of 'rationalization' common among gamblers: in connexion with food, for instance, that something will turn up, or has already turned up, to change luck.

Science gives no warrant for believing anything of the sort. In sober factual terms, science denies that the gamble can ever be won.

Whether the game is now regarded as something as simple as Snakes and Ladders or something far more complicated, the ending of it is predictable. It is that Man must sometime come back to Square One, with most of his technological advantage lost and his fancied 'command of Nature' seen to be an illusion. The population will be reduced again to a level very similar to that which existed when the stakes began to eat into natural resources, a century or two ago.

These endings are to-day perceptibly certain—for machines and Man alike—because all the rules and elements of the gamble are known. There are two players. One is Nature; the other is Man. The game will take unpredictable courses towards its quiescent but certain termination.

Instead of calling the use of fossil fuel to gather food for feeding an abnormally large population a 'game', other figures of speech will serve equally well; but they are all grim. One might speak about a fixed capital being spent increasingly fast to meet growing liabilities; but that is only to borrow from accountancy to express the idea of making a bet which there is no possibility of winning. The game could be likened to two-handed bridge, in which some of the cards are visible, yet, since it is known that the pack has fifty-two cards of a definite composition, the kinds of those not yet seen can be deduced by an intelligent player who is familiar with the ordinary rules of bridge, during the course of play. That particular analogy is faulty because each player has a chance of winning. In the great game of using fuel to support bigger populations, human intelligence cannot do more than prolong the play. It cannot possibly win the game for Man.

That can now be seen; because the game of using fossil

fuel for Man's purposes has been going on long enough for the complete set of rules to be deduced. A few people have dispassionately appreciated that Nature holds not only all the trumps but disposes of enough high cards to turn the winning tricks.

Man has been a little slow in assimilating the consequences of facts on which his existence as a technically-advanced, well-fed, and numerous population depends. He has, on the contrary, been quick in inventing myths to nourish hope against expectation. Myths about the origins of food are firmly established among that part of the population whose hearts are sounder than their heads—or, at any rate, as much of their heads as is acquainted with what science indicates.

Possibly it is the way of gamblers to ignore not only mathematical demonstrations but to throw away business-like considerations such as the fact that all the outgoings of 'the house' —including the gamblers' own winnings—have to be paid for somehow. Like true gamblers, refusing to acknowledge, or even to enquire into, the facts of their own temporary successes, and cherishing the hope that something will provide a favourable solution to their problems, an increasing proportion of people have begun to look to impractical methods. A favourite among these is to base upon nuclear energy expectations much beyond what it is able to meet. The old belief in the efficacy of sunlight to produce illimitable food is not dead: it has been supplemented by pseudo-scientific appeal to discoveries actual, or hoped for, like nuclear and fusion energy.

A modern folklorist could take this new phenomenon to be fresh evidence that belief in the occult is still strong in a reputedly scientific age—which has adopted belief in what many people suppose to be science as the germ of a myth, while ignoring the spirit and teachings of science. That comforting myth of unlimited electrical power and food to spring from it, and other gains to come from peaceful uses of atomic energy, can hardly be older than 1945, the year of Hiroshima.

2

The nineteenth-century roots of fact about food and population

'What does it live on?' Alice asked with great curiosity.
—Lewis Carroll: *Through the Looking-glass*

By 1866 all the fundamental conditions were known that can now be seen to govern the size of the possible and potential human population of a selected political and economic fraction of the world (such as a country) and therefore of the world as a whole. Since the 'sixties of last century all those principles which regulate the exchanges of energy and substance throughout the animate and inanimate kingdoms on this earth have been formulated with exactitude (the last was worded in 1888). [MI]*

All these propositions have been repeatedly tested in every manifestation of science: throughout the experimental sciences and in all applications of science to industry and technology. Whether they are 'laws' or should be called by some other name is a topic for scientific philosophy and is a side-issue in a discussion of population. The essential and material point is that the scientific rules or laws governing, and limiting, exchanges of matter and energy that were discovered last century have never been controverted by the most alert attention to experience. [M2]

* An entry [M] in the text refers to Marginal Notes at the ends of most chapters. These contain amplifications of topics mentioned in the preceding text, also bibliographical references and other notes.

What these rules amount to in practice is summed up exactly, and with scientific precision, in the words *Nothing for nothing*.

In connexion with the production of food and of people and other organisms that comprise a population there is no need to invoke such transcendental subjects as the exchanges between energy and matter as are invoked by Einsteinian relativity and theories of the formation and decay of stars; nor is there any need to mention them, except to point out that they are regulated exchanges, typified by the famous equation $E = mc^2$. For more mundane affairs the knowledge acquired a hundred years ago has shown itself, by test and by logical expansion, to be a sure and sufficient framework: however remissly that knowledge has been substituted by fancy and groundless belief about the sources of our existence as a human community.

So fanciful is the prevailing corpus of substitutes for knowledge about the origins of food—and consequently of the subsistence of populations—that, to a scientific observer, it looks as if the last hundred years of science had passed without corporate notice among students of the growth of human population. Thus, something has surely gone wrong in leaving the subject of human population out of discussion in a completely scientific and unemotional sense. Two, possibly blended, reasons may account for this enormous neglect of facts that lie at the basis of all science and technology, some of which (like the magnitude of use of fuel in modern farming for making fertilizers and powering mechanical cultivation) are well known to economists as well as to scientists 'pure' and 'applied'.

One reason is that demographers, historians, sociologists, and the like usually have no knowledge of science—excepting the historians of technology who tend to be engineers without much insight into any branch of biology. If that is not a reason, it is difficult to suggest why no professional sociologist or ecologist appears to have noticed the full implication for man of what has been done to fossil reserves during the development of technology. There have been many expositions of what has been gained through technological progress. Those are usually flattering to Man and ignorantly unfair to Nature: who, it is generally implied and often stated in those effusions, is well on the way to being conquered by 'Man's increasing mastery' (or some such phrase).

The second reason seems to follow in large measure from the first. There are some ancient cobwebs on much of academic ecology, which sets out to discuss the relationship of life to its environment. Nearly all this 'classic' ecology is descriptive; but without scientific persuasion it does not adventure much beyond pictures of plants and animals in some more or less idealized 'wild' state. If it be granted that teaching about the relation of modern man to the whole of his environment has been formed on constructs more appropriate to the eighteenth century than to the nineteenth or twentieth, it follows that there has come from universities no scientifically-nurtured check to the delusions about 'mastery over Nature': but rather that such delusions have been fostered by default and reiteration as if they represented reality. Whatever the reason, it has come to look as if Man increasingly regards himself as a special sort of creature subject to natural laws in only the narrower physiological connotations, yet not bound to, or not perceptibly conforming to, the rules to which every other thing on and in the earth is subject.

Paradoxically, this supposed immunity of Man from the operation of natural law has been conceived by non-scientists (or by scientists not completely wideawake) who have started from the premiss that Man, alone among the animals, has intelligence.

After a survey of engineering and other technical achievement during the last few centuries or millenia, history is appealed to, to show that it is by use of his intelligence that Man has learnt to conquer Nature, and can increasingly expect to extend his mastery. Consequently, in the matter of provision of food (as in any other aspect of technology), the argument preposes that for the feeding of any number of millions of people—who are, moreover, to be maintained at an ever-rising standard of living 'thanks to the (expected) triumphs of science'—there is, or need be, no problem: provided only that Man uses intelligence.

That idiosyncratic idea of Man's having any command whatever over Nature is the greatest of the fallacies which becloud discussion of future population. What is now generally taught, or at least, generally believed, about the sources of human food seems to have originated from careless reading of what was known and printed at the beginning of last century. It has been promulgated by careless teaching, ever since, of that same inchoate, and now antique, appreciation of Nature in relation to Man.

The essential principles which decide the *substance* of life on earth were stated in a few words by the British astronomer Sir John Herschel [M3] (1792-1871) in his book 'Outlines of Astronomy' published in 1833. I quote the relevant passages as they were quoted by the British physicist John Tyndall (1820-93) in the fourth edition of his book 'Heat a Mode of Motion', published in 1870: [M4]

'The sun's rays are the ultimate source of almost every motion which takes place on the surface of the earth. By its heat are produced all winds, and those disturbances in the electric equilibrium of the atmosphere which give rise to the phenomena of lightning, and probably also to terrestrial magnetism and the Aurora. By their vivifying action vegetables are enabled to draw support from inorganic matter, and become in their turn the support of animals and man, and the source of those great deposits of dynamical efficiency which are laid up for human use in our coal strata.' Herschel went on into further physiographic description.

Herschel could not, in 1833, know about the indispensable role of microbes in keeping the life-cycle turning. The role of soil microbes in bridging the gap implied in old sayings about 'dust to dust,' and in bringing continuous life to fill the gap, was first seen by the Frenchman Louis Pasteur (1822-95) about 1864, a few years after he had experimentally laid the foundation of modern microbiology. Also not until the 'sixties did petroleum products become widely important. [M5]

If we include microbes among 'vegetables', and if for 'coal strata' we understand that all mineral fuels and metallic ores ought to be included (if only because nothing of what Herschel called 'dynamical efficiency' of modern importance can be obtained without use of machines and equipment that involve metals), the rightness of Herschel's quoted words is unimpaired, however much his language remains old-fashioned [M6]. His word 'equilibrium' is notable; for although he applied it to a small sector, it is a key word in discussion of all natural phenomena. There is no terrestrial manifestation into consideration of which the concepts, variously called balance and equilibrium, do not enter.

These remarks are not special pleading on behalf of Herschel. They are meant to bring out the circumstance that whether we are concerned with food and population in relation only to coal, or to all fuels and ores, the distinction is of method or material, not of principle. Also, very little is known of the way in which life is carried on near the floor of deep oceans—a topic not mentioned by Herschel: nor is much known about the details of life of, for example, marsupials.

Now that we have been alerted by Pasteur, it can be safely assumed that at the bottom of the ocean, as elsewhere, there is some mechanism for bridging the gap that corresponds to 'dust to dust'; yet, even though we are almost totally ignorant of details about the life-processes of most species of animals and plants, there is no reason for bringing in a vitalistic slant to principles of living in any mode or medium, or for adopting a pseudo-scientific approach to any question of life and vitality: possibly along the lines of 'if you don't understand something, give it an impressive name'. [M7] To-day's science gives a picture of the principles that is complete and coherent because any and all lines converge: whichever line is followed, it leads to the same conclusive point, and it avoids fallacies and impossibilities that could be obstacles for non-scientific thinking. Only minutiae await further discovery for an enormous increase of descriptive detail, none of which can be more than marginally relevant to any well-founded thesis about food and human population.

By about 1870 the broad principles governing life and other

natural transactions had been enunciated. Those are the fundamental rules—expressed in human language—by which
Nature governs the motion, substance, and fate of all matter.

In 1824 the Frenchman Nicolas Sadi Carnot (1796-1832)
had given an outline of the laws of exchange of energy; he
had thus stated the impossibilities, to a commercial and scientific community which had not quite abandoned the belief that
it might be possible to build a machine which could operate
to yield perpetual motion—and thus produce something for
nothing. In 1858 the Italian Stanislao Cannizzaro (1826-1910)
effectively stated the basis on which modern chemistry
operates in its dealings with exchanges and transformations
of non-radioactive matter. The German Rudolf Clausius
(1822-88) had by 1864 refined the thermodynamical propositions of Carnot into the forms (if not the wording) in which
they stand to-day. [M8]

So, about the words of Herschel quoted above, John Tyndall
(1820-93) could write in 1870 (or a year or two earlier): 'This
fine passage requires but the breath of recent investigation to
convert it into an exposition of the law of conservation of
energy, as applied to both the organic and inorganic world.'

Insofar as we are concerned with principles underlying the
growth and size of human population, nothing needs to be
added to-day to that single sentence of Tyndall's if it is held
to include conservation of matter and is taken in conjunction with Herschel's wording once that is modified as I have
suggested.

No theory or fact of chemistry or physics that has turned
up more recently than 1870 has altered—for everyday life,
and for the increase or decrease of human population as far as
changes in size of a population are conditioned by increase or
decrease of food supply—the significance of what was known
in the 'sixties of last century about the relations between forms
of energy, between matter and energy, and between substance
and substance.

It is the operations of Man himself since about that time
that have brought about an unprecedented, irreversible, yet
almost unnoticed, alteration in the relation of Man to his
world: by threatening his food supplies. By using, and wast-

ing, fossil fuel Man has for more than a century been very busily and happily engaged in cutting away the branch on which he sits.

In view of the technologically far-reaching discoveries which have been made in the last hundred years—radioactivity, isotopes, and aviation are but a few of the many examples that everybody knows about—the statements in the three preceding paragraphs will probably excite surprise; so, comment on recent philosophical developments will not be amiss before passing to the next Chapter.

In 1900, Max Planck introduced quantum theory. That brought in the entirely new idea that the energy of light existed—or could be thought of as existing—in little packets of action named quanta, and that it could perform as indivisible packets: atoms of light, so to speak. The quantum theory has led to considerable refinements in understanding of detail of some energetical changes; it also ushered in Einsteinian relativity. From that followed the idea that in some transcendental conditions (as in the stars) matter could be produced from energy alone; and (as in the H-bomb) annihilation of matter produces vast energy. Atomic physics showed that energy and matter are fundamentally interconvertible. However, conditions for conversion of energy into matter are unimportant outwith the domain of theoretical physics, and then only for particles whose speed approaches that of light.

The mightiest of our electricity generating stations could hardly be thought of as able to produce a mouse's mouthful of matter under any conceivable terrestrial condition.

The discovery of radioactivity and isotopes has revealed new phenomena and ways of behaviour peculiar to those kinds of matter (at bottom: to the behaviour of atoms) but has not produced any new rules applicable to human nutrition or production of food. By yielding fresh knowledge and correcting old errors, experimental and diagnostic use of isotopes has been useful and suggestive in many studies pertaining to the ways in which 'vegetables' and animal organisms deal with their nutrients and otherwise conduct their interior economy or personal housekeeping—in a word, their metabolism [M9]; it has also fathered many new tools, such as the Geiger counter. But all this has been done within the old practical frameworks of energy-exchange. The only philosophical novelty has been the finding that emission of radioactivity by atoms cannot be altered by heating or any chemical or other treatment: for example, radioactive cobalt is sometimes used as detector in blast-furnaces, in which its radioactivity is identical whether it is hot or cold.

Whereas the thermodynamic and chemical principles discovered a hundred years ago apply to all terrestrial exchanges and are of supreme practical importance on earth, the expression $E = mc^2$ presumably applies to *all* matter and *all* energy. However, in our earthbound problems of getting enough food to feed our future populations, we are not materially or directly concerned with it (unless the H-bomb should help to solve the pressure on food-supplies by substantially reducing the population). Its importance for us as people remains—short of a catastrophe—because it *is* an equation. Its message is the same as those of the laws known before 1870: namely, that equilibrium in some definite, and therefore calculable, exchange is the essence and the rule of what is manifest throughout terrestrial and transcendental operations of Nature. By quantifying some matters (mainly in the domains of astronomy and atomic and particle physics) it has made them amenable to intellectual treatment in spheres where the Newtonian rules of the eighteenth century could not assist; yet, in any but a philosophical sense, its operation does not affect our life. As an equation, it is a statement of insistence of something for something, while telling us what those somethings are and in what realms they are likely to be important for us personally, if at all.

We do not need an Einstein to tell us that, in the ordinary governance and conduct of life, energy cannot produce substance—whether it is food or any other thing that we aspire to have.

How has it happened that after more than a hundred years of scientific endeavour that set the bounds of what is possible, many—even educated—people firmly believe that all food comes from the energy of daily sunshine? The reasons must be partly psychological; and to the extent that they are psychological it is not the province of this book to discuss them. However, the hard facts by which food is produced have been known since the 'thirties of last century: as the quotations from Herschel (1833) and Reid (1836) [M5] show, there was at that time no belief that food came from sunshine, but there was explicit acknowledgement that food-materials came from inorganic matter.

So, it is easy to point out *what* went wrong: though much less easy to show how or when a heliocentric belief in the origin of food originated. That impossible and quasi-religious belief must have arisen from a careless reading, and thus a seriously flawed understanding, of what was known, and had been printed with substantial correctness, before 1840.

This careless reading—with its accompaniment of bad teaching—enshrined the errors:

(1) Not noting the significance of such words as '[the sun's enabling plants] to draw support from inorganic matter' and 'By absorption from the soil, the roots of plants take up a large share of nutritious matter'.

(2) Failing to observe the significance, for Man, of the observations made by Sadi Carnot (and of his successors during the next forty years) on the principles which govern the conservation of energy. Along with that went what was known to chemists as the law of the conservation of weight or of matter (or of mass, as we might now say), well before the end of the eighteenth century. The indestructibility of matter, and the total impossibility of creating something out of nothing, was adumbrated by Democritus (*fl.* 400 B.C.) in the words *ex nihilo nihil fit, et in nihilum nihil potest reverti*.

So there was not much excuse for scholars after say, 1850, to lean upon—still less to propagate—a doctrine on the lines of 'all life from the sun'. No doubt the authority of the astronomers was early appealed to in support of the burgeoning belief; and astronomy may well have been deemed a more fit subject for polite teaching—even if the humanistic essence was missed in the process—than the ideas of rude mechanicals like Carnot and most of the chemists.

(3) There was, however, another factor that must have been especially agreeable to scientifically uncritical minds. That was knowledge of the discovery of photosynthesis (the process by which the leaves of green plants provided with chlorophyll have certain chemical actions directly energized by sunlight) in steps taken by several investigators about the year 1800. There were some serious errors in their reasoning (one is mentioned on page 19, and others are discussed in Chapter 20); but the linkage of some effect of the sun's rays with growth of green plants was broadly correct; it was also an astonishing novelty.

Coupled with what it was supposed that those great scientists, the astronomers, had taught about the all-pervading influence of that mysterious and awe-inspiring body the sun, the new knowledge about the action of the sun on plants was, it seems, enough to start an educational myth about the origins of food that is far from being quashed yet.

We here have some introduction to the ironies that beset a study of the facts about the origins of food. One is that Théophile de Saussure, a Swiss who made the last and greatest of the steps that revealed photosynthesis about 1800, published a book ('Recherches chimiques sur la végétation': Paris. 1804) which showed that he was well aware that green plants needed, and took up by their roots, inorganic substances from what we should to-day call ionized salts. Thus he cannot have been responsible for the myth about sunlight and carbon dioxide being a sufficient agency for growth of plants: though, because he is primarily associated with photosynthesis, his name is frequently invoked in connexion with that myth. In other words, it is now necessary to be clear that plant nutrition, and formation of the entire tissues of plants and of all our food, proceed from what is taken up from carbon dioxide *and water* through the direct influence of the energy of sunlight: *supplemented* with what can be gained from substances dissolved in the water of the soil or the sea.

What was known to people such as Herschel and Reid and de Saussure in the early decades of last century was, if properly interpreted, quite adequate as an explanation of the modes by which food was *then* obtained: however lacking the explanation was in detail. It is another, and much greater, irony that similar ideas have become embalmed, unchanged except in detail, in popular notions about the support of population in our own time; yet, circumstances of gathering food have changed so greatly as to make it impossible to sustain a modern population from the actions of sunlight on green plants grown and harvested by nothing more than the resources available up to 1840.

To borrow some words of H. Butterfield about another subject, it is necessary to clear the board and redistribute all the pieces on it in order to clarify the situation in which we stand now.

[MI]   This was the principle or law enunciated by the Frenchman Henry Le Chatelier (1850-1936) in 1888. It is sometimes called an expression of the laziness of Nature; more exactly, 'the principle of opposition of a natural system to further change' (beyond what it has already undergone).

It may be doubted whether it should be regarded as an independent law; it seems more likely that it is a product—a kind of portmanteau—of what was already known to Clausius, Kelvin and other physicists and chemists.

Le Chatelier's law, being a principle of equilibrium, applies to systems which are confined in such a way that individual particles are free to react with and upon each other and their environment. It cannot apply to political conservatism; its clearest application in living systems is to the behaviour of soil microbes towards the nutrients, air, and water that are at any moment at their disposal.

[M2]   Statement of the fact that the laws have never been controverted does not apply merely to the experience of little more than a century. If a historical view is taken further, it will be seen that nothing has been known that controverts or infringes them. The impossibility of perpetual motion was a tenet of Galileo and his successors in the development of mechanics (A. E. E. McKenzie, 'The major achievements of science': Camb. Univ. Press, 1960). McKenzie's book gives a very readable account of the history of some of the fundamental themes mentioned in this book; but, like many academic chemists and other scientists, he shows scant notice of agricultural scientists or any science directly concerned with food and nutrition.

The impossibility of perpetual motion is almost the only scientific tenet, besides gravitation, to permeate into general education. This book is about the impossibility of illimitable food; its scientific grounds are the same as those which reject perpetual motion. The one deals with people; the other with machines.

[M3]   Son of the astronomer Sir William Herschel (1738-1822), whose sister Caroline Lucretia (1750-1848) made a notable contribution to astronomy.

[M4]   London: Longmans, Green & Co.

[M5]   Burmah petroleum, as Rangoon oil, is mentioned in D. B. Reid's 'Text-book for students of chemistry,' 2nd edn.; Maclachlan and Stewart, Edinburgh. 1836.
    The first oil well in the U.S.A. was drilled in 1859; before then, Scotland was exporting its domestically-produced shale oil to the United States and other countries.

[M6]   The remarks on 'Vegetable chemistry' in Reid's book (ref. above) are interesting; some of them are pertinent. Thus: 'By absorption from the soil, the roots of plants take up a large share of nutritious matter; they also receive a considerable proportion of nourishment through the medium of their leaves. . . . Light has a very important influence, not only on the colour of plants but also on the process of respiration, favouring very much the decomposition of carbonic acid, the absorption of carbon, and the elimination of oxygen.' Reid's statements about plant growth are well balanced, though there is the error about 'the decomposition of carbonic acid' that is discussed on page 210.

[M7]   Empty terms like *élan vital* have seduced many non-scientific intellectuals into taking them as substitutes for explanations about the forces that condition life. To use *élan vital* in that way is like asking 'What makes a train move?' and accepting *élan locomoteur* as a satisfying answer.

[M8]   Every scientist stands on the shoulders of his predecessors. This citation of only four people (Carnot, Clausius, Cannizzaro, and Pasteur) as founders of statements about the terms on which the operations of life are conducted is for brevity and for the reason that their statements collected in ineluctable fashion what had been previously known or divined. Carnot and Clausius were mathematicians and physicists; Cannizzaro and Pasteur were chemists. Pasteur's insight in 1864 into the agency by which life is kept revolving is the more astonishing because no earlier meditator on the philosophy of life and immortality had got further than what had been expressed by Alexander Pope (1688-1744) in his 'Essay on Man':

> Fix'd like a plant on his peculiar spot,
> To draw nutrition, propagate, and rot.

Cannizzaro—as is well known to chemists—had many intellectual forbears; the brilliance of his achievement in 1858 is that he durably synthesized their theories and observations.

In the 'forties and 'fifties of the last century many people were actively engaged with discovering the principles of exchange of energy and the principles of chemistry. A list of them would recall the long-winded passages in Jules Verne's science-based romances; but since the reader may here be assumed to be interested more in the humanistic meanings of the discoveries than in their history or the frustrations and persistent ironies suffered by the discoverers, only a few more pioneers need mention.

Grateful mention is thus given to the Welsh lawyer-chemist (Sir) William R. Grove (1811-96), the Englishman James Prescott Joule (1818-89), and the Ulster-born William Thomson (Lord Kelvin; 1824-1907). These aimed at finding the physical and mathematical principles. Special mention is due also to the German medical man or physiologist, Julius Robert Mayer (1814-78), who thought along lines independent of any of these (though he may have been influenced by Carnot's ideas) and in the early 'forties showed that exchange of matter for energy applied to the human body. Mayer may be called the founder of human thermokinetics.

Mayer's work seems to be unique in having founded a popular legend—that the human body renews itself 'every seven years', as I recall from childhood. The fact of continuous renewal of the parts of the living body was not established until isotopes became available recently. In championing Mayer on this topic, John Tyndall (page 13) wrote one of the most magnificent sentences of scientific history: 'Like changing sentinels, the oxygen, hydrogen, and carbon that depart seem to whisper their secret to their comrades that arrive, and thus, while the Non-ego shifts, the Ego remains the same.'

For the main theme it will suffice to retain the names of Carnot, Clausius, Cannizzaro, and Pasteur. I would guess that none of these is a household word, except Pasteur and that for a reason that is ironically wrong in associating him with causes of disease and death instead of with the workings of life which was his constant preoccupation.

[M9] Metabolism is a convenient word which means 'all the chemical changes occurring in any organism (animal, plant, or microbe)'.

3

Understanding the modern set-up

Books must follow sciences, and not sciences books.
—Francis Bacon: *Proposition touching Amendment of Laws*

This Chapter is a letter to the layman, to remove some fancied hurdles from his path and to reassure him about his ability to understand.

To comprehend the size of human population—say, the possible size of world population at any time from this day onward—it should be borne in mind that Man is always subject to Nature and to natural laws of chemistry (exchange and transformations of matter) and to those of thermodynamics (exchange and transformations of energy). He is never, nor can be, in a position to command or alter the rules that govern the whole environment of which he himself is a part.

It matters not at all—except to people specializing for part of their life in particular branches of science—whether we class the study of numbers of human population as biology, ecology, chemistry, thermodynamics, biochemistry, or under some other name.

Because ecology is the study of relations of organisms to their environment, and since human populations are now linked with the origins of their food in essentially a chemical way, I would prefer to call the study of sizes of, and prospects for, human population by the name of 'chemical ecology' [MI]; but that may be because I am a chemist. In any case, the preference is a personal one, and doesn't matter.

All quantitative sciences are branches of observation under the same natural auspices: they work together and to rules that coincide exactly and always throughout every department.

Consciousness of particular laws is not always uppermost in daily practice. As an example from just one field of development: a plant-breeder may be an empiricist or a complete amateur when he crosses varieties to produce new varieties. So was Donald Mackelvie (1867-1947), the Scotsman who raised the famous 'Arran' varieties of potato: having done his arduous work just for fun; and he was such a wretched businessman that at first he gave away his new (and valuable) varieties. Or the breeder may work on almost strictly scientific lines in complete accordance with what he expects from Mendelian laws of inheritance, and then call himself a geneticist; yet, both the amateurs and the geneticists would be surprised if their soil produced new plants like giant bean-stalks that contained much more of the sorts of substances yielded by soil for the nourishment of plants than the soil ever had or was capable of supplying. Anyone who observed such a happening would indeed have material for a new law to the effect that he had got something more out of Nature than she had put in. The general expectation among growers is more business-like; it is that they will not get more soil matter out of soil by growth of plants than was 'on hand' (or perhaps I should say, 'on root') during the growing season—however much sunshine the plants enjoyed and however amply they were supplied with only water and carbon dioxide.

But, any scientist would be sadly at fault if he stepped beyond scientific limits and expressed even a hope that someday it would be possible to breed plants that could yield more human food by 'capturing more energy from sunshine' without letting on how that extra energy was to transform more substance into food, and precisely where that extra substance to feed the soil to feed the plants to feed animals or people was to come from. Feeding the population is not in the least like Jack-and-the-beanstalk magic; but it is much like the House-that-Jack-built story, because it has to start with something and follow a chain of circumstance that is all about things and people.

If an amateur believed a story about fresh magic from sun-shine, we could say 'Poor chap, he doesn't *know*'; but if a scientist accustomed to working with plants said something like it, his statement would be evidence that he had forgotten all the thermodynamics he ever heard about and had been incautiously unscientific for the nonce. Sometimes plant physiologists do talk like that—even from the high table at botanical congresses; and occasionally illustrious physicists show, not that they have forgotten their thermodynamics (which I take to be impossible), but that they have not tried to connect their knowledge properly with their discourse on the future of Man. Which shows, I submit, that even Fellows of the Royal Society are only human after all.

In natural principles there is neither contradiction nor in-novation: only mutual consistence, support, and convergence.

There is not the slightest need for a layman to take fright at the introduction of the word 'thermodynamics', or an ap-peal to thermodynamic propositions. I single out thermo-dynamics for this assurance, because many non-scientists look upon that word as an especially baneful shibboleth; many people feel that they are, if not beyond an intellectual pale, at least disqualified from understanding any science-based argument because they are unable to recite the Second Law of Thermodynamics (incidentally, many scientists don't know precisely what it is) and haven't the faintest notion of what it is—still less how its operation might affect them and their grandchildren. I should also explain that I have taken the liberty of using the one word thermodynamics as a convenient portmanteau to include all the physical, mechanical, and chemical rules that have a bearing on production of food.

Two more clarifications before going into detail to show some of the ways in which Nature limits the amount of food that it is possible to produce in any given circumstance. For scientists these points are, or should be, part of the intellectual air they breathe. Accordingly, I use colloquial language.

Firstly, the objection that nobody need believe what I hap-pen to say or write in a book. 'How do we know that you are right in saying that the laws (of chemistry or thermodynamics) forbid the doing of this or that?' Fair enough; honest scepticism, particularly about what a person says whom you don't know, is never exercized in vain. So when I appeal to the laws or rules you might think that I am being somewhat Kipling-esque (though Rudyard Kipling was never definite about what he meant by The Law); more to the point, you might well object that scientists are constantly altering their hypo-theses and ideas, and that any law is apt to be scrapped or substantially altered from time to time.

Thomas Huxley said that the greatest tragedy in science is a hypothesis killed by an incongruent fact. A hypothesis is like an embryo law; when found not to fit the observed facts, a hypothesis or law (being only a man-made idea) has to be either killed, or brought into more viable shape. One answer to the objection just made is that the laws or rules discussed in Chapter 2—which is the basis of this book—have never (as I remarked in that Chapter) been found to be contravened yet. They appear, in the testimony of millions of earnest ob-servers, to be as much a part of Nature as the expected rising of the sun to-morrow; and if the sun should not rise, or if something happened so grossly contrary to experience as to show that one could produce energy or food by a wave of the hand, the world would probably be at an end anyway.

There is no such thing as absolute certainty: only accumu-lated experience. And as Einstein showed (and acquaintance with still newer scientific philosophy would confirm) ideas about the ultimate working of the universe are in, or are, a flux of probabilities. It is theoretically possible that an ordi-nary brick or stone could by itself rise from the ground (with-out supposing the force of gravitation to be diminished); but that has never been known to happen and therefore is not reckoned with in ordinary living. As we accept the law that bricks stay on the ground until picked up by hand or thrown up by an earthquake, we should accept the less familiar, but even more immutable, laws of thermodynamics: those laws are not affected by earthquakes, but regulate them.

Another possible objection could come from unfamiliarity with the mere terminology of science. It will be recalled that until about the nineteen-thirties radio waves and light were often supposed to go through an imaginary substance called 'the ether'. In the early days of broadcasting there used to be letters to the Editors of popular wireless journals protesting against saying that a programme had been 'put out over the air' and pointing out that it should have been said to have been transmitted 'through the ether'. Up to about 1920 there was hardly a physicist who would not have cheerfully gone to the stake to defend the notion about an 'ether' as carrier of electro-magnetic waves; but since about 1930 the idea of the existence of such an 'ether' has been quietly dropped, and has totally vanished except in historical records. Everybody accepts 'on the air' as a convenient manner of speaking about a radio or TV transmission.

Surely that is enough to shake a layman's confidence in the ideas of scientists about fundamental matters? It need not, if the layman understands that the poor ether-concept was a mental prop of a word (like *élan vital*, already deplored on p. 19): used to account for something not understood (in this case: how force could be exerted at a distance). People could understand how action could be exerted by a push of a stick or a pull of a rope, and physicists pretended they could understand how electric energy could be transmitted through a tangible wire; so 'ether' was invented to 'explain' action at a distance when there was no obvious medium.

However, the important distinction between the idea of an ether and the conception of a natural law is that the ether was merely a hypothesis and could be cast aside without anybody being a penny the worse once the concept had been found to be unnecessary, unprofitable, and superfluous. It was merely a guess; never a law. A law is a concise description of behaviour which has been observed to occur regularly and unfailingly; it has, as it were, been seen in action. Nobody ever observed the ether or how it behaved; nor did the most painstaking experiments give the slightest reason for believing that it existed. So, out it went as Planck and Einstein came in; a shadowy but useless figment in the history of ideas. It was not even 'killed by a fact'; it just died of inanition. So perish—albeit sometimes very slowly—all hypotheses and constructs that do not fit repeatedly-observed, or any, facts.

The next point is also about facts. It is well known to

scientists though unfamiliar to laymen—of whom I take as type the borough councillor or a 'Pro Bono Publico' who, confronted with some local problem, calls for 'the facts'. It is possible that, given some or all the facts, he would be unable for lack of appropriate training in methodology to draw any useful conclusion from them; though he might draw some subjective conclusion coloured by his own or his party's inclinations. But whether the conclusion in science or in the council chamber is right or wrong, it is never the facts that lead to a conclusion: it is always the relationship between the facts that matters. Sometimes the discovery of the relationship calls for abstruse mathematical analysis, whether the problem is one of the laboratory or of local or national government; and what seems to be an obvious conclusion (according to which set of people it is 'obvious') may be the wrong one if it is reached by subjective introspection or without seeing what further facts need to be brought in to make a correct linkage. (Some examples are given in the last Chapter but one.)

A 'food' example is the undoubted fact that so far there is broadly enough food to feed all the people. A second set of related facts is that much of this extra food has come from 'new' lands not farmed until recently; from more intensive fishing and greater use of fertilizers; and so on. But are those facts of observation and record sufficient to establish a confident prognostic, or a new 'law', that things can and will always continue thus? In other words, the facts are correct; but what is the relationship between this extra food and that extra population? Can 'science' be relied on to find a method for feeding many millions more?

In dealing with facts it is not always necessary to have them expressed with a high degree of accuracy; very often a rough set of facts is as useful as, and more intelligible because less confusing than, more sophisticated ones. That is especially true of numerical data; they need do no more than satisfy the principle of necessity and sufficiency. In a general talk about food and what the body does with it, it is not necessary to learn more about the oxygen in the air than that it makes up one-fifth of the air by volume. Nothing is gained by expressing the fraction to three places of decimals; and indeed the figure 21 % suffices for most purposes, including those of an engineer who is trying to put figures about coal and air in relation to one another when he calculates the efficiency of a boiler.

There are many unreal images of science, and of what scientists do and aim at (apart from the quite wrong notions that 'science' is the same thing as technology and that technology is an expression of man's increasing mastery over Nature).

There is on the one hand the idea that scientists are a pernickety race spending their time refining measurements ('in obtaining accurate facts'); on the other hand is the idea that 'scientists' means little more than nuclear scientists who spend their time evolving, however unwillingly, new means of death and destruction. You will see that the one idea is wrong because the facts, however accurate, are of no use by themselves (as the scientific workers know); the second is an invention of political journalists. To be fair, these same journalists do sometimes extend their conception of 'science' to artificial satellites, and to such matters as the economics of petroleum or food grains; but their concern for Man and current affairs does not usually embrace real conceptions of what science is or of the scientific mode of thinking.

It is for such reasons that though everybody knows that petroleum or food has to be paid for in money terms, the would-be popularizers of science and sociology have missed the point that food in quantities greater than what was available about the time of Napoleon Bonaparte has to be paid for in coal or some other part of the capital of fuel. That knowledge about payment is the most important scientific fact (provided you think that people are important); and its usefulness is that it puts people into correct actuarial relationship with fossil fuels on known scientific terms which—like mortality itself—cannot be dodged or circumvented.

It is possible that I have missed something pertinent in my rather casual sociological reading; there is fairly probative evidence that that is unlikely. The British Broadcasting Corporation, before putting on a half-dozen talks, on the lines of Man and Progress, by a London sociologist, printed a foretaste in *Radio Times* to the effect that, reckoned in centuries, the development of modern man could be expressed as a series beginning with about 60; and the quoted series ended with 2 or 3 to mark the beginning of the age of industry. The speaker thus referred to may be assumed to have been familiar with the works of other sociologists; and, because adoption of fossil fuel to feed an increased population became important about 1880 and has been the most pregnant, as well as the most unprecedented, change in the relation of Man to his environment since the invention of agriculture, the omission of 1 from the quoted series was suggestive. Seemingly, neither the specialist speaker nor the educated public as typified by the programme planners, had seized on either the novelty or the social importance of the technical change lately introduced into human ecology.

Yet the B.B.C. aspires to education and to maintaining a high standard of awareness in what are called 'current affairs'; but those seem to be about politics and personalities, without serious reference to Man's having become a technically-conditioned animal. 'Pop science' in which TV and illustrated articles seek to amuse us with technological marvels is hardly science and seldom serious; it is a form of entertainment which invites recall of Chesterton's saying that we should not laugh at the people of the Middle Ages for being so greatly taken with the reports of two-headed calves in monkish chronicles. In any case it assumes an indefinite abundance of fossil fuel without raising any question about that. It is almost as if our thinkers about the philosophical relations of Man himself (as distinct from his machines) had not advanced beyond the age of David Hume (1711-76) and Jeremy Bentham (1748-1832).

A principal object of the whole of accrued science (not within inverted commas) is to tell us, through the laws of thermodynamics, what *cannot* be done. Science thus defined tells us within precise limits how far the world can go in applying its capital of fuel to feeding its population, keeping them warm (or cool, in hot countries), or moving, or well clothed, or anything else that is asked from technology.

Perhaps, as layman, you have been confusing science with technology?

Arising out of a confusion of science with technology and art (in the sense of craft, skill and inventiveness) there is another point which demands a full answer if the reader's confidence is to be retained. If that challenge is not squarely met, there will lurk the question: 'How can you, a scientist, declare that anything is impossible? Haven't there been many things which someone (sometimes of great eminence) has pooh-poohed and declared to be impossible to do, but which have been done?' There have been many such; but all the examples have referred to *phenomena*, not to laws; they have been in the sphere of invention and technology. The makers of the predictions about impossibility have thus made their objections on technological grounds alone—not from grounds of fundamental science. Their objections have sometimes arisen from an imperfect acquaintance with contemporary technology, and sometimes from not having the benefit of later discoveries in the technological field and about phenomena. The discoveries of the ionosphere, and of human dependence on vitamins, are examples of new knowledge about phenomena of which the operation is bounded by laws already known, and still binding.

To say that a technical feat is impossible because it contravenes a thermodynamic or chemical law does not require any knowledge about the technique or the skill involved; the block is absolute. What is here written about impossibilities in relation to food-production and everything else is not a prophecy whether any particular technological feat will be accomplished. The conclusions are perfectly general: not being founded on any idea about technology or skill (except that all technology is founded on thermodynamic principle whether that is acknowledged as implicit or not).

Thus—to take an example apparently most humane and remote from machines—'spare-part' surgery may well develop, during the next few years or decades, to a degree of perfection that is at present only a dream. It is no part of the thesis of this book that such technical advances will not continue to be made or that they will not reach great heights of achievement, for as long as fuel is available, or allotted, to support any or all of them. But the extent to which they can be practised must (like the population at large) depend on resources of fossil and other fuel for making and servicing the technical equipment required by any technology or practice of skill.

That all technology depends absolutely on chemical changes which involve fuel is as indisputable as the acknowledgement in modern business that nothing can be bought without money. The main difference is that payment in fuel for food and for the upkeep of people has not hitherto been recognized in terms of science. It is not I, but the impersonal operations of Nature, that declare the impossibilities recorded in this book.

Bacon's rejection of authority now means that you do not have to believe something just because Aristotle or Carnot or Cannizzaro or Tyndall or I said it was or is so. In scientific matters, you do not have to believe in a person, but in the record of facts and the relationships between repeatedly observed facts as expressed by the laws which embody experience of how things behave. It is open to anybody to challenge the laws, or their wording; but it would be somewhat rash for any writer to found a discourse on the future of population without taking into account not only the facts that might be known to him (about human nutrition, or fertilizers, say) but also the ultimate laws about exchange of matter and energy that express the relationships which bottom all facts about food and its production.

In informing you what those ultimate relationships are, and that—whatever way they are looked at—they converge on having something to burn in order to support a population no greater than the present one, my role is simply that of reporter and transcriber of knowledge which has long been available. For your part, you do need to have confidence that what is in this book is a reasonably true report and transcript written by a person who is implacably a scientist, subject (of course) to human error. I hope I have engendered the necessary confidence; nevertheless, you need not believe me personally. If you have doubts, you can look up details in the record of the whole of science (whether it refers to food or not): and thus carry into practice a well-tried scientific maxim: 'Always check your references.'

This book is not, in the main, a thesis about my personal opinions (or the mere opinions of anyone quoted or mentioned herein). Topics not verifiable because they are opinions are consigned to a later part of the book that is clearly labelled to keep opinion distinct from a discussion of scientific consequences.

Bacon said 'We cannot command Nature except by obeying her'; that is true, being only another way of saying *Nothing for nothing* or that you cannot command your capital or income—if that is fixed—except by conforming to its dictates; though, as somebody said, the man who has sixpence is master of the world to the extent of sixpence: in ordinary commercial matters, understood.

However, it was in a possibly despairing moment that Bacon put out the absurd idea that Nature could be tortured into revealing her secrets. That seems to be, some four centuries later, the prevailing notion about science (meaning, technology) as a means of reaching a result desired by Man after he has 'wrested' her secrets from Nature and has put some, previously arcane, knowledge to his own use.

There is nothing arcane about the practical limits of what can be done: for those limits on what Man can do and the consequent limitations are stated by the laws of thermodynamics. Also, there is no 'wresting' or other violence: every secret of Nature is open to be seen by anybody who has the intelligence to perceive the abstract nature of the *relationship* between things and behaviour: as Carnot and Cannizzaro and many others did last century.

A common idea of a scientist is that of an inventor such as Edison, who put mechanical knowledge into relation so as to invent the phonograph. Whether an inventor of a process or gadget has any knowledge of science or not, or deliberately disregards a scientific hypothesis such that radio waves travel in straight lines through the ether as Marconi did when he (successfully) tried to send wireless messages across the curved surface of the Atlantic, he is showing only what can be done. Making that sort of statement does not in any way depreciate

the efforts of successful inventors and technologists of any
kind : but it brings out the fact that, by concentrating its attention on successful inventions and practical innovations that
conduce to comfort and amenity, the general public—through
the agencies which supply it with one-sided notions about
'science'—loses sight of the other, decisive, part of science.

No Edison, Marconi, or Whittle would pretend that a process or a machine is a product of pure intelligence and does
not require both material to make it and energy to keep it
going. There is no technical operation that does not have to be
quietly paid for in terms other than money. This in spite of
what you have frequently been told about your belonging to
an age that is on the way to 'conquering' Nature. In your
anxiety about population and in your zeal for more food, do
not nurse the hope of 'wresting' anything from Nature, or of
becoming able to do anything which resembles knocking down
a fairy godmother with her own wand.

As a person with some knowledge of how business is conducted, or perhaps knowing about equations in science, you
will see how silly that idea is. No matter now often the idea
about 'mastery' of Nature is repeated so that you, possibly,
have been brain-washed into half-believing it, it is entirely
without foundation because there still is no way of getting
something for nothing : out of Nature, at any rate.

[MI]   A term I first used in 1959. If the term 'human ecology'
had not been bespoken as an offshoot of anthropology it might
have been still more fitting. Human ecology, like the classical ecology
of animals and plants in the wild, does not seem to have assimilated
or to have been touched by disciplines of quantitative sciences like
chemistry, or to have given effective note to the fact that Man has
become an animal depending for a large part of his food on substances lying beneath the surface of the earth and otherwise beyond
the reach of consociations which continue to be in a feral state of
development.

4

The prospect; and the lag of knowledge about population

In two words, im-possible.
—Mr Sam Goldwyn (*attributed*)

More than a century of miseducation about vital subjects has led to a firm rooting of the notion that all food is produced from the daily energy of sunlight alone: without the general public having had a proper opportunity to obtain, comprehensively and in modern terms, knowledge about the inorganic materials of earth and sea and the ways in which those materials are now provided and utilized to produce food.

It seems that nothing that is to the point about the support of modern populations has reached the text-books and treatises on sociology, the life-cycle, and such themes as 'what chemistry does for Man'; and, in spite of the positiveness of the scientific indications, many writers still treat the subject of producing vast new quantities of food in a speculative but optimistic manner embroidered by fancy freely indulged in. Those disquisitions are written without much foundation of science—substitutes (mostly from some superficial acquaintance with the deeds of technology) being offered instead. Being taken by writer and publisher and reader to be some contribution to knowledge, they breed other disquisitions also smelling rather of acquaintance with the candles in the study than with balanced concepts derived from accountancy and the laboratory.

The basis of methods of obtaining food has changed greatly since Herschel's time: using fossil fuel to win food is a technique that was unknown to the contemporaries of George III of Britain (1738-1820) except that some of them used soot from coal-burning domestic chimneys as a manure; nor was there much change up to the accession of Queen Victoria in 1837 except for use as fertilizer of a small amount of ammonium chloride from the new gasworks. Use of coal-fired steam-driven machinery in food technology had grown slightly since George III had visited a London brewery thus equipped; and though William Harley (?1770-1829) the Glasgow dairyman, was about 1812 said to be doing everything by steam in his mechanized cowshed except milking the cows, such applications of coal to purposes directly connected with food remained exceptional for many years.

Use of coal and petrol and other combustible minerals for procuring and gathering food has become a commonplace feature of everyday life. Yet, the archaism of current sociological thought is illustrated by the fact that much of the burden of economic and sociological discussions about future human populations and about the increases of population during the last hundred years or so is whether Malthus was right or wrong in writing as he did in 1798. Malthus's only novel point was a simple mathematical one that is no longer found difficult to grasp or is seen as self-evident; yet writers declare themselves to be 'neo' or some other brand of Methusian as if they derived fresh inspiration from a quasi-arithmetical point which would not detain a schoolboy. In our technological age, no variety of 'Malthusian' controversy is worth while unless substance is given to it by substantial reference to supplies of fuel.

The vacuity of the intellectual climate wherein Malthus soliloquized in 1798 is indicated by the fact that there was then hardly a single scientific piece of knowledge having a bearing on the production of food: and such facts as were known and can now be held to be relevant to a treatise on population (for example: about geology, combustion, conservation of matter) had not been usefully correlated with the chemistry of living matter. People who spend time arguing about the fitness, for our time and future time, of what Malthus said in 1798 or later (he died in 1834) are not merely showing themselves ignorant of any part of science verified since 1870; they are also unaware of the tremendous consequences of dependence on fossil fuel: to which an increasing part of the population has yoked itself during the last hundred-odd years. [M1]

In suggesting that the public has had little opportunity to learn comprehensively about the ways in which materials of earth and sea are now utilized to produce food for a greater population than has ever existed, I have not forgotten that sections of the public attend schools of agriculture, botany, marine engineering, and many more kinds; thus, many people come to learn about aspects of modern life and the ways in which food is produced and harvested. The engineers learn about the laws of thermodynamics in at least their simpler applications; and such examples could be multiplied.

Leaving aside the point that professional sociologists and humanists seem (to judge by their writings) largely indifferent to opportunities to learn scientific principles, the main thing is that what is learnt from conventional sources about the origins of food is fragmented. For example, the agriculturists know about fertilizers, and that sulphur is used to make some of them, whilst coal has to be burnt to make others; the marine engineers learn about fuel economy; and the botanists learn something about the actions of fertilizers. Do these twigs and other branches of knowledge foreshadow a tree, or do they become confluent?

The operative words were 'learn comprehensively'—about the bases of human population. One result of these educational mischances and misfits is that there is no place where quantitative forms of science in relation to people are taught in a manner which is basic and well-rounded. [M2]

Another result is that whereas there can be hardly a boy of school age living anywhere in the world who does not know that aeroplanes are kept up by fuel, or that motor-cars require fuel to keep them going, it would be rather hard to find an adult (however well educated) who is primed with the fact that about a third of the human population has its numbers kept up by food gained by fuel.

Man's concern about fuel during the last hundred years has been about fuel for machines. About the future of food to sustain an increasing population of his own kind, he seems to be content with substitutes; for example: by expecting great things from nuclear power that are either visionary or impracticable without expenditure of ordinary fuel. All of which is very odd; and what is perhaps odder (if one may try to compare incommensurables) is that none of it is widely seen to be odd. Both food and fuel must (in these suppositions) be simply taken for granted as illimitable. That is an 'explanation' which does not explain; but can anything explain the rise and persistence of a myth that flourishes in opposition to science and commonsense?

Man and Science should be conjoined in considering the relations of Man to the organic and inorganic world: for no better reason (if there is a better) than that Man, being part of Nature, can never be apart from or above Nature in any respect. The best that Man can hope for it to be beneficially subject to the rules of Nature for as long as is permitted by natural resources of *every* kind. I italicize the 'every' because phrases like 'conservation of natural resources' have, in some quarters, come to be mean a sort of landscaping involving only surface resources. That implies a view which is literally as well as mentally superficial; for it is the resources beneath the earth's surface which will decide the dimensions of food.

Because the stocks of fossil fuel are fixed and irreplaceable, it is they—according to the uses to which they are henceforth put—that will decide:

(1) the size of the maximum possible human population which the world can attain;

(2) the time at which that maximum is reached;

(3) the miseries and loss of amenity that will be undergone, both: (a) while the maximum of population is being approached after it is seen that fossil fuels are likely to be insufficient for all needs felt to demand satisfaction at the time when that prospect has become clear; and

(b) when the first decline in population growth will occur, and a further decline in amenity and culture after the maximum of population has been reached.

There need be no fear that Man need become extinct. Nor will fossil reserves of fuel or ores ever be truly exhausted. Stocks of fossil fuel will decrease exponentially [M3] and become increasingly costly (in money terms) to raise. That is to say, the level of what is regarded as economic will alter. A question whether what are now regarded as 'economic' sources of metals should outlast fuel is beside the point; soils contain virtually inexhaustible amounts of e.g. iron and aluminium, so the point is at what stage it becomes economic (in fuel terms) to extract them.

After fossil fuel is effectively exhausted—that is, by the time when its availability to man is very nearly, or practically, nil—human population will again be in equilibrium with virtually only those natural resources that are renewable in perpetuity. The population, together with such amenities, culture, and comfort as it can conjure up from those resources and a trifle of mineral fuels, will again be in a state similar to that of the population of a few centuries ago.

It is not *Homo sapiens* that need be a casualty; but sooner or later—depending on the wisdom of the choices he makes henceforth—the almost total casualty will be Man's technological skill: for lack of sufficient fuel to exercise technical skills for satisfying every need for food, amenity, and possibly, warfare.

Associated with the fallacy that energy derived from the sun or otherwise can by itself, without substance, yield food, there is the belief that Man has acquired a 'mastery' over Nature that is likely to go on increasing. By exerting his mastery (it is argued) Man can live comfortably throughout the foreseeable future. That is pompous where humility and the most exact recognition of subservience are called for.

To support such errors about the relationship between people and Nature it is common to appeal to recent technological history to produce a review, and a set of hopes, from which men's needs and the warnings of science are equally left out. In particular, it is common to argue on the lines that history, in conjunction with advances in technology, has so far proved the fears groundless that an expanding population could not be fed. The fears have seemed so far to be groundless; but, as a reading of history, that sort of allegation has so little perception and valid content as to remind me of the story about the town child evacuated to the country, who, on being introduced to milking of cows, said disgustedly: 'Garn! We useter get our milk from nice clean bottles, not outa a dirty old cow!'

A connexion between fuel economy and one aspect of food was recognized during the Second World War by the British Ministry of Information in putting out a propaganda film. *Punch* recognized it with a picture of a woman and her friend chatting while standing before their front garden fence on which some empty milk-bottles were perched. One of the women is saying: 'And there was a very good Government film about not putting empty milk bottles on walls.' (Fig. 1).

Because every mode of viewing the prospects for Man comes to the same thing when it is scientifically based, I have divided the subject for convenience into several different approaches in the following expository Chapters. There are:

the business-like approach of 'nothing for nothing';

the historical approach to show how fossil fuel has increasingly been put to minister to comfort and choice, and (since about 1880 especially) to feed the increasing population;

a purely mathematical approach which is independent of fuel and of chemistry;

chemical considerations which govern food and its procurement.

Other chapters give and discuss additional geographical and sociological information, which, though not absolute or fundamental, may serve as a basis for informed discussion of the food situation and for making sound inferences.

The convergence of the arguments has the advantage, for the layman in science, that if any of the expository Chapters, or any section of them, is found to be too technical, they may be skipped without loss if he has read (say) the approaches by Accountancy and History, or any other two or three: since they all make what is necessarily the same case, though put in different dresses.

Fig. 1. 'And there was a very good Government film about not putting empty milk bottles on walls.'

Reproduced from the issue of *Punch* of 26th January, 1944, Vol. 206, p. 73, by kind permission of the artist (and present Editor) A. Bernard Hollowood. Photographed by Shoreham Photographic from a volume kindly lent by Borough of Hove Libraries.

[MI]   It is remarkable how closely the most seminal publications of Charles Darwin, Clausius, Cannizzaro, and Pasteur synchronized —almost to a year—around 1859. Darwin had taken note of new observations from the emerging sciences based on geology.

Some fuliginous modern writings about a continuous evolution— of technological progress and prosperity rather than of Man in the Darwinian sense—suggest a wry comparison with the geochronology of Bishop Ussher (1581-1656). When he was calculating the date of Creation as 4004 B.C., Ussher could benefit from no factual guidance such as Darwin enjoyed two centuries later. The modern secular Usshers-in-reverse appear to have divested themselves from the last hundred-and-seven years (approximately) of scientific discovery and reasoning; so it is hardly surprising that, in spite of the differences in mechanical and theological atmospheres, their cogitations about the future have an insubstantiality not unlike that of Ussher's writings.

Ussher argued backwards with a definite purpose in the light of careful scrutiny of the records available to him; the others argue vaguely forwards. Malthus's essay of 1798 appeared almost exactly midway between Ussher's time and the present. It was pre-scientific by roughly half a century. That it should still be in considerable vogue is not the least of the ironies of adult education in 'this scientific age'.

[M2]   Although the subject of chemical ecology is people, it is independent of personalities; it does not depend on opinion except within the limited field of choice about the way people conduct their affairs (*e.g.*, in preferring war as an alternative to starvation or other threat). Management decisions about courses of action always have to be made by people, however the facts or probabilities have been arrived at. The field of choice of human action is always limited by what is thermodynamically and logistically possible (if only as regards supply and fuelling of machines). In the ultimate matter of equilibrium-size of population there is no choice (unless Nature is personalized).

The mathematical approach to problems of decision as used in operational research—for example—may appear to be an exception; but operational research, though the aim may be to relate some kinds of people to their occupational environment, is (so far) a different thing from the complete study of Man in relation to the whole of his environment.

As 'operational research' people know, the modern corpus of techniques of mathematical statistical analysis of variables and probabilities had one foundation in the investigations of an Irish brewery chemist into enumeration of yeast cells, and it matured in the biological atmospheres of genetics and agricultural experimentation. Thus it had a wholly biological foundation. Its first application was to enumeration of soil bacteria at Rothamsted (Agricultural) Experimental Station in England. (H. G. Thornton, *Ann. Appl. Biol.*, 1922, Vol. 9, 241-71; R. A. Fisher, H. G. Thornton, and W. A. Mackenzie, *ibid.*, 325-59).

The successful application of the mathematical techniques devised before 1938 for probing into agricultural problems and expanded as 'operational research' in application to problems of convoying of ships, splinter damage to fighter aircraft, and numerous other problems in war and in industry, goes to show that the scientific method is independent of the material.

[M3]   Exponentially: in accordance with a progression well known to mathematicians. That fixed reserves will decrease (roughly) exponentially means that decrease of their availability will follow (roughly) a course like that of capital compounded at a negative rate of interest. They can never be absolutely exhausted: there will always be something left—if only in abandoned mines, for instance.

Consequently, talk about actual 'exhaustion' of fuel or ores is loose; it needs to be bridled with economic common-sense.

5

The approach through basic principles of accountancy

What God hath joined together no man shall ever put asunder: God will take care of that.
—George Bernard Shaw: *Getting Married*

Principles of exact equilibrium or balance being at the bottom of all workings of Nature (or God, if you prefer to say that: and please note that the quotation from Shaw has here been selected because he wrote 'what', not 'whom'), it is still true that the idea of being able to get something for nothing never —or hardly ever—fails to attract. It is not the rule in business to give value away; yet, there is a widespread and strong feeling, or hope, that food for a very large world population can somehow be legitimately got without paying something for it. A belief like that is contrary to the facts of observation and to every construction that can be put upon the relations between the two sides of any equation in Nature, or in any business transaction.

There is nothing new in the idea of Nature's working within a strict business-like framework of accountancy. Last century the physicist James Clerk Maxwell (1831-79) wrote: 'The transactions of the material universe appear to be conducted, as it were, on a system of credit. Each transaction consists of a transfer of so much credit or energy from one body to another. The act of transfer or payment we call work.' That statement may be compared with the bankers' maxim 'Every credit creates a debit.' Both are true.

You will be familiar with the idea expressed in advertisements by people having a little capital who want to buy a substantial share in, or perhaps the whole of, a small business. There is always a sentence like: 'Accounts must bear investigation'; if it is not printed, it is implied as a matter of ordinary prudence about getting correct information in every business matter.

There is an old story about a lady who was told by her bank manager that her account was overdrawn. 'That's impossible', she is reported to have said; 'I still have plenty of cheques left.' One needs to be slightly less innocent about money to see that that simple story, like its continuation that she promptly offered to make out a cheque to meet the deficit, represents a misunderstanding about the difference between real capital and belief in its paper representation. Not everybody will be as quick to grasp that the story is an almost faithful burlesque of what is commonly believed about not having to worry about supplies of fuel—and especially what is thought about infinite supplies of energy having come into sight now that 'progress' has brought nuclear fuel on to the practical, everyday, horizon. As with printing unlimited notes or cheques, so will no form of energy be encashable for food; nor does nuclear fuel drop from the skies to be had for the picking-up. It is obtained from a complicated process of chemical concentration of metals that is quite expensive in its consumpt of ordinary fuels and sulphur. As Oscar Wilde wrote in 1895: 'Even these metallic problems have their melodramatic side.' In 1895 that was only about money.

As regards food and population—there has been a lack of that kind of accurate, dead-pan, impersonal scrutiny of the facts resembling the way in which every business is audited, if only for income-tax purposes. Confidence-tricksters flourish because of people who are at the same time greedy and credulous—as well as not sufficiently well informed about the actual ownership of Brooklyn Bridge or the Eiffel Tower—when they expect to be able to get hold, for almost nothing, of something very valuable.

To remind a businessman of that is not to suggest that teachers of elementary biology in schools, or apparently more learned sociologists of the kinds discussed in Chapter 3, have been deliberately fooling people by informing them wrongly (or not informing them at all) about the origins of food. It is not as if there had been a deliberate attempt during the last few generations of teachers and taught at running a kind of Fagin's school; it is rather more that they themselves have not known. They have therefore been supposing the material currencies of Nature as never-failing and thus to be taken for granted—without enquiry or audit. Teaching about the origins of food has been kept deliberately—like that in Dotheboys Hall and schools of agriculture—strongly 'practical': which means that it has been conducted on pragmatic lines aimed at immediate profit and nothing beyond; and any enlightened businessman will agree that the short-term views are not always the best. For example, at Dotheboys Hall the boys were taught on the lines: 'w-i-n, win; d-e-r, der; now go and clean it.' The intention was good and economical; but it will be agreed that both the methodology and the matter of what was taught left something to be desired.

About food, the simplicist notion is part of the established order of things that food is produced by nothing more than each day's ration of sunlight and carbon dioxide (which cost nothing); hence, large numbers of otherwise educated people have no doubts about it. Consequently, qualms are not commonly excited (unless by thinking how crowded the world may become) by the prospect of sustaining a world population many times larger than now exists.

The fallacy could not have arisen, nor could it continue to exist among educated people, if it had not been supported by a wholly false view that science is practically the same thing as technology and 'progress' in all material directions. Technology, like food-production, depends on fuel; but the continuance of fuel, and the emergence of some substitute if fuel becomes scarce, are taken for granted; which means, without scientific or any other kind of thought being brought into the question. Instead, a wish-fulfilment that is evident in believing that food comes from origins which are inexhaustible as well as 'free' takes the place of recognizing the businesslike necessity of always having something to exchange for food; and 'science' is looked upon—again magically—as a sort of

Aladdin's lamp able to fulfil almost any material wish. Since (it is alleged) science, on the basis of past discovery, will surely, in the form of future research, discover the correct way of stroking the magic lamp, where is the problem even if the method of solving it is not yet apparent?

If you recall what was in Chapter 1, you will see that that is not only fantastic but is a totally wrong view of what real science is. You do not conduct your business solely on a basis of fantasy buoyed up by the hope of a beautiful picture of what your balance and credit will look like in ten years' time. You are more realistic.

Since it is often said that production of food by agriculture and fishing in any technically-advanced country has become a science-based business, why not treat it as a business, and a science-based one?

As a scientist, I don't know much about the details of business; and if I go wrong, you will be able to correct mistakes. I need, however, not stray far from the broad principles of trade—which, in the main are (I repeat) the same as those by which the business of Nature is invariably conducted. Indeed, if we take the American word 'trade' (in the sense of exchanging one thing for another) we have the whole thing summed up for both Nature and business.

In Nature there is never any profit; neither is there loss from the standpoint of thermodynamics. Loss from the human point of view in trading one thing for another—that is, what engineers and agricultural scientists would call 'losses in conversion', of coal into electricity or hen-food into eggs—are normal, almost inevitable; and the human gain is in convenience. The balance sheet in energy and matter is always balanced, when everything is taken into consideration.

A large part of science is concerned (as already explained to some extent in Chapter 3) with what cannot be done. That has two aspects: it embraces (a) what cannot be done at all—like getting perpetual motion; and (b) what cannot be done without incurring those almost inevitable trading losses which are cheerfully suffered by Man because he temporarily gains something by way of comfort or convenience. Thus, Man cannot eat grass and similar fodder; so he is prepared to

pay a high price (up to 80 % of what he puts in) in order to get
20 % or so of eggs or meat or electricity or whatever it is that
he can enjoy. Nature has employed the full 100 %; whether
it is to warm the hen (and her egg) and thus warm the
atmosphere, besides keeping her active and alive; or to warm
the air around the electricity station or whatever. Not only
does the sum of what Man uses as fuel or food (etc.) *plus*
all the 'conversion losses' invariably add up to 100 %, but it
is known to be impossible to get more than 100 %, of what is
put into any process, out again. The one example I can think
of of getting exactly as much out of a device as is put into it, is
the ordinary electric bar fire. That device yields, as heat, the
exact equivalent of the electricity that reaches the ends of
each bar; but there has been a big fraction of loss before
the electricity gets into the house.

We seem to have wandered a little from a straight comparison of business with natural operations in general, but
on the way I have repeated the point that natural laws are
explicit about 'nothing for nothing'; and the point about
conversion losses has been brought in, so as to suggest that
in any technological operation conducted by man there can
reasonably be no other hope than to expect a big loss.
Whether it is convenience, or food, that you are after, you
must expect to pay for it: and pretty heavily in terms of
natural resources. The modern use of sulphur, coal, and other
combustibles for making fertilizers to produce extra food is
decidedly expensive in raw materials—to say nothing of trans-
portation charges which (under modern conditions) all have
to be paid for in fuel.

'Something for nothing', as a creed for obtaining food,
perhaps begins to look a little groggy. In business there is
often the appearance of getting something for less than cost
as anybody will recall when he (or she) thinks of loss-leaders,
sales of water-damaged salvage stock, or any one of thousands
of other examples. Part of business depends upon inducing
the housewife—by means of coupons, 'free gifts', and other
psychologically attractive devices—to believe that value is
being given for less than cost. Some of the price-reductions
may be below actual cost; but does any person, if not men-

tally simple, not believe that somewhere along the line everything has to be paid for—even if 'only' by the insurance companies and those further along the line of value for value?

Businessman and scientist thus have much common ground
in deciding that food, also, always has to be paid for in
modern conditions. Once upon a time—and this is not a fairy
story, but fact—primitive man gathered wild nuts and fruit
and killed animals with stone axes and lived off what he could
find to eat and to clothe himself and his women and children
by his own muscular efforts alone; if he failed to find enough
food, he died: either of starvation or by going to war with
the next tribe so as to reduce the numbers of mouths in
both tribes to a working equilibrium [M1]. It was as simple
as that; furthermore, a similar state of affairs—including cooking with wood, but refined by use of implements made from
metal smelted with wood—lasted substantially into the recent
historic period. So long as that state lasted, man was always in
equilibrium (though a rough and often painful one) with perpetually-renewable natural resources. Nature saw to it that
the balance was kept.

In our modern highly-developed economic societies based
on trade and on extensive use of fossil fuel not only for producing food but for making and producing comforts and amenity, we have changed all that; or have we? The change will
last approximately as long as the stocks of fossil fuel last. It is
as simple as that.

Fossil fuel is the exchange-material for all our amenities as
well as for much of our food: and when fossil fuel becomes
scarce there will be a struggle for it: because there will not be
enough timber and vegetable products to burn; fossil fuel is
the only other material to exchange not only for food but for all
the kinds of weapons and comfort to which technically-advanced Man has become accustomed, and all the 'progress'
he has come to expect.

That follows from business principles: or—if you prefer
—from the natural requirements of always being obliged to
exchange one thing for something else: whether that 'something else' is food for keeping people alive or for satisfying any
other of people's demands.

If you are an actuary, you may be thinking that some, perhaps all, 'laws' in science are really theories that apply strictly only to mathematical models; or that the laws are a sort of statistical shorthand; and that the basis they really have is statistical. You may be right; is a point I would love to discuss with you (but not here), along with such semantic points as whether any of the laws can be held to be 'true' or 'valid'; or whether there is such a quality or virtue as truth and validity in an absolute sense. The only postulate for which I ask acceptance now about the laws of Nature is they are good working rules which have been found immensely useful in practice: like those of business and life assurance where chances are offered against payment; while nobody expects, in the long run, to get something for nothing (or, as the French say, because he makes lovely eyes). The example of the brick that does not jump suggests one probability as a sufficient guide to sound belief and action. We need not argue whether thermodynamic laws are senior to inferences properly drawn from bills of mortality, the postulate being that they all are reliable as the basis of some corporate bet or gamble (to refer you to Chapter 1).

There is nothing difficult or occult whatever. It is just as easy for anyone who knows about business to grasp the idea of equilibrium being the basis of science as it is for a scientist to tell you that that is so: the businessman already is equipped with the basic ideas of exchange and 'nothing for nothing' and balancing something against something: which are also Nature's own.

What will, very likely, be a novelty for any but a handful of scientists is the notion that most food does, nowadays, come in exchange for fossil fuels. This book may have been your first opportunity of learning about the necessity of having fuel to exchange for population; but once you know about the relation of fuel to people (and not just to keep machines running) the rest follows.

The course of the evolution of the practice of exchanging fossil fuel for (a) manufactures first, and (b) for food a little later, is the subject of the next Chapter.

[MI]   The White King in 'Through the Looking-glass' made a
note: 'The White Knight is sliding down the poker; he balances
very badly.' In this semantic discussion—of the sort of problem
that seems inseparable from popular exposition of scientific matters
—I leave it as 'an exercise for the student' to decide whether anything would have been gained in precision—apart from any question
of suitability of language to the childish occasion—to write that the
White Knight is very bad at maintaining his equilibrium. Hint: it
is a question whether he was at any time, and in what sense, in
equilibrium: of which, and of logical language, Lewis Carroll was
an expert judge.

6

The approach through historical fact:
the introduction of fuel

Agriculture is the series of processes whereby a given area of land is
artificially induced to yield food for more animals and people than
it would naturally support.
—slightly modified, without change of sense, from the paper by John
Bennet Lawes: (1814-1900): *On agricultural chemistry, J. Roy.
Agric. Soc. England,* 1847, Vol. 8, 226-60

Agriculture includes cultivation of non-food crops such as
those which produce rubber, fibres (hemp, ramie, sisal), drugs
and essential oils (mint, opium, quinine, ylang-ylang), as well
as products in an intermediate category such as cocoa and tea,
and some (like cotton) producing both food and fibre. Nevertheless, Lawes's remark holds good today, as a statement of the
relation between agriculture and food.

The statement testifies to the amazing percipience of a
young Englishman at a time when agriculture used almost
no fuel for any purpose, use of fertilizers had barely begun,
and there was practically no agricultural chemistry or other
agricultural science except what Lawes had discovered for
himself after absorbing some hints from Justus von Liebig
(1803-73) and others. Liebig's pioneering ideas about the
ways in which plants obtain nutrients from soil were not all
sound; because he was a pioneer, that cannot be held against
him. Lawes was almost invariably and uncannily right, yet
Liebig remained unwilling to accept Lawes's clear demonstrations of the relations between plants and the sources of
their nutrition.

Because a mention of fertilizers is liable to arouse emotional overtones—especially in a discussion of artificiality—

it seems necessary to clear the ground towards a rational presentation of the food situation past and present.

Fertilizers were probably not, about 1846, uppermost in Lawes's mind; but, instead of speculating on the state of his thoughts, I emphasize that *every* form of agriculture always is artificial whenever practised by primitive or advanced peoples. As a minimum operation of art, the native trees must be removed, or the grass sod dug up, in order to make room for agriculture and to be only one step beyond the hunting-and-fishing and nomadic stages of relying on wholly natural produce.

After the seeds are sown or the fruit-bushes planted, some attempts must be made to keep the soil free from weeds and tree-seedlings which, by springing up, declare that they, and not crops, are the natural types of vegetation. A stage further is the growing of crops on dug or ploughed land, in straight evenly-spaced rows of only one kind of plant; and that is highly artificial—there being nothing like it in natural conditions.

The agriculture most nearly like Nature's own way is grassland husbandry, wherein a mixture of species are between them allowed to compete and cover the soil in order to be eaten by animals; but that always involves a high degree of human interference extending to both herbage and animals. (The technical name for it is management; it can involve much skill where it is possible to grow good agricultural grasses at all).

On land which is naturally covered with 'grass'—say, the American prairies—no system of human management will, in general, 'work' to produce (in Lawes's words) 'food for more animals and people than it would naturally support': because there is not enough rainfall; the greater part of the former prairies are put to growing an endless succession of wheat crops for the good reason that hardly anything else which is acceptable to Man will grow there except wheat.

On the point about artificiality Lawes was absolutely right: because every form of agriculture is inherently artificial, whether fertilizers and tractors and other modern devices are used or not. On the point about agriculture's

yielding more food (and hence more people) than the soil
would produce if left to itself, he was right also. It was because
he put that matter in a nutshell that I quoted him.

I may here attempt to avoid another possible miscon-
ception. It might arise because I quote Lawes or anyone
else. In this book no words are quoted in support or re-
buttal for the unscientific reason that their author, in his
person, is regarded as an 'authority' about the argument.
There is nothing like an attempt to count heads or to
muster opinions. The case stands on its natural strength, of
which the foundations have been visible for a long time. In
seeking to direct attention to these foundations I can do
no more than point them out: they are there, whatever anyone may say. Quotations are given simply because they are
beautifully worded, apposite or suggestive, or just amusing.

The history of the rise of industrialization based on fossil
fuel is so well known (at least in outline) and is for the
most part so amply documented that it is unnecessary to
make more than a few remarks about it. The main chrono-
logical facts are diagramatically outlined in Fig. 3, Chapter
17. For the purpose of this survey, uses in industry and/or
machines can be taken to include cooking and space-heating
(in Britain, almost exclusively based on coal until the end
of the last century); and, because industrial and manufac-
turing uses of fossil fuel may be said to have originated in
Western Europe, and indeed to have been for a long time
almost confined to Britain, the remarks about early industrial use will refer mainly in Britain. [MI]

Accounts of the Industrial Revolution usually give un-
due attention to the rise of importance of coal for driving
steam-engines and other machinery, and for making iron
(and later, steel) to make the machinery and its associated
constructions such as railways, ship hulls, and fixed buildings. In spite of the good stories which have come down to
us from all that, it should be recalled that use of coal for
what may be broadly called chemical manufactures ('engineering without wheels') as well as for space-heating, became

important earlier than did its use for machines and smelting of ores. The early chemical manufactures included making of glass (notably in the north-east of England), and of salt by evaporation of sea-water in many coastal parts of Britain. Gunpowder, fireworks, sulphuric acid, bleach, and many other chemical products were manufactured on a relatively large scale in Britain and France before the 'Rocket' locomotive ran. These were possibly Less Memorable though leading to good stories (one is mentioned in Chapter 16, Appendix II, Note A7) and to the establishment in Glasgow of what was for a time the largest chemical works in the world. The relation of coal to food remained indirect and mechanical for many years (Chapter 4, page 34; and page 58).

Sulphur (in gunpowder) was the first combustible mineral to be put to use for power and for gathering food. In firearms, gunpowder helped to bring down wild game, the explosive being an early form of power. Until about 1840 sulphur, either as element or in sulphuric acid and other compounds, found no other important use in production of food; though sulphur-containing ores yielded metal of which some was used for agricultural and related purposes.

Until about 1860 the chief use of coal for purposes connected with food was in land transport; coal then began to assume importance for sea transport [M2]. After about 1890 steam vessels were increasingly used for fishing. Petroleum and natural gas could hardly be said to be important for any food purpose before 1910; and their use for making fertilizers became notable only after about 1922.

It is worth noting that in the United States wood ceased to be the principal fuel for all purposes as late as 1907; and in that country animal power in agriculture—typified by the famous multi-mule teams on the prairies—reached its peak about 1918. Mechanization and electrification of agriculture in the United Kingdom took off rapidly after about 1937. Use of coal for making iron (steel after 1860) and for cooking increased throughout the period; and spread of canning and, more recently, refrigeration also increased demands on fossil fuels in many spheres of food technology.

Use of fertilizers to augment the proportion of soluble

nutrients released by renewable natural agencies from soil can be said to have begun in 1840. In that year, large quantities of guano began to be imported into Britain from Peru; importation of nitrate of soda began from Chile; and manufacture of superphosphate began on a commercial scale in 1842 [M3].

Guano may be called a recent fossil; it consists of an accumulation of droppings, dead chicks, feathers, and other mainly organic material from islands in dry climates where sea-birds have nested [M4]. It is usually regarded as both a nitrogenous and a phosphatic fertilizer, but its calcium should not be overlooked. [M5]

Nitrate of soda is an ancient fossil which occurs in deposits of unknown—possibly bacterial—origin in Chilean deserts; the commercial article is nearly pure sodium nitrate. It is regarded as chiefly a nitrogenous fertilizer, but is especially valuable in farm practice because, unlike most nitrogenous fertilizers, its sodium provides the exact equivalent of alkali for neutralizing its nitrate; whereas many nitrogenous fertilizers set up a strong demand for lime or chalk to be supplied to neutralize the acidity bacterially produced in soil from unneutralized compounds of nitrogen. [M5]

Superphosphate and its small-scale predecessor known as 'dissolved bones' provide phosphate, calcium, and sulphate.

Up to 1860 there were no more novelties; but by-product sulphate of ammonia from gasworks was a useful supplement to nitrogen and sulphur derived from other manures, though (like many organic manures) it was not capable of avoiding the loss of alkaline minerals that followed its use on soil. [M5] Since the sulphate of ammonia was a gasworks by-product which conserved the nitrogen (which would otherwise have been wasted) from coal, we need not debit that fuel against the production of sulphate of ammonia; nevertheless, the 'sulphate' part of it had to be obtained by burning sulphur. [M6] Potassium is supplied in relatively large proportion by farmyard manure and other materials of recent plant origin. It has not been mentioned because potassium salts did not come into common use as fertilizers until the last quarter of the century; until then, farmers had to do without a concentrated source of one of the most important needs of heavy crops. [M7]

Farmers in some districts could obtain lime and a little supplementary phosphate by digging local deposits—often directly under the soil—of chalk and 'marl'. 'Burning' of limestone to make quicklime for agricultural use was one of the earliest [M8] uses of coal in agriculture; it was chemically unnecessary but saved transport and was a convenient substitute for grinding a hard material.

The position of fuel in farming remained until the end of last century much the same as has been set out here— apart from the expanding use of fertilizers in Britain and Western Europe, and, with some lag, in the 'new' countries. Novelties like 'potash' required little but mechanical power for mining and a crude processing; and basic slag (a fertilizer valuable because it is rich in phosphate and lime, and makes a useful contribution of magnesium) is a by-product of steel manufacture and cannot be debited against fuel, except that it is very hard and requires much power for grinding to a high degree of fineness. Use of steam-power on farms never caught on to involve much coal, in spite of having enthusiastic advocates who early prophesied a 'revolution'—which did not arrive much before 1930, with the internal-combustion engine.

It is not the purposes of this Chapter or book to provide a detailed survey of fertilizers such as is better given in text-books like that of A. M. Smith [M9]. What is socially important to know is that use of fuel in fertilizers is only one factor in farm management for an increased production of food; hence, this historical discussion must return to broader themes after one more note on fertilizers as they looked before about 1860.

The novelty of 'artificials', as they were called, consisted in their carrying in small bulk a large poundage of plant nutrients (with the notable exception of potassium) that had been provided in massive bulk by farmyard manure. Consequently, users of nitrate of soda, superphosphate, and guano were often derided as 'Wheel-barrow farmers': though partly for the wrong reasons [since farmyard manure on account of its content of straw and other plant residues produces naturally good effects on the *structure* of soil (page 120) that cannot be matched by supplying nutrients alone]. However, in some respects the wheel-barrow farmers were on the right lines; they had to convince doubters about the efficacy of adding supplies of nutrients to soils which had been partially exhausted by years of traditional farming. Such a one who 'proved by doing' was Wren Hoskyns: demonstrating his large crop after an application of guano, he said: 'The Penguin of the vast Pacific was the Wizard that had made this crop, not I.' [M10]

[M1]   In an article 'Domestic life in Sardinia' (*The Philosophical Journal*, 1966, Vol. 3, 19-30) Professor M. F. M. Meiklejohn remarked *à propos* of the mountainous region known as the Barbagia: "The fuel is wood, for coal is unknown, as it was on the mainland of Italy until the eighteenth century. Then it was considered impious for man to burn rocks, which the Lord had not intended him to do, and this might be thought in remoter Sardinia even today."

[M2]   The Suez Canal was opened in 1869; between 1860 and 1870 the registered steamer tonnage increased from less than half a million to over a million; by 1880 it was nearly three millions. 1870 was the peak year for sailing vessels, with a registered tonnage of $4\frac{1}{2}$ millions.

[M3]   Sulphur is not usually regarded as a fuel. Sulphur provides several instances of the traditional preoccupation with machines rather than with people. At World Conferences devoted to problems of power and energy, sulphur is never mentioned because it has not been commonly burnt under boilers. However, in making sulphuric acid for superphosphate or other end-product the first step is to burn the sulphur in air. In a modern factory using elemental sulphur the greater part of the electrical energy needed by the whole works is produced from steam generated by burning molten sulphur, of which the supply is regulated by turning a single valve: just as if the sulphur were fuel oil.

Most elemental sulphur is produced by the ingenious process invented by the American, Dr Herman Frasch, in 1904 for melting-out (by steam) underground deposits occurring in the southern United States and Mexico. Sulphur is also extracted from sulphur-rich natural gas occurring mostly in North America, though France has lately found so much of this 'sour' gas that she is producing from it about a million and a half tons of pure sulphur annually.

There are other large-scale methods of obtaining sulphur and sulphuric acid; all those methods involve use of carbonaceous fuel.

It can be estimated that sulphur produced by the Frasch process alone has, after its conversion into superphosphate, generated enough protein to keep alive about a sixth of the population of the countries using superphosphate. That would be no mean claim to make on behalf of the enterprise of United States citizens in making 'Frasch' sulphur available to a hungry world; but it has been left for a British publication to make it. 'Brimstone: the stone that burns' by Williams Haynes (New York: D. Van Nostrand Company, Inc. 1959) is the 'official' story of the Frasch process, and was issued under the auspices of the biggest U.S.A. sulphur company; the point was not mentioned in it.

W. H. G. Armytage, a British engineer, published in 1961 'A social history of engineering' (London: Faber & Faber) which does not appear to mention the Frasch process, though that is a clever engineering device and has had considerable social consequences.

[M4]   Now that the guano deposits known before 1860 have long been exhausted, some countries having suitable islands 'crop' guano by letting fresh deposits accumulate during a few years.

A substitute for guano (but principally employed as a protein-and-phosphate supplement in animal feeding) is the meal produced directly from small fish which abound off the coast of Peru; in the last few years the meal has become one of Peru's two principal exports, large quantities of it being sent annually to Europe. The fish provided the principal food of the guano birds; and it is possible that the Peruvian sea-birds may decline in numbers because of a shortage of their food.

[M5]   Acidification of soil after application of some nitrogenous manures has been tardily recognized to be important. It was first scientifically noticed by J. T. Way in 1856 as a consequence of use of the organic manures sheep excreta and shoddy (woollen rags); what Way wrote stands true to-day. The phenomenon of soil deterioration from acidification became acute on many British farms in the 1920's as a consequence of unwise use of much sulphate of ammonia without liming. That led to an unfortunate confusion between soil scientists (who sometimes got the blame) and fertilizer salesmen.

It is only since about 1935 that disinterested agricultural advice to farmers has seriously stressed the necessity for liming in conjunction with fertilizer use of concentrated nitrogenous materials other than nitrate of soda (also nitrate of lime, popular in Europe but not used in Britain). It was recently estimated that fertilizer use of sulphate of ammonia alone sets up a requirement for a million tons of ground limestone to be added to British soils each year.

Farmyard manure does not acidify soil, because it happens to

c

contain enough alkalies to neutralise its nitrogen; nitrogen-free superphosphate does not acidify soil. It may be noted that this adverse effect from combined nitrogen in fertilizers is wholly independent of its origin (animal, organic, or 'synthetic').

[M6]   Until about 1905 sulphur used for making fertilizers was largely a by-product of smelting of sulphur-rich metallic ores, purification of town's gas, and other industrial processes; so, like the nitrogen of sulphate of ammonia, it could hardly be debited as virgin fuel.

A large proportion of modern sulphate of ammonia is made from synthetic ammonia by combining it with sulphate from gypsum, thus avoiding use of either elemental sulphur or sulphuric acid; it nevertheless makes relatively heavy use of carbonaceous fuel.

Until expansion of industry in Western Europe produced sulphur (or sulphuric acid) as a by-product as just mentioned, all the world's sulphur was obtained either from volcanoes or from sedimentary deposits (of marine bacterial origin) like those of Sicily. The Sicilian deposits were so important for early industry that in 1838 the British Government sent a gunboat to make sure that virtual monopoly did not interrupt supplies of sulphur at reasonable prices.

Pizarro, having left ships and stores on the eastern side of the Isthmus of Panama, obtained sulphur from Andean volcanoes during his first voyage southwards along the eastern coast of the Pacific.

[M7]   From about 1800 an increasingly important source of potassium in British farming was imported oil-seeds. These were mainly imported for their oil-content (for colza-oil lamps and other uses). After the oil had been pressed out, the residue was used directly as manure (rape cake); or, if fed to cattle (linseed cake or cattle cake) much of its potassium reached the soil via the dung and urine.

[M8]   Making salt by evaporation of sea-water around British coasts was possibly the earliest use of coal in connexion with food and trade. It was typified by the works at Prestonpans (Firth of Forth) which used local coal, and by numerous salt-pans along the English eastern and southern coasts that relied on coal brought by sea from the neighbourhood of Newcastle when inland carriage of salt from the Cheshire mines to the neighbourhood of those coasts was difficult. The salt was mostly used for preservation of meat and fish. A notable outlet for salt meat was victualling of ocean-going shipping. Since some of that brought back food, and spices esteemed because they helped to disguise the flavour of, as well as preserve, much nominally 'fresh' meat, an indirect role of coal in food technology was not negligible in the days of sailing-ships; also, export of salt fish must then have accounted for an appreciable tonnage of British coal. Incidentally, and showing how recent is disuse of methods of making use of renewable resources for providing food, the prosperity of Poole (Dorset) depended until almost the end of last century on its imports of sun-dried cod from Newfoundland.

[M9] 'Manures and Fertilisers' (Nelson, Edinburgh and London; various editions) by A. M. Smith gives a succinct account of origins and composition for those who can follow chemistry.

[M10] Wren Hoskyns, 'Talpa: or the Chronicles of a Clay Farm,' 2nd edn. 1853. The farm being clayey, it is probable that the soil naturally released enough potassium to suffice, with guano, for a good crop. 'Talpa' is one of the minor masterpieces of English literature. The chapter devoted to Hoskyns and 'Talpa' makes one of the many stories in Crichton Porteous's book 'Pioneers of Fertility' (Fertiliser Journal, London. 1949).

7

The historical approach: The two Agricultural Revolutions—protein the axles

At twelve he [T. H. Huxley] had read Hamilton's essay *On the Philosophy of the Unconditioned*, with the result, he tells us, of stamping on his mind 'the strong conviction that on even the most solemn and important of questions, men are apt to take cunning phrases for answers.'
—Edward Clodd: *Thomas Henry Huxley*, Edinburgh: Blackwood. 1902

Hoskyns may be left gazing at his guano-fed turnips, while we go back a hundred years beyond his time to the beginning of what is usually called 'The' Agricultural Revolution, but which on account of its completion and fulfilment by a second major innovation, at the turn of the present century, is better called the First Agricultural Revolution. The inception of that was contemporary with the Industrial Revolution; unlike the Industrial Revolution, it is historically remarkable for having had its real bases misunderstood and misrepresented in almost all sociological studies, which have also missed what has happened in the important matter of producing protein in our own time. [MI]

Since the reader will probably have little difficulty in finding an incorrect statement of the development of 'the' Agricultural Revolution, a potted version of the customary one will suffice here.

The exordium is the introduction of Enclosure with hedges and wooden fencing, of what was formerly common land, so as to divide it into privately-owned fields; the economic and agricultural benefits to the landlord, and indeed to the soil and its products, are stressed; as are the miseries of dispossessed cottagers. 'Yields of corn and turnips were improved'; so was the output and quality of Meat, partly because the breeds of cattle were improved, and partly because growing turnips provided the novelty of cattle-food which could be stored throughout the winter, so as to keep the cattle alive [M2]. Mention will, most likely, be made of prominent agriculturists like 'Turnip' Townshend (a farmer who pioneered the four-course rotation of crops now known as the Norfolk rotation), Coke of Norfolk, and others: also with a strong emphasis on turnips alongside wheat, barley, and other cereals, and meat-production.

The story usually ends there. Many writers (though not Jacks [M1] a scientist; or Crichton Porteous, *ref.* M10, p. 59, who was a farmer) fail to give prominence to, or even to mention, the broad-leaved, 'arable', annual, or 'Dutch' clover which was the axis of the whole thing around which the First Agricultural Revolution revolved and on which it all depended as the chief agency by which extra protein was brought into the system. [M3]

Since turnips and cereals are poor in protein, and meat cannot be produced alive without a rich source of protein, the story from Enclosure to Meat does entirely lack the most elementary human or animal nutritional sense if it leaves out the essential clovers from any Agricultural Revolution. (To anticipate a little, the Second Agricultural Revolution also depended on clovers and their leguminous allies, but mostly perennials). Incidentally, the same sort of nutritional nonsense is exhibited by writing that the growing population of the Industrial Revolution were fed by increased imports of cereals from overseas—and leaving it at that. 'Turnip' Townshend's nickname typifies the old-fashioned neglect of the humble clovers; he was given the name more than two hundred years ago, long before anything was known about protein-accumulation and nitrogen-fixation in leguminous crops (of which clovers are the type); but is there a reason for modern historical writers to show ignorance about protein equal to that of farmers of the eighteenth century?

Up to about 1860 in Europe, and until forty or fifty years later in the 'new' countries, most agriculture was performed without direct use of fuel; imports of oil-seeds and guano and so forth were in sailing ships until almost recent times. There were still until, about 1860, 60 million bison or buffalo roaming the western plains of North America [M4], and not much agricultural inroad had been made into the eastern forests (wherein the largest native animal was the turkey). The 'white' history of New Zealand had barely begun, and that of Australia was hardly seventy years old. In none of these countries—except for small areas of eastern North America—were there by 1850 any agriculturally useful grasses or clovers. New Zealand and Australia did not possess a single native forage legume, and the native grasses and legumes of North America were good only for free-ranging beasts such as the bison.

The 'new' countries all lacked—except for what had been sporadically imported by Spanish and other colonists—not only productive livestock, but the means with which to feed them on a proper farming scale. This brings up an oddity of British public consciousness. Thanks to publicity given to high prices paid by overseas buyers at auction sales for individual animals of pure-bred stock such as the Hereford and Aberdeen Angus breeds of cattle, everybody knows that the animal foundation of American herds (and some others) is British or European; and some people known that New Zealand mutton is largely derived from the Romney Marsh in Kent. The white faces of Hereford cattle are conspicuous in many 'Western' films.

In 1860, not only were the present vast herds and flocks of protein-producing farm livestock absent from the 'new' countries, but so were the means to feed them and the knowledge about land management that often had to be gained by painful trial-and-error lasting almost until our own day. The agricultural history of all this protein-production as meat, milk, eggs (also beans for direct human consumption) effectively began only in the 'eighties of last century; and some of its most dramatic episodes—such as the sudden realization of the value of the soya bean for the United States—occurred only after the First World War.

Until about 1880, then, all the 'new' countries lacked almost entirely all the essentials for producing protein in quantity. Besides most of the livestock and the know-how (especially that about rotation of crops) (given the climate), these lacks were: (*i*) the grasses and the clovers and other legumes that are agriculturally productive in European terms and could be incorporated into a rotation of cropping or could form the basis of good pastures for a grassland economy of animal husbandry (which is New Zealand's principal mode of farming); and (*ii*) the phosphatic and other fertilizers with which to sustain the new protein-rich crops and keep them productive, for the animals especially.

The well-known injunction 'Go West, young man' is of this mid-century period; it was addressed to settlers in regions east of Lake Michigan that had been colonized by people who had come down from the Appalachians into a plain which they could not farm properly. The saying was not simply advice to the adventurous (as it is often taken to be); it meant that the only method of getting better crops was to shift from soil almost exhausted after a few years' farming without fertilizers and without any rotation which included a legume: and then to make a fresh start by breaking up virgin soil a few miles west.

Just at that time seeds of the legume alfalfa (known as lucerne in Britain) were being imported into the United States. That the fruition of that was not to come for almost forty years is attested by references to alfalfa in some stories by O. Henry (1862-1910), in which it features as a comparative novelty. By O. Henry's time superphosphate and other fertilizers were being manufactured within or imported into the United States; and grasses and clovers also imported from Europe had spread enough to be able to complement alfalfa and to form the basis of modern North American intensive production of protein for human consumption.

Except for the soya bean (a modern introduction from Eastern Asia) and some warm-temperate forage crops of lesser importance, it remains true that all the 'balancing' protein of the 'new' countries is produced, with the aid of appropriate fertilizers, by grasses and clovers (including alfalfa) brought from Europe and the Mediterranean region.

Before the days of commercial farm seedsmen, many of

the seeds came accidentally in the baggage of the early settlers, having been brought in sweepings of hay-lofts for filling pillows or for feeding hens on the voyage; and, of course, that brought European weeds as well (but that is another set of stories). Subterranean clover—or just 'sub'—a Mediterranean clover which is now the principal legume forage of Australia, is said to have been introduced by the wreck of a ship going to another destination in the Pacific; I do not guarantee the truth of that detail, and many actual and attempted introductions of grasses and clovers capable of producing good yields of protein were made consciously: sometimes at great trouble and expense incurred by bodies concerned with improvement of agriculture.

Just in that sort of way that 'Turnip' Townshend's nickname indicated oversight of the annual clover which was his chief contribution to a productive rotational system of arable (ploughland) cropping in Britain, so has there been a complete oversight in popular idiom of the perennial, creeping, 'wild white' clover which is the basis of productive grassland farming in every temperate region of the world; excepting the warmer parts, as in Australia, where the closely-related 'sub' clover does similar office.

Grassland farming does not, except in Scottish practice, lead to production of vegetable crops directly edible by people. It is associated with animal production and thus with meat and milk, and sometimes horses. Kentucky is famous for its 'bluegrass' pastures and for its racehorses. Neither the bluegrass nor its indispensable companion and prop, the perennial clover, is native to America, let alone Kentucky: but it is the grass that has unjustly had all the limelight and has acquired not a little glamour.

Possibly because of the limestone soil, as well as because of the presence of the Kentish-type clover, the grass known in English as smooth-stalked meadow grass flourished in Kentucky to the extent that the name by which it is known in the United States became attached to the Kentucky pastures. Smooth-stalked meadow grass (*Poa pratensis*) is common all over Britain and temperate Europe but rarely becomes as conspicuous or, as the agricultural ecologists say, 'dominant', in herbage as it does in Kentucky.

There, as in all other grassland, a grass sward of any kind requires an ample supply of assimilable nitrogen around its roots; if nitrogen compounds are not added as animal excreta or as fertilizer, the nitrogen has to come from clover or other suitable companion leguminous plant able to fix nitrogen biologically from the air: and that nitrogen-fixation by the legume has to be aided by adequate fertilizing to bring the supporting minerals, needed by both grass and clover (to say nothing of the needs of the animals for production of bone, flesh, and milk). The minerals necessary in the fertilizers are phosphate, sulphate, calcium, trace elements, etc. where the soil does not naturally supply them in quantities ample for a continuous high level of production of whatever it is that Man wants from the grassland.

There may seem a need for a pause for breath; but this will have exemplified how the story of increased production of human food and other crops is always a chain which is at least as long as that of 'The House that Jack built.' The words 'where the soil does not naturally supply them' (the nutrients needed for a high and constant level of production) means, in practice, 'almost everywhere'. Jack has built his roomy house in just the last few decades, and has undertaken to use quite a lot of fuel in that process; moreover, he is bound to go on using fuel, for as long as he can, to keep all the inhabitants fed who have come to occupy the new house.

Throughout Europe the problem of increasing the output of protein for human consumption after about 1750 had taken a different shape from that which it was to assume in our own time in the 'new' countries. In the British Isles the annual clovers (like the one used by Townshend), and the perennial 'wild white' clover and its relatives, were already present practically everywhere.

The annual clovers were not suitable for grassland; but even the poorest 'grass' contained a sprinkling of 'wild white' and its allies such as what children call 'eggs-and-bacon'. These perennial legumes, especially 'wild white', were fully if instinctively, appreciated by graziers, who jealously refrained from ploughing up old grassland (like that of the English midlands) which bore a good proportion of them. That reluctance arose because if the pastures were ploughed up, there was no means of replacing the 'wild white' and other perennials except by the slow process like that which foresters call 'natural regeneration' (*i.e.*, in this instance, relying on seed brought by birds and other accidental agencies), or the ancient process of 'inoculation' which consisted of bringing turves from a clovery pasture and allowing the roots to spread. Quite simply: pastures were not portable; and regions rich in clover and therefore able to produce much meat, wool, and milk from grass remained agriculturally as well as geographically isolated.

In the eighteenth century something was done to strengthen existing perennial clovers and to restore losses of calcium and phosphate incurred from traditional dairying and grazing, by manuring pastures with bone wastes from manufacture of buttons and cutlery; but the problem of making 'wild white' available to every farmer in Britain remained unsolved until the twentieth century: when 'wild white' seed was first put on commercial sale.

The Second Agricultural Revolution in the United Kingdom began in the early years of this century: because it was only then that 'wild white' seed was available *together with* knowledge about the need for lime, phosphate, and 'potash' to make grassland highly productive. Also, a farming tradition was upset: because in our own time it has become possible to plough up and renew English clovery grassland without fear and even with advantage. In Scotland the ploughing of grassland every few years has long been standard practice; but the clovers always had to take their chance until suitable manures and 'wild white' seed could be bought and used together.

In the 1880's experiments were begun with sowing seeds of Kentish wild white in parts of England and Wales distant from Kent; but the plants failed—probably because the need for sowing lime and phosphate fertilizers as well as the seed was not understood. The first of these lots of seed were collected by hand by Mr William Body who farmed at Shoreham, Kent. In 1896 William Somerville, the first Professor of Agriculture in the University of Durham, began experiments of improving poor natural grassland at Cockle Park, Northumberland, by treating it with fertilizers of which basic slag (supplying lime and phosphate) was the chief. The response of the native clovers and consequently in the productivity of all the herbage was astonishing. Somerville's work was continued and extended by his successor Thomas Middleton; in 1906 Middleton was succeeded by Douglas Alston Gilchrist (1859-1927), a Scot trained in Glasgow and Edinburgh, who began sowing seed of wild white while continuing the manurial treatments. A little earlier, another Scot, R. V. Mather (1854-1925), principal of the seed firm of Laing & Mather Ltd., of Kelso, Roxburghshire, had brought seed from Kent and after preliminary trials had in 1905 sown a field or two with it (in mixture with grass seeds as is normal practice) at Ellemford in Berwickshire, and put the seed on general sale.

From then on—owing chiefly to the great fame of Cockle Park—wild white seed has been increasingly appreciated, to the point that it has come to be looked on by farmers and agricultural advisers alike as the foundation of Britain's most important crop—namely, grassland. The fertilizer requirements have been correspondingly understood.

The Second Agricultural Revolution effectively began in the United Kingdom in 1905 [M5], when it became possible for the first time to establish clover in grassland and to finally close a protein gap: just as the annual clovers had been brought into arable farming to fill an earlier need for protein. Wild white seed has been of great value to the United Kingdom in both World Wars, especially the Second when the potentialities of legumes in both arable and grassland farming with appropriate non-nitrogenous but fuel-consuming fertilizing had been properly understood. It is an odd thing that British farmers are incredulous that the introduction of wild white is so recent as the beginning of this century; for thirty years the seed has been so readily obtainable that they all think it has 'always been' (probably through confusion with 'Dutch' clover).

Wild white seed has for some years been imported into Europe from New Zealand and elsewhere; new strains of the plant and its companion grasses have been produced by breeding; so it is interesting that the rather scarce seed of 'original Kentish' still commands the highest price.

Jonathan Swift (1667-1745), whose phrase about the man deserving better of mankind than the whole race of politicians if he could make two blades of grass grow where only one grew before, is so frequently quoted as to be almost a cliché, was a contemporary of Charles (whom we *should* call 'Clover') Townshend (1674-1738). If any men deserve to be awarded in Britain and in the most exact sense, the encomium foreseen by Swift, they are R. V. Mather and D. A. Gilchrist: though Mather apparently was not greatly concerned about improvement of mineral status of the soil that is an essential accompaniment of sowing the seed, and Gilchrist was building on the clear demonstration of the necessity for phosphate and lime that was given by his two predecessors at Cockle Park. The influence of Mather as the first commercializer of the seed has been unrecorded except in local publications [M6]; and though Somerville and Middleton were given knighthoods (they had many contacts with Whitehall committees), Gilchrist died in comparative obscurity; his immensely valuable and permanent work for Britain was not recognized by any award; nor has a plaque been put up to commemorate William Body's significant contribution to our agricultural output.

In like vein, I mention that it will be found difficult to discover a mention of any clover in poems, even when the subject is of the most bucolic. In spite of the crucial importance of legumes for maintaining the whole world's population, unless the legumes are of the kinds that produce edible grain they are not often seen by poets, or noticed by compilers or users of agricultural economic statistics. In the warmer parts of China, the legume indigo keeps up the fertility of the soil and supplies the blue dye characteristic of peasant dress; useful as a forage crop while it is young, it also becomes useful as a nitrogenous fertilizer after it has been processed for manufacture of the dye, the waste organic matter being returned to the soil.

Fencing makes an indispensable contribution to higher production from grassland even where the grazing is of poor quality; a fortiori where the farming is clover-intensive. Fencing serves many purposes in management of both livestock and land; it may suffice to mention that the practical alternative to fencing is of the type of the traditional peasant goose-girl. Where there are traditionally no fences, and no grass as in the up-to-date farming of the Sénonais (some sixty miles south-east of Paris), it is necessary to have human aid during grazing of cereal stubbles in order to protect the perennial crops such as lucerne.

The fuel component of fencing in modern agriculture is often overlooked. Adoption of barbed wire about 1880 was one of the major factors in opening-up the United States and in making a settled, protein-producing, agriculture possible in the West and Middle West; the enormous importance of metal fences for Australian production of meat and wool may be better known in Europe.

Annual consumption of metal (i.e., fuel) in fences is large. To divide a continuous area of land into fields or paddocks of about 25 acres would require 10 miles of fence per square mile; 20 miles if the fields were the often more handy size of $6\frac{1}{4}$ acres. Those reckonings allow nothing for access roads, so the mileage needed in practice is greater. They are independent of kind of fence; but if the fencing were of stranded wire, the mileage would have to be multiplied by the number of strands; the total tonnage of metal would be greater than that of the wire alone. A wire fence has to be renewed every few years.

In 1913 it was estimated that the capital laid out in fencing of all kinds in England and Wales was equal to that of the capital invested in all the railways. The figures for the fencing must be imprecise, since fencing includes stone walls, live hedges, and wooden fences as well as wired ones. Nevertheless, the quoted comparison seems to be fair. That it is the only estimate of its kind that I have seen suggests that the implications of fencing so necessary for intensive production of protein-rich food are often neglected; but local costs are well known to agricultural economists. In upgrading poorer British land to produce more meat, fencing alone may involve a new cost of about £50 per acre; since a couple of adjacent 10-acre paddocks require 1320 yards (nearly a mile) of wall or fence to be constructed.

Under equilibrium conditions, in certain kinds of country, the fencing could be constructed by human labour from nothing but local stone, without using fuel; but fortune of such kinds is always tempered by other limitations.

[M1]   A sound ecological account of soils and their relation to Man is in 'Soil', by G. V. Jacks (London: Nelson. 1954). Some readers with a sociological bent may find special interest in the chapter 'The History of British Soils'.

[M2]   Previously, cattle were commonly killed before the winter to make salted meat, which would keep. Only the minimum of cattle were kept alive over winter, often half-starved. Gentry had doocots or dove-cotes; many of these remain as stony evidence of acute winter shortage of fresh meat in most parts of Britain up to about 1850.

[M3]   It was called 'Dutch' because, like 'Brussels' sprouts and other vegetables, its seed was introduced into Britain from Flanders towards the middle of the seventeenth century.

[M4]   The estimate of 60 million head of bison does not differ greatly from the known recent number of cattle in the U.S.A., so it may be puzzling to understand how the natural herds lived on wholly wild resources. Only two points about that can be touched on here.

One is that the bison, though similar in size to domestic cattle, yielded no milk for human consumption; therefore, though the protein represented by bison flesh was not much less in total bulk than exists as bovines on the hoof on present-day U.S.A. farms and cattle ranches, the annual output of protein for human consumption is much greater now than the bison could ever yield. Part of this increase is due to keeping of animals other than bovines; the whole being associated with practices including cultivation of imported forage plants (mentioned later in this Chapter: see also Chapter 8), so that animals tied to a farm could obtain—at least in theory—enough protein to give them a balanced diet at all seasons.

The bison roamed freely over the western plains and hills covered with rough grass that was normally not very nutritious as judged by farming standards, and some of it poisonous to ordinary livestock; their range extended from the U.S.A. into Canada. By going from north to south and *vice versa* over a distance of about 1,500 miles, and by varying their elevation, the animals were able to choose from a range of climates and seasons for their feeding and for rearing offspring. In particular, by being in an area while the herbage was young, they benefited from its temporary richness in protein (Chapter 12), and continuously moved to fresh pasture—following the spring growth, enjoying a mild summer, and later going south or downhill to avoid the worst of winter (when the ground would be snow-covered and growth of plants at a standstill as it was in a hot summer). This migration of bison is a vivid indication of the ecological importance of vegetable protein; its story could be regarded as an animal appendix to Chapter 11.

Under human guidance a migration, of sheep principally, is an important part of animal husbandry in mountainous regions of Europe having hot dry summers in the lowlands. In these instances the migration in search of protein and other 'keep' is mainly up-and-down. It lasts many weeks or several months. It may be quite local—as in Alphonse Daudet's charming little story *Les Etoiles: récit d'un berger provençal*—but considerable distances are sometimes traversed with a vertical range of several thousand feet: across the Italian Apennines, for example.

This operation is known as *transhumance.* That international word is of Spanish derivation and means 'change of (grazing) ground'; it has nothing to do with the Latin word *homo*, and may be of pre-Roman origin. In Spain the migration-routes are signposted *ganado* or *cañada* where they cross main roads. In Madrid the crossing of a large square in a fashionable quarter is indicated by small stone posts incised CAÑADA which are worth a tourist's attention if he can find them.

The British climate does not permit transhumance in the full sense, though Britain has several partial agricultural analogies to it. The 'burning' of hill heather is a means of inducing old woody vegetation to yield an abundance of young shoots in territory where they are the main source of protein for grazing animals, including game. A form of transhumance in search of carbohydrate (principally) is the autumnal moving of hives of bees to the heather so that the bees can benefit from a second crop of flowers after most lowland wild and cultivated flowers, such as clovers, have finished blooming.

[M5]   In 'Microbes and Us' (Pelican Book A 326: Penguin Books.

1955) also in 'The early history of wild white clover seed in Britain' (*Fertiliser FeedStuffs J.*, 1951, Vol. 37, 775-7) I awarded the whole credit for pioneering the commercialization of wild white seed to Gilchrist in 1906. I am glad to put that matter right and to give the correct name of William Body. The other details of the history and utility of wild white (plant and seed) as given in those publications are unaffected.

[M6]   Mather's contribution was unknown to me until Mr Anthony Whitworth, through his interest in the history of Shoreham (Kent), got into touch with Mr Richard Body (still farming in Kent), grandson of William; he kindly put us on to the trail of Mather as the real pioneer of general sale of wild white clover seed in Britain: albeit only one year earlier than 1906.

8

The historical approach:
managed energy on farm and lawn

If, in your minds, you replace the factory by the farm, and accept
that there is more individual ownership and smaller units—although
this too is changing—then you will agree that modern mechanized
agriculture looks more and more like industry: it represents a
managed effort to produce goods such as milk, meat, and vegetables
for our human needs.
—Lord Beeching, *The Industry by which we live*: Ford (Dagenham)
Trust Lecture to young people, *Chemistry and Industry*, 1966,
128-34

It is often said that mechanization (meaning especially tractor-
ploughing and cultivation, and its associated mechanical harvesting) has greatly increased farming yields. That can be
accepted as true for temperate agricultures; in countries like
Britain having changeable weather, mechanization adds to
the direct advantages indirect ones. For example, it enables
ploughing or harvesting to be done in short time during
fleeting periods of favourable weather. In extreme instances
that may make all the difference between a good crop and a
poor or lost one. The advantages from machine power in
and out of doors bring gains that are more than convenience;
but they have to be paid for. The payment is made in fossil
fuel instead of by human or animal power maintained by
daily sunlight and other renewable resources.

Agricultural economists of last century may have occupied
themselves with calculations of the efficiency of animal motive
power on the farm; if they did, I have not heard the results.
Some organizations like tramway and omnibus companies,
being big users of purchased fodder, devoted much attention to the money economics of their motive power; and in
a related connexion, tramway companies used the principle
of maximization and may have pioneered its use in practice

earlier than Kelvin did mathematically for electric power. [MI]

Having seen no estimate of the cost of animal motive power in terms of land, I obtained the help of an agricultural colleague. We arrived at the estimate that in average British arable farming having only about a third of the farmland under grass, about a seventh of the farm area has to be devoted to producing food for work animals. Since the greater part of British farmland is devoted to dairying and other types of farming of which 'permanent' grass is the main feature, and because grassland requires less horse (or tractor) work than does ploughland, a fair weighted average for the whole of the cultivated area of Britain might be that animal power was, before horse-work was almost completely displaced, 'fuelled' by produce raised on about five per cent of the total farm acreage; whereas in arable farming about 14% of the land had to be devoted to providing food for the work animals. Those estimates are not close enough to say that the farmer's personal transport is included or not, though horse-drawn transport of heavy loads between farm and market or railway station is included.

It is possible that the temporary advantage of increasing the overall production of food in Britain by the order of four or five per cent on an almost constant acreage has been attained by mechanization of agriculture; and similarly for other countries on a per-acre basis of acres of cultivated land. Outside Britain, gains from taking in new land should be allowed for in any estimate of increased national farm production after a general introduction of mechanization. It should not be overlooked that 'mechanization' includes a general increase of consumption, on the farm, of energy derived from fossil fuel that could not have been supplied by animal power: for example, electricity and oil put to small 'indoor' jobs and especially to lighting; as well as the extra consumpt of fuel to make and renew extra tonnages of machinery. Probably the farmer, too, covers many more petrol-fuelled miles than the displacement that was allowed by horse and gig or surry!

Going a little further, it is a question whether longer-distance inland transport of farm exports (crops, milk, etc.) and imports (fertilizers, feeding-stuffs, etc.) is not more expensive in fuel if conducted mainly by lorry than almost entirely by rail.

Certainly, the over-all domestic production of food in Britain—whose agriculture is now the most highly mechanized in the world—has increased by more than four per cent since farm mechanization became common in the mid-thirties; and by much more than 4 % if a comparison is made with 1900 or a little earlier. However, not all that increase can be attributed to the accidentally simultaneous rise of mechanization: probably the greater part of it is owed to introduction of new varieties of crops and prolific breeds of animals, and to greatly improved management of land (especially: much more knowledgeable use and management of clovery grassland) that can bring great improvement of yields, whether cultivations and harvesting are performed by horse or tractor. The increases have been secured by heavier use of fertilizers (involving fuel consumed at a distance from the farm) of which the use is also independent of kind of motive-power; and the tonnage of lime used on farms has increased to an extent creditable to the farmer: though not without extra use of fuel in road transport.

The most evident of the gains in production had been brought about by the general encouragement of 'wild white' clover in pastures and meadows, in many of which it was a scarce plant before 1930.

This clover has a special place in upholding and increasing production of animal products, especially meat and milk; and—as with all other plants which contribute to greater removal of soil minerals in vegetable and animal crops taken from the land—the increased productivity has been gained only by applying an additional weight of fertilizer. [M2] This, especially in conjunction with clover, makes the soil richer in nutrients and organic matter. The extra fertilizer involves greater use of fuel in its manufacture (necessarily) and, in usual modern practice, for its transport also.

If one is not satisfied with the yields consistent with the soil's natural stock of plant nutrients, then, obtaining a greater production of crops and animals per unit area of land compels, as a minimum, heavier use of fertilizers and consequently of fuel; additional knowledge and skill in various aspects of management are also called for. Three examples from practice will make this clear.

One is the necessity for greater use of lime and phosphate and other earthy fertilizers in order to increase and sustain nitrogen-gathering and protein-output by clovers and legumes generally (as it was preached from Cockle Park and other centres of agricultural instruction, and now performed as a matter of routine by farmers all over the temperate regions of the world).

A second, and especially useful example, is the much-publicized increase of yield of maize grain from adoption of hybrid instead of ordinary maize on a similar area of land. Laymen may be inclined to think that such increases are brought about solely by an application of science to plant-breeding; and therefore it may be thought that the increase is solely due to the hybridization. That that is not so is attested by the fact that the distributors of hybrid maize seed inform the purchasers that heavier fertilizing (with nitrogen, phosphate, and potassium) is necessary to obtain heavier yields. What hybridization has done in this and similar instances is to increase only the *potentialities* of the seed for producing a heavier crop; but those potentialities have been realized only when all necessary plant nutrients are artificially added to support the heavier growth of stems, leaves, and seeds in the whole plant, and therefore to compensate for an increased removal of nitrogen and mineral nutrients when any part of the crop (including animal products to which it may have given rise) is removed from the soil that bore it. If all the consequences of heavier-than-natural cropping are not punctiliously attended to by Man, the result is deterioration of the cropping power of the soil. [M3]

A third example is, in a way, the converse of the farmer's problem; it may especially appeal to laymen who take pride in their lawns. A weedy lawn is invariably a starved lawn. The ideal is for a lawn to bear only true grasses (graminaceous plants) [M4]; but if the owner wisely attempts, by using fertilizers, to encourage the grasses to grow so as to assist them to smother the weeds, he becomes aware that he has to use the lawn-mower more frequently. He does not want the extra crop; but he has to apply energy in some form as part of the price for achieving a pleasant close turf obtained by interfering with Nature's selection of the plants ecologically suited to the existing soil and environment. From the owner's point of view there is an improvement; yet— like everything else—it has to be paid for in energy.

As with any farm crop, a sowing of what are supposed to be the right kinds of seeds can never achieve the intended aim unless all the soil conditions are artificially adjusted to suit the intended crop. There is ancient precedent (*Matt.* XIII, 5-9); for ecological lessons like this; it is always and inescapably true that Nature can never be defeated or circumvented.

[MI] Attention to the economics of tram-horse lives was mentioned by G. B. Shaw in '*The Intelligent Woman's Guide to Socialism and Capitalism*,' (London; Constable. 1928); maximization of electricity-distribution costs was pioneered by William Thomson (Lord Kelvin) in preliminary calculation for the first Niagara Falls generating station (direct current).

[M2] This general improvement and preservation of soil is a fact of farming experience rather than scientific record; though data exist which show that growing of a grass sward is the best mode of improving the structure of soil (page 120) and thereby assisting in combating soil erosion.

This neglect is an example of the lapse of 'agricultural chemistry' into being a branch of economics, more concerned with yield and cash values than scientific thought. Chapter 9 gives some other examples from fertilizers; and since soils and fertilizers (of which the behaviour is essentially electronic) are the foundations of modern farming, the right of modern farming to be called 'scientific' is questionable unless the meaning is that farming is not much more than application of technology.

In 1848 Lawes & Gilbert instituted an enquiry into the roles of annual clover in a four-course rotation; it included *inter alia* an investigation of effects on soil, and was continued at Rothamsted for a hundred years. The only other enquiry into the effect of clovers on soil in a rotation that the initiative of a further 100-odd years has produced was conducted in the East of Scotland by A. M. Smith and L. A. Mabbitt (*J. Soil Sci.*, 1953, Vol. 4, 98-106; A. M. Smith, *Scot. Agric.*, 1953-4, Vol. 33, 123-6.)

In spite of the patchwork character of scientific investigation into the rationale of food-production, sufficient information can be pieced together from observation of world-wide farming practices and from various branches of science to make sound generalization possible about human food and population. For example, farm animals are crops; and animal and human nutrition has been investigated so extensively as to make the essentiality of protein indubitable. From this and historical considerations (of which this book is a digest without specific reference to every detail) there is no room for doubt about such generalizations as that production of real food (see Chapters 11 & 12) from the land depends on protein-rich crops, and that a population larger than that of about 1830 or 1900 requires a correspondingly larger expenditure of fossil fuel for procuring its food.

[M3] In rather uncommon instances, some ingredients necessary for rendering a soil highly productive are naturally supplied from outside the soil. The best example are volcanoes which disseminate what geologists call 'basic' rocks containing lime, potassium, and phosphate. Java and Sumatra, both actively volcanic, show the contrast. The soils of Java (also of Bali and Madura) are frequently replenished with plant nutrients (except the nitrogenous) from above (or below!); and food crops, including the leguminous ones, flourish accordingly without much human aid. Human aid is needed to supply nitrogenous fertilizers for heavy crops of sugar-cane. The nearby island Sumatra receives mainly 'acidic' rocks from its volcanoes; accordingly it remains for the most part covered with tropical wet forest which is agriculturally unproductive and supports only a low density of human population.

[M4] Special lawns are made by using camomile and other low-growing non-leguminous plants to cover the soil closely. I have referred to graminaceous plants as the main constituent of ordinary lawns. The same principles of growth, nutrition, and competition, apply throughout.

9

Present imperfect

Pipe to the spirit ditties of no tone.
—John Keats: *Ode on a Grecian urn*

It was no coincidence that the increase of population in the technically-advanced nations was accompanied and sustained by an increased use of fossil fuel; though in the developing nations such as the United States it was for many decades marked by devastation of surface resources such as forests.

The rise of sulphur (in sulphuric acid) to being the most important fuel for producing enough protein to give what is now called 'nutritional balance' in feeding hundreds of millions of people and farm livestock was almost entirely empirical. It was found, before 1840, that sulphuric acid is the most convenient agent for 'dissolving' bones and rock phosphate, in the quest for making their contained phosphate quickly available to crops. [MI]

The connexion between phosphate, sulphate, and calcium (all being contained in superphosphate) and production of protein was not understood until the close of last century; and indeed what is called agricultural chemistry has not for many years been encouraged or allowed to show much chemical curiosity about the relations between soils, fertilizers, and crops.

The first comprehensive trial with a fertilizer was made by a Dorsetshire clergyman, the Rev. F. Huxtable, in 1845. He had been inspired by lectures given by and published by James F. W. Johnston on the composition of crops. In 1838 Johnston had noted the tapering of cereal straws, and had deduced that the chemical composition of plants must differ not only between various parts of the plant but at different stages of growth and maturity of the whole plant. His analyses proved that that was so. The search for knowledge of that seemingly important kind has been virtually abandoned since 1866, so there is no comprehensive modern knowledge about what any plant does with its materials.

Thanks to the theories of Liebig and the investigations of pioneers among whom special mention is deserved by the Frenchman J.-B. Boussingault (1802-87), who started the world's first experimental farm in Alsace in 1839; the Englishmen J. B. Lawes (1814-1900) and his collaborator J. H. Gilbert (1819-1901), also J. T. Way; and the Scots Johnston and William Anderson, the gross or over-all composition of the more important British kinds of crops, and consequently the indispensability, to them, of chemical elements of which nitrogen, potassium, phosphorus, calcium, and sulphur were the chief, was known in outline by about 1865. Fertilizers supplying potassium did not become common articles of commerce until about 1890 (somewhat earlier in Germany); however, among agricultural chemists the practice became established of looking upon fertilizers as supplying only nitrogen, phosphorus (as phosphate), and potassium: and of putting cash values to them on that basis.

This has persisted although the chemical nature and composition of fertilizers have been well known since about 1860. The habit of referring to fertilizers—whatever their composition and effects—as virtually consisting only of different percentages of the 'major' nutrients 'N, P, and K' (nitrogen, phosphate and 'potash') is also accompanied by relics of chemical theory as it was in the 1850's.

Fortunately for the lay reader, this archaic concentration on (some of) the nutrient needs of plants makes an outline of 'nutrient theory' easier to follow because it avoids most of the chemical and physical complications which attend a fundamental understanding of the relations between soils, fertilizers, and plant and animal growth. It thus leaves the ground clear for discussing some novelties associated with food-production that have emerged since 1880, and have given many laymen an impression that modern science has offered some brilliantly successful short cuts to increasing the output of food.

The Chapters on history will have brought home the *fact* that use of fossil fuel in farming and fishing has increased very greatly since, say, 1880. If the reader cares to draw upon his own knowledge to compare the human populations of the technically-advanced countries now and in (say) 1880 or 1910, he will see that a large proportion of the present population does rely for its very existence on fossil fuel put to maintaining enormous herds of animals and vast acreages of high-yielding crops that either did not exist, or were just beginning to exist, at that time—according to which date is chosen for comparison with the present 50-odd million people in Britain or the 180-odd millions in the United States, and so on. Such a simple comparison should be conclusive, if it is made in conjunction with the kinds of information supplied in Chapters 6, 7 and 8.

Mere correlation is not evidence; if the reader still doubts that much of the extra population (of people and livestock and crops) has been paid for in fossil fuel, a great deal more of probably unsuitable explanation would have to be offered and read through. There is no 'instant food-production science'.

One of the difficulties of explaining any 'food' problem in simple terms is that, whilst the fundamental chemistry and the thermodynamic necessities remain inalterable at all times and in all fields, as soon as chemistry has to be linked with plant and therefore with human biology the subject 'explodes' over many different fields and aspects. Because the forms of life differ, it is not possible to adopt the apparent clarity of explanation which suffices for the one-to-one correspondences of cause and effect in classical physics (*e.g.,* a bar of known material and length expands by a predictable amount when heated through a known range of temperature; or else it melts while remaining the same substance).

Soils and fertilizers as sources of plant nutrients are fairly complex studies in themselves; then there is the relation of Man to plants; that is complicated by the different kinds of nutrients needed by Man, and is further complicated by the frequent interposition of a chain of animals between plants and Man. Nor would the subject be made more simple by writing for vegetarians alone: complications of a different order arise and are outlined in Chapter 11.

An explanation of all these facets would require very many words. To attempt it is liable to provoke the exclamation: 'Why can't you scientists tell us in simple language?'

The answer to that is that the ways in which life manifests itself with different species and habitats contrive a complication whenever a reader is sufficiently curious about food to want to know (for example) why ruminants can benefit from grass and hay directly, and people can't. If the basic rules are not already known to the reader, answering two or three questions like that could fill a small book.

Scientists *can* be concise when they can assume a knowledge, in their hearer, of the basic rules; and then an explanation of even such a comprehensive subject as the relation between any human population and its environment can be put into a couple of paragraphs by using scientific shorthand. That is done in the Laws of Population stated on page 148. It is again done, in more ordinary language but with less conciseness and with some loss of precision, at the end of Chapter 19. It has already been stated in the three words 'Nothing for nothing' which sum up all our existence; but that probably sounds like an asseveration, so the rest of this book seeks to bring evidence that the asseveration is made not by scientists but by Nature.

What scientists have been doing for the past couple of centuries is to find out what Nature does asseverate about the conditions for human and other existence. When Nature has plainly expressed that she will give nothing for nothing, but that something extra can be had by exchanging something else for that extra, scientists have ascertained exactly what has to be paid or given in exchange. As far as food is concerned, we may say that those conditions of exchange—

very imperfectly reckoned with in what is called 'agricultural' chemistry—are the basic laws of chemistry; this book is holding them up for the reader to see how they apply to human ecology. You would not blame a lighthouse because on a dark night its beams warn ships of the existence of the rock on which it stands.

To understand the most concise forms of statement of the conditions on which most of the world's population now stands, the only knowledge additional to the basic rules is about the main lines of the human needs for proteins on the one hand and of non-nitrogenous nutrients on the other; together with as much detail about vitamins, minerals, and water as is thought desirable.

For the present we may keep to the subject of what has been supplied to plants during recent history to make plant and animal crops grow to an abundance much beyond what the soil would support by itself. Thus, we do not have to go far beyond the pragmatic kind of enquiry that has turned the main effort of what is called 'agricultural chemistry' into a branch of agricultural economics: by applying certain powders called N, P, and K (which might just as well be labelled A, B, and C) and finding the increase in yield, without much scientific curiosity being engaged by the processes which occur between applying these powders and harvesting the crops.

However, it is necessary to keep two steps ahead of agricultural chemistry (as she is practised) by recognizing that, in addition to N, P, and K, the powders contain and supply much calcium (Ca) and sulphur (S) needed by plants as nutrients.

That brings in another of the apparently endless bifurcations. Calcium and sulphur (as sulphate) are valuable for their ameliorating effects on soils as well as by being nutrients for plants. As soil amendments, calcium is usually given as lime or chalk; sulphur as calcium sulphate (gypsum). The chemical effects of calcium are quite different in gypsum and lime, though the plant-nutrient effect is the same. Almost half of superphosphate is gypsum; and if I mention that superphosphate is the biggest chemical product (tonnage-

wise), that some 400,000,000 tons of it have been used in this century for dressing the soil, that since 1842 only four experimental enquiries have been launched—one each in the U.S.A., New Zealand, Australia, and Scotland—to enquire into the effect on soil of the gypsum contained in superphosphate, and that a bare handful of modern experimenters have acknowledged a nutrient effect from the calcium in superphosphate, you can see why it is about as sensible to call the various powders A, B, and C as to give them the pseudo-scientific labels N, P, and K. It will be apparent that convention rather than scientific assiduity has dominated the chemical questions underlying production of the world's food.
[M2]

Spectacular results from applying an ounce or so per acre of trace elements have been brought vividly to public notice. Reports of astonishing results from using these trace elements have led to extravagant notions that by doing everywhere what has been accomplished in, for example, some parts of Australia, after adding small quantities of trace elements to soil, the world's food output can be multiplied. It is desirable to try to restore proportion. Trace elements are required by animals, plants, and microbes (particularly by those bacteria which fix nitrogen from the air). They have been responsible for many good stories, including the only Red Indian legend in agricultural chemistry. To avoid a trifurcation I will keep to the 'plant' side.

Existence of some trace elements in plants has been known since the eighteenth century; but the first hint of the importance of trace elements for the well-being of plants was obtained in 1923 by a young English botanist doing her first piece of research. By showing that a minute quantity of the element boron (chemical symbol, B) is essential for growth and reproduction of broad beans (a protein-producing plant, as it happened) this girl founded not only the minor industry of adding compounds of trace elements to ordinary fertilizers but opened up a vast and still-growing field of research into the importance of trace elements in living matter. The trace-element alphabet began with B. One outcome of that was knowledge about Vitamin B_{12}: needed by animals and containing the element cobalt (Co); another was about fluorine (F) for good teeth.

However, trace elements are simply another set of nutrients. The fact that very small amounts of them are effective towards plants in regions like those of Australia, where Nature had neglected to supply one or more of them to meet man's agricultural requirements—must account for the almost magical attraction the subject has provoked; just as a century earlier the ability to supply nutrients in wheelbarrow loads had seemed marvellous to people who had never known nutrients to be supplied except in cart-loads of dung. Trace elements always have to be given in conjunction with normal amounts of ordinary fertilizers containing nitrogen, phosphorus, sulphur, calcium, and potassium as and whenever those 'major' elements are required either to improve soil or to make up a deficiency of nutrients.

Important as trace elements are for agriculture, they do not use more than a small total of fuel. Because vitamins are likewise quantitatively unimportant, I omit discussion of them beyond saying that part of the function of trace elements is as an indispensable constituent of some vitamins and other cell-catalysts; in the dentine of teeth, fluorine is a structural constituent. Sulphur, required by plants (as sulphate) in a proportion nearly as great as phosphate, is not a trace element; its importance for animals is that, combined in some amino-acids which are constituents of proteins, sulphur is indispensable for animal growth and health. To take nitrogen to be the essential or type element of protein foods, is to overlook the sulphur which is *equally* as necessary; because the sole form of sulphur that animals can use is what is combined in two or three amino-acids contained in proteins.

Industrial fixation of air-nitrogen to make 'synthetic' fertilizers and other nitrogenous compounds has probably raised more false hopes about 'conquering Nature' in food matters, or becoming able by means of intelligence and 'science' to get round the limitations she has imposed on food and population, than any other single technical feat. Once again, science (properly understood) shows the ineptitude of such ideas; they do not lead to a permanent solution of the problems of keeping more people alive than there were before artificial fixation of nitrogen became commercial.

Once again, the subject splits into several directions; and, once again, each of them leads to the same conclusion when they are considered naturally—that is, along the lines set by Nature.

Fixation of nitrogen in factories has been of paramount importance in war (see page 260) and for industry (making synthetic fibres and other plastic, for instance); but it is easily possible to overrate the importance of synthetic nitrogenous fertilizers for food, now and in the future. Any idea that bringing down nitrogen from the air in factories has abolished the threat of famine, or that all that is needed to abolish that threat is to build more synthetic-fertilizer factories, is a delusion which is wrong several times over.

The chemical or thermodynamic reasons are:

(a) nitrogen-fixation is expensive in fuel. That is because much energy has to be used to 'activate' the inert nitrogen of air;

(b) nitrogenous fertilizers do not, in general, produce 'balancing' protein even when they are used in conjunction with other fertilizers. That might be called Sad Fact No. 1. Green plants do not, in general, act that way; special agricultural methods restricted to temperate climates have to be adopted to induce green plants to convert combined nitrogen into protein-rich crops;

(c) it is a pipe-dream that effective fertilizers could consist of only the gases of the air. Apart from the use of fossil carbonaceous fuels that the manufacture of synthetic fertilizer entails, earthy materials like chalk have to be *either* contained in, *or* used in close conjunction with, nitrogenous fertilizers not only to supply sulphur and calcium as nutrients for plants and microbes but to prevent damage to the soil from the activity of certain classes of microbes on nitrogenous compounds of any origin.

Taking these in order for further discussion:

(*a*) To fix a ton of air-nitrogen necessitates use of 5 tons of coal-equivalent; roughly a ton of coal has to be exchanged for the nitrogen (alone) of a ton of synthetic fertilizer. If natural gas or oil is used instead of coal as the starting-point, the tonnage of carbonaceous fuel is less though still substantial. For plastics and synthetic fibres the consumption of fuel per ton is high. That puts paid to the idea that by using plastics as substitutes for metals, or making synthetic fibres instead of growing animal or vegetable fibres, more than a temporary advantage can be gained, or that food-production can be advantaged. That synthetic fibres release land for producing food that might have been devoted to producing textiles or wool is a silly idea; at least, wool-growing produces mutton! (Also, the wool and mutton are produced at a minimal cost in fuel).

However, those ideas are of the type of the many about 'progress' in general and about food-production in particular that will not stand a moment's examination—given the sort of knowledge you are now acquiring about our dependence on fossil fuel for almost everything we do.

Incidentally, to make any kind of foodstuff synthetically from coal or oil or natural gas is fairly expensive in fuel if, like alcohol or fat, it contains no nitrogen; if it is a synthetic amino-acid the fuel cost is quite high—partly because of the fuel cost of the nitrogen and other elements, and partly because of the high conversion-losses.

(*b*) Only the leguminous tribe of plants such as clovers, beans, and peas, have the ability in practice to convert air-nitrogen directly into protein-rich plant tissue. They do not benefit in practice from synthetic fertilizers or any other compound of nitrogen. Leguminous plants or legumes can utilize combined nitrogen; but that is so expensive and unnecessary to give them (unless in the ordinary use of farmyard manure when there is any to spare) that it is usually uneconomic.

Leguminous crops are the centre-piece of all self-sufficient agricultures, as has been suggested in Chapters 7 and 8. What is meant by a self-sufficient agriculture is one which grows food for the whole of its resident population—unlike the prairie wheat mentioned in Chapter 6, and the example of Hawaii, Chapter 17, note M3. Legumes are the mainstay of all durable agricultural systems; they are the main source of protein for vegetarian and most flesh-eating peoples; in addition (or, if you prefer it, therefore) they enrich the soil with nitrogen utilizable by succeeding crops and by their companion grasses in pasture; and they help to maintain the soil itself in good condition.

In farming conditions, leguminous crops do all these things abundantly and well if the soil is dressed with fertilizers supplying calcium, phosphate, sulphate, and potassium (and trace elements if necessary).

The principal combustible for keeping up modern populations is sulphur; because (as explained in Chapters 6 and 7) of its use in making sulphuric acid to make superphosphate: for clovers, alfalfa or lucerne, soybeans, and other leguminous crops. Sulphur for this purpose can also be obtained from gypsum (anhydrite) by roasting it with coal. Any road (as they say in Lancashire) there is no escape from using fuel of some sort if we want protein on the scale to which we have become accustomed.

In 1900 Lawes and Gilbert published a voluminous paper in which they pointed out *inter alia* that in non-leguminous crops such as cereals and turnips, in the state in which they are usually harvested, a characteristic effect of nitrogenous fertilizers is to increase yields per acre of starch, sugar, and fat—the *non*-nitrogenous constituents. [M3] The incuriosity of agricultural chemistry is well shown by the fact that this magisterial statement has not been mentioned in any textbook, as far as I know. A result of this inertia about the ascertained principles of production of food is that in order to publish a general statement that shall be sound as well as comprehensive for all important crops it is necessary to go beyond the scanty experimental data and to invoke what practical farmers have everywhere done by finding out in the hard way, without much benefit of agricultural 'clergy'.

New Zealand farmers have maintained a relatively huge output of protein by relying on clovers (and associated young grasses) and earthy, non-nitrogenous, materials as fertilizers.

Elsewhere, growers of starchy and sugary crops and some non-leguminous oil and fibre crops, such as sugar-cane and sugar-beet, cereals, potatoes, and cotton, have—by becoming the chief users of nitrogenous fertilizers—shown the correctness of the 1900 dictum just quoted.

Chapter 21 outlines the reasons why nitrogenous fertilizers are unable to produce protein, in most crops, to the extent of keeping any land animal alive unless it obtains additional protein from another suitably rich source: beans or fish-meal, for instance. For the present, it will suffice to drop the hint that the tendency of Nature is to keep a constant ratio of total (organic) carbon to total (combined) nitrogen in various parts of her living empire. That is the chief bio-chemical means by which the entire life-cycle is regulated and kept going. It is part of the natural condition which was long ago built into the make-up of every species of plant and animal. Because nothing that Man can do will alter the constitution of any species, it will be seen that it is useless to expect that supplying extra nitrogen (in synthetic fertilizers, for instance) will yield any extra protein for Man, except on Nature's terms. (It is similarly hopeless to expect more food from any known or prospective method for increasing photosynthesis, unless fossil reserves are drawn upon—for as long as that may be possible—to supply additional nitrogen and earthy materials to meet the equally reasonable requirements of the extra plant-growth that is hoped for).

The richness in protein of the young herbage of grassland (not counting the clovers and other legumes) was discovered in 1926 at Cambridge University by H. E. Woodman and two colleagues [M4]; skilful graziers must have empirically been aware of it. That is the latest major piece of scientific knowledge used in this book: it completed the knowledge needed for making a complete survey of food in relation to population.

Lawes-and-Gilbert had missed a trick, for they had never considered young graminaceous plants as sources of protein. Nor was it until 1931 that C. J. Willard of Ohio State University [M5] explained that the reputation that alfalfa had ob-

D

tained as being slightly richer in protein than annual clover was due to alfalfa being cut several times a year, so that it was its new growth that was harvested, whereas clover was cut for hay only once or twice (and being more mature when cut, its protein was 'diluted' with fibrous matter). When cut at similar stages of growth, the two legumes carried similar percentages of protein.

But why should ideas about sources of protein have been left at the stage where they happened to be in 1900? During the quarter of a century that intervened between the last publication of Lawes-and-Gilbert and the investigation instigated by Woodman, Einstein had published both the Special and the General theories of Relativity (the British Government lost no time in sending an expedition overseas to make astronomical observations to test them as soon as a suitable eclipse of the sun occurred in 1919); and there had been many technical advances with machinery. The new knowledge about trace elements had begun to attract attention among scientists; but the knowledge about the potentialities of 'wild white' clover had, in Britain, been almost forgotten in an agricultural depression.

Woodman's investigations of 1926 showed that young grasses are able to convert combined nitrogen from sources outside themselves into a high proportion of protein. Hence, the chief value of 'synthetic nitrogen' for protein production comes when it is applied to grassland having undeveloped clovers but cut every few weeks—either by the teeth of protein-seeking grazing animals or, more artificially, by machines which involve fuel.

The only common kind of crop able to convert combined nitrogen into protein-rich food directly edible by man is the cabbage tribe: not that they are a group of plants specially rich in protein, but because they are harvested at a fairly early stage of their development.

(c) Ideas that the discovery of synthetic nitrogenous fertilizers has by itself banished the real fears about eventual exhaustion of natural Chilean nitrate are misconceived. The nitrogen of any nitrogenous fertilizer is, by bacterial action in the soil, converted into nitric acid (if it is not a nitrate already) whch leads to undesirable consequences for the following crops by damage to the soil, unless the nitric acid (and sometimes other acids) are neutralized. It follows that any kind of nitrogenous fertilizer, whether it is of natural or synthetic origin, must either (*i*) carry enough material to neutralize all the possible acidity, or (*ii*) compel the farmer to incur extra expense and labour in applying chalk or limestone. Condition (*i*) is satisfied exactly by Chilean nitrate of soda, also by I.C.I. 'Nitro-Chalk' to which chalk has been added during manufacture; it is also satisfied by mixed farmyard manure—though not by urine, poultry manure, and most other 'organic' manures—through the accident of its composition.

Thus, there is no superiority of any manure just because it is a 'natural' or 'organic' product; in practice, everything depends on their composition, nothing on their origin. Seductive advertising is trying to tell farmers and us about immense progress alleged to have been achieved in making fertilizers more and more concentrated to the point of sometimes entirely eliminating the neutralizing material. [M6] The farmer can, of course, supply lime or chalk as an extra; but the main point of the advertising is the alleged saving in transport and labour costs through putting more and more N, P, and K in a given size of bag. Something has to be left out? An alert farmer will surely want to know more about the all-up costs when nitrogenous fertilizers are sold without any neutralizing material? [M6]

It may appear very old-fashioned and unprogressive to suggest that some of the older fertilizers like nitrate of soda, guano, 'Nitro-Chalk', and farmyard manure have certain definite advantages which cannot be matched by fertilizers containing a high percentage of nitrogen. Plants and soil microbes are old-fashioned also; they never change their feeding habits. So it may be as well to know what those habits are, and what the consequences in fuel, lime, food, and disappointment can be from believing that Nature will behave otherwise than according to her own rules.

[MI]   The essence of the superphosphate patents of 1842 was to use fossil phosphate because there could not be enough fresh bones. The name 'superphosphate' did not imply a technical or agricultural superiority; it was a term borrowed from eighteenth-century French chemists.

[M2]   An American fertilizer chemist, A. L. Mehlich, blew one gaff by pointing out (in *Soil Science*, 1948, Vol. 65, 9-25) that on the average, fertilizers then contained a higher percentage of calcium (as calcium oxide) than of the nutrients of the conventional N-P-K triad. Also, an agricultural chemist who writes that part of the good effect of superphosphate may be credited to its supplying sulphur as nutrient for plants (in addition to the P) usually seems to be looking over his shoulder as if he were expecting to be chased for daring to defy the unchemical nutrient-theory convention that N-P-K and trace elements are all that matter.

The convention that all fertilizers whatever their composition can be represented as percentages of N, P, and K has even eaten into the otherwise impeccable logic of mathematical statistical methods (Chapter 18). In statistical analysis of results of fertilizer experiments it is normal to attribute the effects to N, P, and K as if they represented entities; in fact, every fertilizer consists of chemical compounds or mixtures having two or more components, each of which must have some effect on soil and plants (though not necessarily an acknowledged nutrient effect). However, should a single fertilizer be a chemical combination having two members of the N-P-K triad, statistical analysis is regarded as impracticable and is not attempted, because the effects of the acknowledged nutrients cannot then be mathematically separated!

[M3]   J. B. Lawes and J. H. Gilbert, *Phil. Trans. Roy. Soc.*, B, 1900, Vol. 192, 139-210.

[M4]   H. E. Woodman, D. L. Blunt, and J. Stewart, *J. Agric. Sci.*, 1926, Vol. 16, 205-74.

[M5]   C. J. Willard, *J. Amer. Soc. Agron.*, 1931, Vol. 23, 754-6.

[M6]   There has been progress—but it is technical (in technology of fertilizer manufacture). Some important biological considerations, including the needs of soil and crops for lime and trace elements, are left out—or, what is worse, soft-pedalled or missed—when that is taken as 'progress' *ohne weiteres*.

More detailed consideration of the farming aspects and dangers is in the book by Michael Blake, 'Concentrated incomplete fertilisers', Crosby Lockwood, London. 1967.

10

The approach by mathematics

'Twenty-four hours, I *think*; or is it twelve? I ———'
'Oh, don't bother *me*,' said the Duchess; 'I never could abide figures.'
—Lewis Carroll: *Alice in Wonderland*

In the present state of awareness about what is called 'the population explosion' a fairly common hobby is making estimates of the size of the population the world can support. That would be no bad thing to try to do, if the estimates were based on any sort of reality, such as the possible production of protein or any other basic necessity for supporting a population. All those estimates I have seen have been based on impractical premises, like the possible output of cereals and/or nitrogenous fertilizers after building more tractors and fertilizer factories: it is along those lines that the problem of feeding x thousand millions of people living in any one year (where x is greater than 2) is expected to be solved.

Gross as that error is, it does not show the most negligent aspect of the various numbers of thousand millions that have been published as estimates of possible maximum population of the world. In fact, there are two grave oversights in publishing any single maximum figure for world population. In either practical or mathematical terms these two blunders necessarily amount to the same thing. The mathematical expression is given in the curves of Figs. 2 and 2a.

One of the oversights has been to state for how long it is expected that the maximum population, once reached, can be kept up. I can assume only that the authors have assumed that their expected total of human beings can be maintained indefinitely; possibly they have entertained some such thought as Goethe's

Über allen Gipfeln
Ist Ruh'.

Figs. 2 and 2a. Maximum populations: two aspects of stating only a single figure for an expected maximum of world (or any other) population.

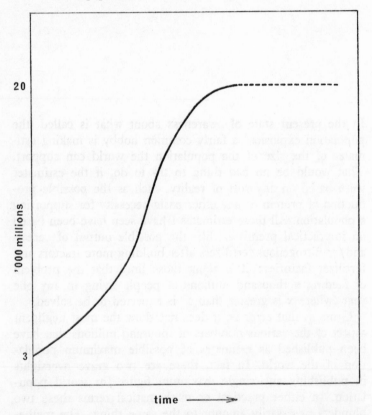

Fig. 2. The approach to a maximum of population is indicated by a growth-curve (here assumed to be of ordinary type) having the usual inflexions, including a *gradual* slowing-down of increase of population as the maximum comes close (in time and magnitude).

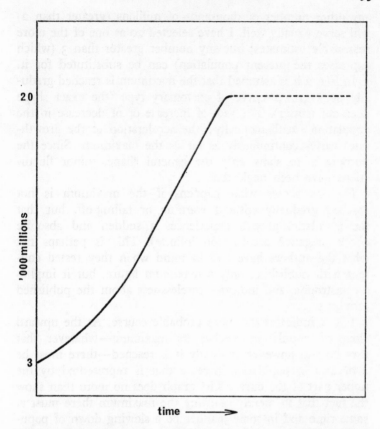

Fig. 2a. An interpretation of the consequence of stating a single maximum of population—and leaving it at that without any saving assumption. Catastrophe (an explosive decrease of population) is indicated by the infinitely sudden decrease of population that is necessary if the stipulated maximum is not to be exceeded after growth following a roughly normal growth-curve: which, nevertheless, does not avoid a gradual, but insufficient, retardation of population at an earlier stage.

Be that as it may, in considering these fanciful exercises in arithmetic there is no harm in adding a little more fancy; accordingly in constructing Figs. 2 and 2a I have carried the maximum figure to infinity along a horizontal line or 'plateau'. For the purpose of the discussion it does not matter what the fancied maximum figure is: 5, 8, 30, 50 or any other number of thousands of millions (greater than 2) will serve equally well. I have selected 20 as one of the more reasonable estimates; but any number greater than 3 (which expresses the present population) can be substituted for it.

In Fig. 2 it is assumed that the maximum is reached gradually by a growth-curve of customary type (the exact shape does not matter). The rate of increase or of decrease in the population (mathematically: the acceleration of the growth-rate) varies continuously as far as the maximum. Since the purpose is to show only the general shape, minor fluctuations have been neglected.

Fig. 2a shows what happens if the maximum is not reached gradually without warning or tailing-off, but that the population-growth experiences a sudden and absolute check (negative acceleration infinite). This is perhaps not what the authors have had in mind when they rested content with publishing only a maximum figure, but it implies a catastrophe, and indicates carelessness about the published estimates.

Fig. 2 indicates the more probable course. As the upward slope of population reaches its maximum—whatever that may be and however gradually it is reached—there must be a *decline* in population-increase that is represented by the upper part of the curve. The graph does no more than show the fact that in merely *reaching* the maximum there must at some time and in some manner be a slowing down of population-increase: whatever happens after the maximum is reached: be it the maintenance of a constant size of population, or (when fuel becomes hard to get) a further decline towards the equilibrium figure of some two thousand millions or less.

That decline *after* the maximum is reached is not shown in Figs. 2, 2a. Its inevitability is discussed in Chapter 15, and may have been already discerned by the reader.

The point is that the deceleration of population-increase before any maximum is reached has to be brought about by some means: it implies fewer births than deaths over a fairly long period—say, fifty years or a generation or two at least. Whether that decrease of births or excess of deaths is to be

brought about by war, famine, disease, or some less un-
pleasant means remains for the future to decide.

There can be no continual increase of population towards
some practically infinitely distant maximum unless most unusual care is taken to husband resources of fossil fuel. The
present stocks of fossil fuel would probably last many thousands of years if they were used only for food purposes.
The proportion of annual consumption of fossil fuel that is
used for all purposes connected with food—production, processing, and cooking—is quite small. There seems to be no
estimate of its size. One might guess five per cent or less:
the other 95 % or more being devoted to generation of energy
for purely mechanical and industrial purposes.

However, the smaller the proportion of fossil fuel that is
used for food purposes after being raised, the greater the peril
to the population of the future, and the sooner will its maximum
numbers be reached. The intensity of the squeeze on future
population is determined by the rate at which fossil fuel is
used for non-food purposes.

It may be noted, as one of the oddities that abound in a
discussion of food, population, and conservation, that forestry
presents the most thorough-going application of practical
ecology. The best forestry management rests on practices
worked out a long time ago in Germany and France; it is
based on elaborate long-term plans for replacing every tree
cut down. As part of the plan, some trees are cut down after
a few years' growth to yield small timber and to leave more
room for those intended to grow big. Since the time for
completion of any forest programme may be a hundred
years, no forester can hope to see the end of what he initiates.

Forestry management is practical, sensible, and well
thought out at every point. The pity is that such far-seeing
thinking and practice are devoted only to one renewable
resource. There seems to be no reason why forestry should
not continue for many hundred years: unless the pressure
on timber for fuel is allowed to become so great through
lack of enough fossil fuel, that the capital of timber is heed-
lessly devastated as it was before management of forests was
recognised as an exact, conscientious, and most useful art.

II

Cherchez toujours la protéine! Sociological notes on cannibalism, vegetarianism, and other ecological features of human population

Perrichon: 'Madame, je voudrais un livre pour ma femme et ma fille . . . un livre qui ne parle ni de galanterie, ni d'argent, ni de politique, ni de mariage, ni de mort.'
Daniel (aside): *Robinson Crusoé!*
—E. Labiche & Ed. Martin: *Le Voyage de Monsieur Perrichon,* Paris. 1860

In trying to make clear the circumstances of the rise, upkeep, or fall of any population at any time, it is always salutary—and, for modern populations, essential—to see how their protein was or is supplied. This is a neglected subject [MI], though its historical and future sociological importance cannot be over-rated. It tends the more to be lost from sight because of shallow emphasis put on cereal grains, as if any population could flourish on cereals.

For the last eighty years or so, the subject has been complicated by the need to look at the fuel origins of protein (and consequently of population) in excess of what was available a century ago; a little further back, there is the little matter of using trimmings from bone knife-handles and the like to replenish depleted stocks of phosphate and lime in old pastures where a phosphate-rich marl was not at hand; but beyond that we are thrown on to inference and guesswork about the ways nitrogen and phosphate and lime were brought into and kept in circulation.

Before dipping into ancient history, it is worth while to quote the estimate of Lawes in his 1847 paper (see page 50) about the value of rotation of crops. For the single English county of Norfolk, and assuming that half its land were under the four-course system, Lawes estimated that rotation had increased what he called the natural annual produce of corn by 10 bushels per acre; and that to produce that increase (and corresponding output of meat) by artificial manure would require an importation of 75,000 tons of guano each year. That was clearly impractical; nor was anything like it necessary at first: because the arable, annual, or 'Dutch' clover and the system of keeping animals and returning their excreta (mixed with straw) to the land was responsible for the enrichment of the soil in nitrogen and for the increase of meat-production. The original rotational system could not go on for ever without restoration of phosphate, lime, and other minerals carried off the land in meat, milk, and other crops; these minerals were henceforth to be supplied increasingly by use of fuel to make fertilizers (superphosphates especially); but Lawes's calculation suffices to suggest the effect of the 'Dutch' clover in producing useful nitrogenous compounds for soil and for all the arable crops.

A few sample jabs into ancient history will suggest the backbone that curiosity about sources of protein can give to enquiries into human ecology. The first thing is to get rid of preoccupation with cereals as the staple of life and reproduction in any land animal. That preoccupation is evident among economists and compilers of tabulated statistics that relate to diet and crops (including, say, tobacco) which collectively, even when edible by man and beast, could not sustain life. There is probably an example or two at your hand; if there is not, you will certainly recall stories by travellers in the Far East whose only mention of diet is on the lines that the Japanese eat nothing but rice, and that a Japanese or a Burmese can work or fight all day on nothing but a handful of that. Belief in these patent nutritional impossibilities is constantly renewed by televised and other pictures that feature the flat or terraced rice paddies without hinting at any nutritional counter-balance; which is normally given by beans and fish; assisted, in Japan, by seaweed. [M2]

It is doubtfully correct to say, as many historians do, that the fall of the Roman empire was due to demoralization consequent on importation of abundant corn from north

Africa. For one thing, at that time Mediterranean regions were benefitting from legumes including alfalfa or lucerne (later taken by the Spaniards to South America), which had crossed the Near East; it has been conjectured that lucerne was the 'grass' eaten by Nebuchadnezzar. In any case, the origin of alfalfa is sufficiently attested by its name *erba medica* (the hay of the Medes) common in Italy. Doubtless other legumes such as lentils and peas and beans had been introduced from the Near East and Egypt and Crete; but although Romans may have been 'demoralized' by too much free corn, they need not, theoretically, have been short of protein; since, apart from land protein, there was fish in the sea never far away. Unless, of course, the historians are right and the Roman populace did eat practically nothing but 'corn' and that that term excluded lentils and other pulses; but then the mass of people would not have been suffering from purely psychical demoralization but from actual under-nutrition through not getting enough protein from any source.

The biblical tale of Joseph bidden to store corn needs similar scrutiny. If 'corn' meant nothing but non-leguminous cereals, no amount of it could have averted famine unless the Egyptians could have taken enough fish out of the Nile. The probability is that, whilst the chief cereal was barley, the 'corn' included lentils and other pulses; also, the barley may have been unusually rich in protein [M3].

Just after the last War harrowing tales came from some of the first British civilians to reach Sicily, who reported that the Sicilian economy had been so much damaged by war that the peasants ate meat only twice a year (Christmas and Easter). The inference was wrong; for the peasants never had eaten meat much more often; they had beans and fish. Their diet was and is wretched; but they do not need meat to give it nutritional balance. All inhabitants of small islands and of long and narrow countries bordering the sea (Norway, for instance) make much use of fish in their diet, though, before the coming of the white man, some Polynesian islanders had brought pigs and were able to eat pork as well as fish.

In the most efficient agricultural systems there is no waste of animal protein. In Denmark, for example, 'the pig hangs on the cow's tail'. That means that the protein in home-produced and imported feeding-stuffs that milch cattle receive and of which the milk not sold fresh or condensed is processed into butter and cheese, the by-products such as whey are fed to pigs, there being the closest possible tie-up between dairying and production of bacon and other pig-meat.

In every instance, the keeping of land animals to supplement indigenous diets does no more than put the question back one stage; so it is always necessary to probe a little further and to ask: Where did, or does, the protein to balance the diet of the meat animals or fresh-water pond fish, come from? When that question is answered—even if only by a reasonable guess—the ecological enquiry has gone as far as it can to account for persistence of a human population in the absence of a developed economy of transport and exchange, or a primitive sufficiency of the two main forms of human nutrients: nitrogenous and non-nitrogenous.

The locusts which sustained John the Baptist were almost certainly not insects but the fruit of the carob or locust-tree *Ceratonia siliqua*. So, most likely, were its pods the 'husks' mentioned in the parable of the Prodigal Son. The ripe pods are unusual among leguminous fruits in being sweet; they are practically a balanced diet. The Italian name is suggestive; the fruit is called *pane di San Giovanni* [M4]. Like lucerne and many plants which yield fruit directly edible by Man, carobs were introduced from the East. The Spanish names *alfalfa* and *algarroba*—obviously of Arabic origin—suggest a fairly late establishment of lucerne and carobs in the west of Europe [M5].

When speculating about the origins of any self-sufficient ancient settlement on a site (such as Jericho) not near a river or large lake, a source of fresh water must be assumed: not necessarily for purposes of drinking and washing only. The water may also be used for irrigation; that, as sole use, implies both cereal and pulse crops. If water is not very abundant, it may first be run through fish-ponds and then used for irrigation; thus producing protein, and possibly reserving the irrigated land for producing a correspondingly large amount of cereals as energy foods.

For Minoan Crete there is scanty but definite evidence of presence of beans: as could be expected from its situation, though they may have been in part imported. Such seafarers as the ancient Cretans could not have been short of fish; but the limestone soil could have borne indigenous legumes so that also cattle and/or sheep could be kept, and the state of Minoan crafts suggests that they were.

Into West Africa the slave-traders brought peanuts (ground-nuts) which turned out to be a major source of easily-grown vegetable protein of great benefit to the present population. It is questionable where the advantage lay in slave-trading times; the matter was not then thought out, but the result may (over a period of years) have been to increase the population potentially available for capture as slaves.

In South America and Darkest Africa even the peanut spread slowly; cannibalism lingered in many places for many different reasons. Nutritionally, there is something to be said for cannibalism; protein of one's own species is fractionally more efficiently utilized by a carnivore than protein from another animal species; and any meat has definite advantages over purely vegetable protein unless an animal is definitely and specially adapted to a vegetable diet. An extreme example of such special adaptation is the koala bear (a marsupial, not a mammal) which is normally restricted to leaves of only a few of the many species of eucalypts in its habitat.

However, aspects of cannibalism go wider than its nutritional efficiency. It is a part—though not an indispensable part—of the ecological necessity for reducing the population to what the available resources can support: so, though killing need not be consummated by cannibalism, in primitive societies some mode of cutting the surplus population down to a fitting numerical size could not, in the absence of catastrophe or imported fatal disease, be avoided. That remains true whether or not tribal warfare was dignified or rationalized by some accompaniment such as head-hunting or cannibalism; or whether some more selective practice such as infanticide and profuse religious sacrifice (as with the Aztecs) was adopted as well or instead.

In his book 'A pattern of islands' Sir Arthur Grimble mentioned a Pacific Island some ten miles long which was inhabited by two tribes separated by a neutral zone about a mile wide. Every so often and for no obvious reason the neutral zone would be crossed and a battle fought. Many were killed in the process, humanitarianly deplorable to the eyes of civilized persons, but ecologically an absolute necessity: given the conditions on that island at that time.

With the coming of white traders and seamen and missionaries into primitive communities the human ecological picture became much less tidy. The missionaries preached 'thou shalt not kill' without telling their hearers how thou shalt keep alive; missionary words were thus entirely anti-ecological. If the early missionaries had been entirely successful there might soon have been no alternative to semi- or absolute starvation. Fortunately (from a dead-pan ecological viewpoint) the other white people introduced killing diseases, their own sort of warfare, and other practices (like indenturing labour) that reduced the population of some areas—the effects being most clearly seen in the Pacific Islands. They also introduced foodstuffs, which were mostly starchy because starchy foods were cheap and easily transported over long distances; and thus further debilitated the natives. The ecological picture rapidly became very confused; and I do not propose to carry the protein argument further beyond remarking that recent medical and therapeutic advances have further aggravated the relation of numbers of people to sources of protein.

In some regions modern methods of using fossil fuel to gather extra protein from both land and sea have staved off the worst consequences. The outstanding example of that is Japan; and such examples deserve much closer ecological study than they have obtained from the United Kingdom. Once again, the accent of British study of techniques has been concentrated on machines—Japan having been looked upon chiefly as an object-lesson in shipbuilding, and almost totally ignored as the largest and most practical demonstration of getting food by means of fossil fuel used to support a population which has been expanding both numerically and technically.

Japan is admittedly a special and probably unique case. The country consists of small islands in a kindly temperate zone; their interior is mountainous so that the resident population is mostly within a day's walk of the coast. Much of the fish is nowadays brought from distant seas, so that disputes between Japan and Russia about fish-protein are not infrequent. However, once the coastal and deep-sea fish has been landed, the problem of distributing it is simple (unlike that of feeding India with fish if the people would eat it). Within living memory, the city and outer suburbs of Edinburgh obtained fish from women who carried it from the fishing ports along the nearby Firth of Forth.

Any increase of protein for hot countries offers peculiar difficulties. Dairying is almost impossible without special expenditure. If the people are vegetarian, they will probably already be producing something near the maximum of protein the land is capable of yielding. In Ghana fish smoked on the shore has long been a useful protein adjunct to diet, especially because the distance a woman can carry a load of fresh fish on her head is short. Smoked fish is carried long distances by lorry—sometimes into inland regions of adjoining countries. Eating that fish may be an acquired taste; but its acceptability in places hundreds of miles from the coast does suggest a local craving for animal protein. In Ghana itself the greatest recent advance in the matter of protein has not been agricultural, but indirect: it is the introduction of ice into the coastal markets and of refrigerated transport to take fresh fish a couple of hundred miles inland. That implies use of fuel and energy for making the ice and extending the range of supply of fresh fish: the gain is apparent, and so is the explicit example it gives of the fact that any gain in quality or quantity of food beyond the subsistence level has to be paid for.

Vegetarianism is with some people an emotional question often beclouded with half-truths about agriculture. There is no need to argue the question about the nutritional suit-

ability of vegetarian foods, since the fact that they can support life is attested by millions of people in hot countries
and by a minority in Europe. However the argument that if
all England (or Britain, etc.) were to rely on vegetable foods
there could be a great increase in production of home-grown
food is untenable. In support, it is alleged that an acre of
soil could produce several—perhaps five—times as great a
weight of carrots, potatoes, cabbage, grain, and other crops
as an average British cultivated acre now does. That argument is doubly specious.

Firstly, it leaves out of account the fact that large areas of
Britain are kept under grass to produce meat and milk for
the reason that grass is the crop best suited to much of
Britain (especially the western half); if the grassland were
ploughed up and converted to arable cropping there would
be grave climatic difficulties—not so much in growing the
crops but in harvesting them when grown. A farmer on the
Lammermuirs told me that he had once brought in the oats
on the first of January, and jokingly claimed that that was
the earliest corn harvest on record in Britain! If that sort
of thing happens in the east of Britain, how much more likely
are damaging delays in the west to crops more tender than
oats? For those curious in such matters, I mention that the
main agricultural and horticultural limitation from water in
the west of Britain comes not so much from what does fall
as rain and snow, but from what does not fall: that is, the
greater cloudiness, and therefore lessened sunshine, all
through summer.

Secondly, another climatic limitation. That is, that no crop
that can be regarded as a protein-rich staple human food can
be reliably grown in Britain. Traditionally vegetarian peoples
all live in hot countries like India where pulses unknown in
Britain (except as imports) can be easily ripened. The nearest
European analogies are in southern Spain where beans here
regarded as exotic are freely grown: the northern frontier
of the haricot bean (*haricots grain*) is south of Paris. Our
only large-scale possible protein-rich crops, edible by man,
(besides the rather second-rate cabbage family) are ordinary
peas and broad beans—which cannot be counted on to ripen

everywhere in England. Nor, in Britain, could production of much vegetable oil be expected.

Earnest Britons who believe in agricultural self-sufficiency to the point of starting their own demonstration farms have in almost every instance chosen a site somewhere in East Anglia; there, almost alone in England, does the climate smile on their ideas.

There is no reason why people in Britain and other parts of Europe north of Lisbon (or say, Washington D.C. in the United States) should not become vegetarians if they are prepared to import food from warmer regions. But that could only come about as the result of a highly-organized system of exports, imports, and marketing something like that which enables the people of Hawaii to live almost entirely on sugar and pineapples (Chapter 17, Note [M3] page 176). Nothing less elaborate will do; and British vegetarians might give the matter more than cursory economic and ecological thought.

Classical ecology has lately extended its concern from plants and animals in the wild along two directions which involve Man, while it remains (as far as I can tell) utterly blind to the prospects of the human species as a whole. Its relative, anthropology, seems to have stayed at the stage of recording tribal customs of the black man 'before they vanish' (from being tribal, that is). Much concern has been expressed about the fate of whales (or should one say, the prospects for whaling?) and of large game and other animals having some economic importance; and that sort of thing has become a topic of conversation in intellectual circles. The other direction of recent ecological thought is about animals and birds threatened with extinction through Man's interference with them directly (as by shooting) or indirectly (by encroachment on their habitat). Much of this concern is admirable and justified; I am not gainsaying that, but expressing surprise that so much of it has been devoted to the outsides of birds and virtually none that is pertinent (apart from purely nutritional and physiological discussions) to the insides of people. I hazard the guess that as much space has been given in the Press and elsewhere to serious studies of the whooping crane as to equally serious study of the ecology of Man.

There is, however, an odd case in the example of the present Kanaka inhabitants of that group of Pacific islands which may for short be referred to be the name of the best-known one, Nauru. These consist of solid phosphate rock exploited by the British Phosphate Commission on which the United Kingdom is represented, though practically all the phosphate rock is delivered to Australia and New Zealand for conversion into superphosphate.

It has been foreseen for many years that the phosphate would soon be worked out (the present estimate is that it will last 20 years). The concern has been about the fate of a few thousand Kanakas thereafter. That is an inversion of the usual thing, since the whole population of Australia and New Zealand are relying on the protein they produce—for domestic consumption and for export—on superphosphate they make from Nauru phosphate; and the geographically next nearest big deposits of rock phosphate are in Wyoming. Possibly we need not worry too much about the Australians and the New Zealanders; they will, no doubt, obtain ample raw phosphate from North Africa. Yet, I cannot help thinking it odd that in the discussions which have come my way about the fate of the Kanakas, I have not heard or read a mention of protein.

There are good reasons for foresight about the fate of the Kanakas; and it is, in a way, creditable to the sociologists for raising that matter. However, if chemical-sounding words like 'sulphur', 'superphosphate', and 'protein' are still not fit to be taken up and used in intellectual society, the only conclusion which seems possible is that sociologists have not *yet* learnt the first of the realities of what makes modern Man tick and enables him to keep up his numbers everywhere—and not just in a remote Pacific group of rather special islands.

[MI]   This subject has been discussed at greater length in my 'Microbes and Us,' Pelican book A 326 published by Penguin Books

Ltd. in 1955. It includes an essay entitled '2154' which accepted the invitation of an incautious U.S. citizen who wrote in a chemical journal: 'If the reader . . . feels any discomfort over the prospects of all our present fuels being gone in less than 200 years, let him relieve it by a little philosophizing sparkable by a backward look for the same distance. Back there, none of our present fuels were considered of much use or dreamed of.' The present book mentions, on page 248, a dream (taken seriously) about magical energy replacing our present fuels.

[M2] Honourable mention, therefore, to Miss Nina Epton for giving a balanced picture of everyday Japanese diet and food habits in 'Seaweed for Breakfast,' London: Cassell. 1963.

[M3] Some modern barleys, apparently not in common cultivation, contain close to 18% of crude protein; they would theoretically give a balanced diet.

[M4] Mr Johnny Morris of the British Broadcasting Corporation pretended to be so much astonished at finding 'beans' growing on trees that in an amusing broadcast about his visit to Majorca he referred to these plants as 'bean-trees': a name which my wife and I have gratefully adopted into our family language. Thus, in describing to each other the succession of crops as the train climbed up from the irrigated citrus groves around Valencia, we pointed out oranges, wheat and ordinary beans, cereals, almonds, and bean-trees; and on the heights olives.

[M5] A forage legume *Vicia monanthos* Desf., which also is called *algarroba*, is the protein mainstay of the livestock in some of the cooler parts of Spain *e.g.* near Salamanca. I am indebted to the Director, Royal Botanic Gardens, Kew, for the botanical name of this vetch.

12

Mostly about protein

'What did they live on?' said Alice, who always took a great interest in questions of eating and drinking.
'They lived on treacle,' said the Dormouse, after thinking a minute or two.
'They couldn't have done that, you know,' Alice gently remarked; 'they'd have been ill.'
'So they were,' said the Dormouse; '*very* ill.'
—Lewis Carroll: *Alice in Wonderland*

Well over a hundred years ago the short-term prisoners in Dundee—not engaged in hard labour but under relatively easy conditions—assisted in showing the necessity of protein and earthy constituents of diet by losing much more weight than did comparable inmates of the three other Scottish prisons. This they did because in Dundee only treacle was served with the porridge; whereas other prisoners all got porridge with milk. The experiment may have been unintended and was not critical; it did not distinguish between the nutritional effects of (say) calcium and those of protein; but at least it showed that a high-carbohydrate diet was Bad for Them.

Since that time a great deal has been learnt about the importance of proteins and 'minerals' in animal diets. The net effect on general nutritional education has been to establish some degree of awareness of the need for having at least a minimum proportion of foods containing materials derived from the soil. In the light of the kinds of information contained in previous Chapters, that general knowledge can be given a little more precision by saying that nitrogen, sulphur, phosphate, calcium, and other food-constituents derived from soil or sea are indispensable for (*a*) the diet of any animal, and (b) for production of green plants or whatever the animal eats.

Minerals normally enter animal diets through the eating of green plants which have taken up the minerals from the soil. It is one of the chief virtues of annual and perennial clovers and of alfalfa that those legumes are not only excellent sources of protein for farm livestock but they are also the best vehicles for carrying calcium and sulphur from soil to animal.

Besides common salt, a few minerals may be eaten directly by ourselves or any other animal. These are chiefly calcium and phosphate. Calcium phosphate supplies both; calcium may also be taken as chalk and some salts of organic acids. Carnivores obtain most of their minerals by eating bones. In farm practice it is common to add fish meal to the rations of animals—including poultry which are not normally carnivorous—to supply not simply balancing protein but also the minerals contained in the fish-bones; sometimes bone meal is added to the rations.

The needs for nitrogen and minerals derived from the soil (or sea) hold for all animals in all circumstances: whether the animal is a fish or dolphin living naturally in the sea, or is a human being living under savage conditions or with the aid of any kind of agriculture. Unfortunately, education about the origins of people's diet still rests largely on the fairy story about the energy of light producing food from the gases of the atmosphere. Even if we ignore the thermodynamic aspects, and also the needs of all plants and animals for mineral substances, the notion that the combination of sunlight and photosynthesis can produce food will not stand up for a moment. Sunlight acting on carbon dioxide and water can transform them *only* into carbohydrates. Most introductions to the life-cycle begin and end with an equation for formation of carbohydrates, and are silent about the proteins and minerals. It is (apparently) assumed that those will somehow get into food through the energy of sunlight making green plants grow; furthermore, when plans are made for producing food for many thousands of millions of people, the calculations are usually based on talismanic invocation of 'more fertilizer' applied to cereals: with or without greatly expanded use of mechanical cultivation and other applications of energy—all of which can come only from fossil fuel.

That sort of thing is unrealistic in every way if it does not pay thorough-going respect for chemistry as shown in plants, animals, and microbes. I would rather go into positive relations of populations with their earth than into the sources of errors that pervade current discussions about food and population; but they are usually so gravely misleading that it is well worth while to show how wrongheaded are the main sources of misinformation.

Knowledge is widely diffused about the desirability of balancing carbohydrate-rich foods such as cereals and sugar with a due proportion of protein to balance carbohydrate-rich food*stuffs* such as sugar and cereals in the kitchen and at table; and that knowledge is the basis of animal husbandry. Beyond that, its implications have not extended far. There is also the point that human nutrition is taught as if all that mattered is the fate of food after it enters the human mouth: the medical men and others who study that subject —often in great detail—seem to have little interest in or knowledge about the ultimate (as distinct from the geographical) origins of food. That could be remedied; but much public misinformation about world food-supplies emanates from semi-official bodies like the Food and Agriculture Organization which tend to be accepted as 'authorities' about food though they do not make much use of knowledge so elementary as the need for adequate proportions of protein. [MI]

In making comments on increases in world output of 'food', F.A.O. devotes its main comments to cereals and sugar, and thereby shows how careless it is about the distinction between foodstuffs or nutrients, and real food. That distinction is thereby lost to the public, unless its members—already primed with the facts that cereals rarely contain more than 12% of protein, and sugar contains none—succeed in putting two and two together to reach the conclusion that any organization which pretends that cereals and sugar are food is talking through its hat. To mention that cereals, potatoes, sugar and such-like are not, by themselves, food unless the word 'food' is used so loosely as to deprive it of nutritional meaning is no academic point; it is a very real one for people and other animals. A Morayshire farmer who pointed out (in the correspondence columns of the *Glasgow Herald* (1951)) that the entire American wheat surplus could not, by itself, rear one litter of pigs was showing himself wiser than F.A.O. and all similar bodies.

The difference between 'food' and 'foodstuff' is commonly blurred at origin in pronouncements and publications of F.A.O. and similar quasi-official and semi-political bodies. The confusion gains further and widespread currency when those pronouncements are repeated, condensed, and commented on or quoted as fact in some argument (usually about population and 'food') by other officials, public speakers, and journalists. They—naturally enough in the present state of uncritical education—take the original pronouncements as authoritative: indeed, everyone could have the right to expect them to be faultless from the scientific and every other point of view.

But it is because the original 'authorities' are careless about nutritional, agricultural, and verbal proprieties that a myth is maintained about our greatest problem.

The verbal distinction is a simple one: it is between food and food*stuff*. Those terms are not clearly distinguished even in some of the better dictionaries. The difference in meaning can be vital: if, for example, one is condemned to try to stay alive on food*stuffs* such as sugar or treacle or cereals (without having enough total protein in the diet or daily intake of *food*); or if—on the other side—one is concerned with drawing up, pondering, or implementing policies about production of more food in the proper sense.

Under the latter, broadly administrative, head may be included governmental projects for 'fertilizer factories' whenever the term 'fertilizer' is used as an omnibus one without clear distinction (in relation to population and not just sales) between synthetic nitrogenous and other fertilizers as sources of foodstuffs and real food (Chapter 9). Again under the latter head, the confusion is multiple: nor could one conceive, from the frequency with which that sinister confusion is made, that world food is really important or that people mattered enough to have the most incisive scientific thinking engaged in their behalf; whereas the runners in this race fall at the first fence by a muddle about words and their meanings.

The explanation of the ineptitude of the Food and Agriculture Organization seems to be that it is dominated by economists; and that scientists in it are either of the wrong kind to make confident pronouncements about food on the world scale [M2] or are not listened to if their interests in food and people happen to be appropriately broad. F.A.O. (or its public relations branch) is failing to do a good job of public education by insisting on the distinction between real food and commercial foodstuffs. If it did that, people would be better informed about the actual state of world food-production. As things are, it looks as if F.A.O. is assuming that there is a widespread lack of perception of the meaninglessness of increases in output of cereals and sugar as pointers to any food situation. Well or badly, the greater part of the population is somehow managing to keep alive; yet, hardly any private or official publication says much about the sources or prospects of the world's protein supplies.

Like more specialized bodies having frankly commercial interests in (say) wheat and sugar, F.A.O. concentrates its world surveys of production on tonnages of *commodities*— that is, of foodstuffs which lend themselves to being expressed in figures because they can or do enter into world trade. Books and articles about world production of 'food' usually follow this model; sometimes by extending tabulated figures so far as to notice commodities such as meat and leguminous grains; but the indispensable clovers and young grasses and other fodder crops that make it possible to produce enough protein do not get mentioned. [M3]

Fodders are sometimes the subject of a swap or agreement between neighbouring farmers; but, being in principle eaten on or near the spot where they grow, they do not, apparently become economically memorable either as tables of yesterday's figures or in the reckonings of writers of books under such titles as 'How famine can be avoided'. Need it be said that these show no general grasp of the facts or the principles of production of real food, or even of what real food is?

Just for the record and without entering into much explanation that would take us beyond the main theme of the sources of human energy, it may be useful to state the sources of 'balancing' protein—meaning thereby those photosynthesizing and other plants that contain a proportion of protein above the 16% by weight aforesaid [MI] and are therefore capable of giving what is called 'nutritional balance' to foodstuffs or human diets supplying less than a sixth of their (dry) weight of protein.

There are only two main sources of this balancing protein. Some vegetables which could be classed as protein-rich are toxic; other plants are unduly fibrous; but, assuming edibility, these two sources are:

(*i*) any young or fast-growing organism (including most microbes) or any young part of any green plant (irrespective of the age of the parent plant—which may be a grass or a tree or other perennial).

(*ii*) any non-woody part of any leguminous plant, or legume, at any stage of growth or maturity up to and including the ripe seeds (pulses).

There are no legumes in the sea; and (*ii*) overlaps with (*i*) as far as young legumes are concerned.

All marine animals (mammalian and other) depend upon the microscopic green algae of the sea at one or more removes (the familiar large seaweeds are not important as food sources for marine animals). All mammals (including sucklings) and carnivores depend on green plants, often at several removes; most fish are carnivorous, so the food-chain between a large fish and the original microbial algal protein may be long. Fungi and other microbes (yeasts, mushrooms) which have no chlorophyll depend on green plants for their carbohydrate. Browsing of young leaves of trees and shrubs by animals in search of protein and minerals is familiar; the best human analogue is eating of asparagus, which is the richest source of vegetable protein known to me. [M4]

A minor third source of balancing protein consists of ripe nuts of some deciduous non-leguminous trees, such as walnuts and brazil nuts. [M5]

[MI] Leaving aside complications which arise from minerals, vitamins, and other constituents that involve the higher flights of nutritional studies: and also leaving aside foodstuffs like sugar or fats (for the reason that they contain no appreciable proportion of nitrogen or sulphur essential to life), there is no *single* standard or value by which the adequacy of a foodstuff or diet can be judged. Calories, weight, or money-value are useless nutritional measures by themselves.

In estimating the dietary value of a foodstuff or mixture of foods, it is always necessary to have at least a rough idea of the proportion of protein to non-protein constituents, since a minimum content of protein in the daily diet is a necessity. Anything to eat is better as a stop-gap than nothing; but no amount of protein-poor food can enable good growth and reproduction. Most farmers are aware of this; if they keep animals, they have to have a pretty shrewd idea about it in order to remain solvent. Cereals usually contain only about 10-12 per cent of protein by weight, whereas a minimum of about 16 per cent of the dry weight of a diet should be protein— as the farmer quoted on page 112 was roughly aware.

There is a stumbling-block in appreciating what the minimum percentage of protein is. That happens because some medical writers reckon by percentage of energy; and since fats give, per unit of weight, much more energy than protein, these writers accept a minimum of about 10% of protein, for human diet, often without stating their method of measurement. Worked out in weight terms, this 10% of protein in a mixed diet comes to about the same thing as the 16% by weight—or about a sixth of the total diet—that I have adopted.

For ruminants, bulk of food in relation to capacity of the rumen is a further consideration which I mention to show how commonsense as well as calories or world tonnages or other single units need to be borne in mind. Just to drive that point home, I mention that for reasons similar to those which make carbohydrates and proteins less effective as energy sources than fats are, the maximum yield of energy from nitroglycerine or T.N.T. is about a third of that from an equal weight of butter (even though about a sixth of butter consists of salt and water).

[M2] I would not leave the reader with the impression that F.A.O. is unaware of the general need for protein or that F.A.O. publications do not frequently mention the subject. An example of its interests in protein is the appointment by F.A.O. of specialists in subjects such as nursery rearing of fresh-water fish to augment local supplies of edible protein in tropical countries; these efforts have been well publicised. Such considerations ignore the question whence the extra protein needed by the additional fish or other meat-producers, is to come from. Unless it is explained how *that* problem is being met, the crude result—as it reaches the public—is to re-inforce the idea that all that is necessary in order to increase supplies of protein-rich or other food is to utilize know-how by importing a person who has specialized in some narrow aspect of the immediate problem, while the basal problems are left unresolved and unexplained. Arguing along similar lines it could be suggested that the world's food problem could be alleviated in a way that would give ample material for the public-relations boys, by hiring enough conjurors to produce rabbits and pigeons out of their professional hats.

These comments are not meant to suggest that what is being done locally to augment food-supplies is not worth doing; the comment about F.A.O.'s emphasis on commodities like cereals and sugar in its surveys of what is called world 'food' is meant to suggest how slight is the Organization's appreciation that production of real food is a matter which needs the most critical scientific attention.

Incidentally, economists could be expected to be specially alive to the hopelessness of trying to get something for nothing; but neither in, nor outside, F.A.O., has a grasp of the practical fact that all food has to be paid for in strict chemical currency been very evident in discussions of world food.

[M3] The reader can test for himself how greatly the common insistence on exported commodities as food has affected his general knowledge. If he were asked which country is the greatest producer of wheat, he would be unlikely to name China unless he had lived there. Yet China held the premier position up to 1938—the latest year for which figures of production of wheat in China are available. Since 1938, production of wheat in North America and other 'Western' countries and in the U.S.S.R. has undoubtedly increased; but it has probably increased in China as well, so China must still be among the world's largest producers of wheat. However, because Chinese wheat has not for many years entered into recognized world trade, the fact that wheat is extensively grown in China is little known in the West—having been obscured by travellers' tales to the effect that the staple diet in China is rice.

[M4] Unpublished analyses kindly made for me by Mr R. H.

Alexander in the Chemistry Department of The West of Scotland Agricultural College have shown that at least 50% of the dry matter of canned asparagus tips and of the edible portion of raw asparagus is crude protein. I do not know of any published analyses of canned asparagus; published analyses of fresh 'asparagus' are misleading because the material analysed has included much of the woody part, which, as every aspirant to culture knows, is not eaten.

[M5]   Brazil nuts have several historical and chemical associations. They are collected from a tree *Bertholletia excelsa* which is found only in Brazil and other north-eastern parts of South America in which it grows wild. It is the sole known member of a genus named by the explorers Friedrich von Humboldt (a Prussian) and the Frenchman Aimé Bonpland who, in the course of a joint expedition to South America, gave the first botanical description of the tree and named it to pay their respect to the French chemist C.-L. Berthollet (1748-1822).

In 1801 Berthollet (who never went to the Americas) had introduced the concept of chemical equilibrium which is so germane to a modern discussion of food and population.

Humboldt and Bonpland ('Plantes Equinoxiales': Paris, 1808, vol. 1, p. 122) made their appreciation in these pregnant words: *Je le dédie à l'illustre M. BERTHOLLET à qui l'on doit tant de découvertes, et dont les travaux actuels promettent beaucoup à la physiologie et à la chimie des végétaux.*

As far as is known, the meat of the Brazil nut is the foodstuff richest in the trace element barium (Ba); it also appears to be unusually rich in the related trace element strontium (Sr; not the radioactive isotope). I am indebted for much of this information to Dr J. J. Swart, of the Biohistorical Institute, Utrecht; and, through a Scottish friend Mr D. K. Jardine, to Monsieur Serge Vérétenicoff, the Documentalist of the Institut Français de Recherches Fruitières Outre-Mer (I.F.A.C.), Paris; and through him to the Centre National de Documentation Horticole, Paris.

Chemical investigation in the South American jungles being a little difficult to perform, it does not seem to have been ascertained whether the unusual richness of the fruit of *B. excelsa* in barium and strontium is due to its growing in soil which happens to be rich in those uncommon trace elements, or whether the tree actually requires them in unusually large proportions.

Because oil-seed cattle-cakes made from leguminous plants, and also non-leguminous plants such as flax (linseed) and cotton, are widely used by farmers to 'balance' cereals and other protein-poor constituents of rations for farm livestock, and are referred to as 'concentrated' sources of protein, it should be mentioned that the raising of the percentage of protein is essentially arithmetical. Cakes are made from soybeans and peanuts (ground nuts) which have a good percentage of protein to start with; but the seeds of non-legumes contain barely enough protein to support animal life. The cakes are made by pressing the seeds to remove most of their contained oil; the proportion of protein in the residue (the cake) is thereby raised to 25% or more. What is gained in that way is not protein but convenience.

13

Soil and water around the world

One may not doubt that somehow, good
Shall come of water and of mud;
And, sure, the reverent eye must see
A purpose in liquidity.

—Rupert Brooke: *Heaven*

All agriculture depends on the management and control of
water; all life goes on in water as the internal medium and
external medium; all aqueous biological media are solutions
of salts and gases. Remembering that all the 'water' that is
useful or harmful to roots, marine plants, red corpuscles of
blood, bones and everything organized in the internal or
external media, produces its effects because of changing
equilibria with the salts, gases, or other substances dissolved
in or carried by the water, we can see one facet of the principle that life is everywhere the same though the details
differ. Rain and snow are virtually pure water incapable of
supporting life, but having profound effects after they reach
an existing solution or can make their own (by dissolving
surface rock, for example).

It is therefore quite permissible to make no more than
incidental references to the sea and other large bodies of
water, while concentrating attention on soil as a convenient
type for all aqueous media.

The most evident function of soil is as a support; but, like
every function and inanimate product of soil, that can be
supplemented or entirely substituted by artificial means if we
pay enough in energy: as is done in soil-less culture (sometimes called hydroponics). No function of soil is indispens-

able; but soil will be dealt with here, in a cursory survey, as the watery system which it essentially is.

The most rewarding way of looking at soil—it is also the most modern and logical—is as a system of spaces which can be filled to varying extents with air and 'water' (a salt solution, I repeat: the inverted commas around the word 'water' being henceforth understood). [MI]

It is the arrangement of the solids to form the spaces— and, therefore the arrangements and the permeability of the spaces to water and air—that decide what is the most important character of soil: namely, its structure. With the structure is bound up the immensely important fact that the spaces are the workshops of the soil microbes which are continually turning-over, and ultimately oxidizing, organic matter so that the cycle of life can go on. Aeration is therefore of the first importance; but, since the soil pores are always 100 % filled with water plus gases (which I have called 'air' for convenience), it is the water that decides the proportion of air and therefore the well-being of plants. Water decides the *kinds* of bacteria and other microbes; if there is not enough air, the equilibrium between microbial species will rapidly alter, and those species which require oxygen for their essential purposes will cease to dominate and will be replaced by others which produce reducing substances that plants cannot tolerate. The plant roots and small animals also require air for their own purposes.

The solid materials of soil have many functions which would require many words to explain. Under the combined influences of chemical solution aided by dissolved carbon dioxide and oxygen, the inorganic particles of rock break down to release nutrients and to form clay colloid; organic residues like old roots, leaves and animal bodies are broken down by microbial actions and thereby their temporarily locked-up plant nutrients are released; organic colloids are formed from them as well as from microbial tissues. The chief importance of all the colloids is to act as chemical regulators; for one thing they absorb ('adsorb' is the technical term) ions of salts that would otherwise be washed out— though that can be a mixed blessing.

The widespread idea that soil is chiefly useful as a store-house of plant nutrients contained in the solid material derived from the original rock was founded on a germ of truth, but is so old-fashioned as to be inappropriate to agricultures which produce protein intensively. It is fitted only to conditions where the equilibrium between soil and its plants, animals, and human population is the natural one, so that the human population is sparse. Nutrients are released very slowly from rock particles: the nutrients in their interior may not become available for centuries. Nor may the nutrients, or the rainfall, or the climate, be suitable for producing heavy yields of protein-rich foodstuffs to sustain a large human population without considerable human aid: as the agricultural history of North America, New Zealand, and other 'new' lands bears ample witness.

This Chapter already contains enough to suggest that soil is a very complicated system; it varies, moreover so greatly with location (latitude, altitude, and other factors) that any study of soil is largely a matter of geography—whether we are concerned with its unimproved state or with what can be produced from it by energy introduced in agriculture. About soil and its food-producing potentialities the main point is that (whether or not it is cropped, fertilized, irrigated, or given any other treatment by man) every process and manifestation occurring in soil is invariably an equilibrium process: of which the natural or artificial state of balance existing at any moment is virtually instantaneous in fact and of short duration in practice, because the soil is always tending to revert to a new physical and productive level which is the lowest possible. In this respect, soil—for all its complications—resembles every other system; it follows Le Chatelier's principle (page 18) in resisting changes of energy. As a simple example, there is the fact that all soil is on its way to the sea: that is, to the lowest position of gravitational energy.

By controlling the proportion of air in the soil pores, water decides the extent and vigour with which plants and microbes can turn over the nutrients left at their disposal from the inorganic solids and organic residues. If the pores are full of stagnant water, the soil is said to be water-logged;

and the chief function of drainage is not the obvious one of taking away water but rather of letting air in. Since growing paddy rice on flooded fields may look like a contradiction, I mention that the water on rice-fields itself brings oxygen chiefly by being kept flowing, so that it brings dissolved oxygen from the air.

After a gentle fall of rain on to 'dry' soil, the water displaces partly-respired air and thereby renews it with the normal mixture of gases richer in oxygen. It is, therefore, not a poetic exaggeration to say that rain, or properly-managed irrigation, enables the soil to 'breathe', and acts as an oxygen-pump. In general, air and water in soil and plants must always be continually renewed from outside: even though the water that is actually used by plants for their internal chemical operations forms a small, or very small, proportion of what the soil receives [M2].

That first function of water in soil may be summed up as its mechanical, aerating, effect. The other main effect on soil is physical, or, more exactly, physico-chemical; it refers to the dissolved and undissolved salts of the soil. To avoid going into detail we may include the colloids—not only because they are much bound up with the salts but also because, like dissolved salts, the colloids can tenaciously hold water. For simplicity I will write 'salts' in discussing the physical effect of water in any soil that bears plants; the soil colloids will get separate mention only incidentally, though it is desirable to add that microbes and plant roots are colloidal, like all other active cells.

Everybody knows that plants need water 'for growth'; but that soil has to be 'moist' is no explanation. Nor is the percentage of water in soil a guide: it can serve as an example of the fact that a single fact is of no use unless it is put into proper relation with other facts. Peaty and clayey soils, which are rich in colloids, may be quite 'moist' without their water being available to plants. Marine plants are adapted to utilizing water containing $3\frac{1}{2}\%$ of salts, yet the $96\frac{1}{2}\%$ of water of sea water is wholly unavailable to land plants (unless it is diluted about 30 times with fresh water). These points are all aspects of energy.

What may be called the 'free energy' of actual water (H_2O) in decreased when anything is dissolved in it. The extent to which the available energy is lessened can be measured in atmospheres of osmotic pressure; for plant roots the opposite is taken and is called 'suction force'. An atmosphere is equal to a pressure of 15 lb. per square inch. Osmotic pressure of soil is set up by dissolved salts and the colloids. The osmotic pressure of soil water (technically, the soil solution) is normally half an atmosphere or less; in blood and other internal body fluids the osmotic pressure (to which the blood sugar contributes as well as salts) is normally about 6-7 atmospheres; in sea water the osmotic pressure is over 20 atmospheres. The suction force which land plants are able to exert so as to take up water and dissolved nutrients from the soil solution is a maximum of about 15 atmospheres. If the soil salts are naturally or artificially so concentrated as to have an osmotic pressure approaching or exceeding 15 atmospheres, the plant is defeated, and wilts (or does not start growing) whatever the apparent moistness of the soil, and however rich it is in nutrients.

Over-fertilizing with soluble fertilizers is a common cause of trouble in glasshouse cultivation, for example; though excess of salts is not always the sole harmful outcome of trying to be over-generous with plant nutrients. Land plants cannot get water from salt-rich soils or water for precisely the same reason that makes it expensive in energy to distil fresh water from the sea: the two things are matters of degree, the principle being the same.

But if it is recalled that land and river plants do the best that is possible with the available nutrients (assuming that aeration and some other conditions are also right) when the osmotic pressure of their aqueous environment is quite low, it will be seen that the chief physical effect of adding reasonably salt-free water to soil is to reduce the salt concentration (or, the osmotic pressure) so as to make it easy for the plant to take up both water and nutrients. It is Le Chatelier's principle again: the plant/microbial system being bound not to use more energy than it need do in given climatic conditions. Since the colloids as well as the true salts come into the picture, clayey and sandy soils need different kinds of farm management; this is largely because although the clayey soils have a larger total pore space than an equal volume of sandy soil, the arrangement of the pores and solids differs; so, therefore do the water-relations and many other things differ with which a farmer is concerned.

In any one set of seasonal and climatic conditions, the chief cause of useless loss of water from ploughed and cropped soil (apart from evaporation where the soil is bare) is growth of weeds. In grassland, a small proportion of what are commonly called 'weeds' constitutes a normal part of the herbage, and may be useful by supplying mineral nutrients of which the grazing animal might not get enough from the true grasses. The 'weeds' of grassland (if not too many or too big) can be looked upon as partners rather than competitors. Weeds in arable crops are in competition with the principal crop for water and nutrients. There is an old saying that 'the best way to grow a poor crop is to grow weeds'; and there is the counsel of perfection that 'the time to hoe is when there are no weeds' (meaning, to remove them before they have grown big.) Like other green plants, weeds lose to the atmosphere several hundred pounds of water per season and per pound of dry matter; that water is used to transport soluble material from soil and through the plant tissues; but it is desirable that the crop—not the weeds— shall use the soil water, as well as benefit from the nutrients supplied by the soil and fertilisers. Therefore, a big problem in all arable farming is keeping the weeds under control.

In arable farming, the chief purpose of ploughing is to control weeds. Preparation of a seed-bed is a secondary purpose; so secondary, in fact, that if weeds can be controlled by any other means (hand-picking, or chemical spraying) there is little need for ploughing to prepare the seed-bed. A decent scratching to loosen the top inch or two of soil is enough, *provided that* the weeds are really under control. It should be remembered that the weeds which will compete with the young seedlings may exist as buried weed-seeds and may germinate at the same time as the crop seeds will; or a little before, so as to become established first and per-

haps cover the ground and smother the young crop plants!
I am writing with British weeds and climate principally in
mind; yet, however contrary it is to general belief among
townspeople, it remains true for nearly all conditions of
arable farming that ploughing is primarily a method of weed-
control. [M3]

The important exception to that is breaking up land either
as a first step of bringing virgin land under cultivation, or
breaking up grassland forming part of a rotation which includes arable farming. But since cultivation of grassland
worth the name is virtually restricted to temperate climates
having a fair rainfall, and because popular interest in ploughing does, most likely, relate to what can be done to support
population in developing countries having warm climates, I
will confine the discussion to arable cultivation.

Since control of weeds is the first thing to aim at, any
simple discussion of ploughing should be taken under two
contrasted heads. Those are (a) hot climates and (b) climates
having much frost in winter. A snag in that over-simple
classification is that much prairie wheat-farming is done
where there is a hot summer and a very cold winter; but as it
is not necessary to examine the details of American or other
agricultures, we can stick to the two-headed climate classification because that fits in with the behaviour of weed-
plants everywhere; it also decides (broadly) the type of
plough, if any, that is used.

American farmers visiting Britain often look pityingly at
the normal British use of the mould-board plough, and take
its continued employment as part of British conservatism.
If the visitors do that, it shows that they have learnt neither
to be humble in face of the British climate nor to recognize
the facts of geography: such as that if Britain were slid due
westwards it would be up against the coast of Labrador and
almost as cold and sunless as Labrador is, and quite several
hundred miles north of any part of the favoured great
American plain.

In almost any agricultural region of North America (except
British Columbia, which has a climate much like that of
southern England) the usual plough is the disc-plough. This

has the great mechanical advantage that its cutters (to use non-technical language) rotate instead of having to be dragged through the soil. It can also work fast. The discs bite into the soil and chew up the surface, leaving the soil and the weeds chopped up, the weeds being up-rooted and left on or very near the surface. Under a hot sun the weeds quickly wither; and if they are about to flower or have set immature seeds, that is the end of the weeds and of their population of seeds not already shed.

Imagine that happening on a sticky soil like most British ones! The disturbed weeds, whether uprooted or merely cut, would grow again in a week or so of damp mild weather typical of our autumn. So there would be not much, if any, control of weeds beyond a little discouragement to them; except in the most favourable conditions.

Accordingly, in Britain and northern Europe generally, the mould-board plough is the general tool for the main ploughing. Any form of this antique instrument deals with the weeds by inverting a slice of the soil, thus forming the familiar furrows; and having chopped off the weed roots at a depth of several inches, it buries them and the green tops. Laborious, but necessary. [M4] Ideally, seeds borne by the weeds are buried too deep to grow up to the surface after germination: in practice, the control of weeds and their seeds is short of perfect; but it is the best that can be done, now that children may no longer be employed to pick the weeds by hand as a supplementary measure.

Setting up furrows by turning up long rows of soil and leaving the clods on edge has other advantages. It assists surface drainage. It exposes the clods to the action of frost whereby the clods are broken down without any further action by the farmer; and his seed-bed is almost ready in the spring, and requires only a light cultivation (a further discouragement of weeds). There is usually no need to break the surface clods with mattocks as must be done in some hot climates.

The differences I have outlined can be seen as between the south and the north of Italy; they are still more pronounced between any Mediterranean country and Central or Northern Europe. The differences are not primarily due to soil, although very broadly, there is an increase in clayeyness as one goes north in Europe. (That is also an effect produced by rainfall in cool conditions). The differences in modes of ploughing, if there is ploughing, are due to prevalence or absence of warm sunshine at time of ploughing and to presence or absence of frost in winter.

Where it is not necessary to kill weeds in cool climates, there is normally no virtue in deep ploughing (as with the mould-board plough) for its own sake. In hot climates just scratching the surface is sufficient to kill weeds; nor is much more labour necessary to prepare a seed-bed, except knocking down by hand the clods produced by ploughing. Ploughing may be necessary to bury the stubble of the preceding crop; but a light plough drawn by one animal is ample on most soils except the most sticky.

Many Western people have the idea that it would be a great agricultural advance if developing countries had tractor-drawn ploughs of European or American types. If mechanical cultivation were introduced, it would save a great deal (perhaps not all) of back-breaking human effort; but, leaving aside humanitarian considerations as well as questions about fuel, it is by no means clear that much agricultural advantage would be gained in hot countries by controlling weeds by tractor instead of with a simple tool like a cutlass or something of a design not much more advanced than a pointed stick.

It has not always been found possible or easy to adapt 'European' ideas about cultivation to 'new' lands even in temperate regions; great caution is necessary before supposing that European or North American ideas about treatment of soil can be usefully exported to agricultures of hot climates.

Caution is especially necessary in considering what are often supposed to be the boundless agricultural potentialities of the tropical wet-forest belt. Many wrong-headed attempts at farming these regions on European models have ended in disaster. The very reason for the supposed 'fertility' of the tropical forests—namely, their luxuriant growth of trees

—is the reason why they are suited mainly to tree-agriculture (*i.e.*, production of crops like cocoa, rubber, oil-palm; some nuts; where the crop harvested is not the timber but an annually-renewable product) except in special conditions which have no analogue in Europe. Tropical forests operate on a different nutrient-cycle from that of temperate climates: as is diagrammatically suggested in Fig. 4, page 196.

That comes about because wet tropical forests have mostly been formed on ancient rocks which have been subject to warm heavy rain for millions of years, with the result that almost everything soluble has been washed out of them except what is contained in the trees themselves and a shallow surface layer wherein the plant nutrients circulate rapidly: in effect, from tree to tree. One result is, that if the forest is clear-felled and exported as timber, a large part of the nutrients have gone; nor can they be replaced by fertilizers applied to the usual kinds of arable crops, because hot sun and rain acting on bare soil destroys the scanty organic matter left in the soil. Like everything else in this Chapter, this picture is over-simplified to the bare bones; but it will suffice to show that in wet-forest soils the useful materials and microbes are almost entirely *above* the soil; whereas temperate agriculture has always been conducted on the premiss of an equilibrium in which most activities of release of nutrients occur within the soil itself.

Indigenous farmers of tropical forest belts have evolved a system for producing their own food by what is commonly called 'shifting cultivation' [M5]. This consists of leaving the big trees standing, and cutting down and burning on the spot such smaller vegetation as can be tackled by simple tools. The patches cut down are usually quite small and are scattered around the villages. After the 'burn', which supplies the soil with mineral nutrients which were previously in the small trees (there being a continual return of organic matter and more nutrients from the leaves of the trees left standing) the soil is cropped for not more than three years with food-producing plants: often grown as an untidy mixture of legumes and non-legumes ('mixed cropping') so that some biologically-fixed nitrogen is added to what is obtained from the leaf-fall. After a couple of years, the patch is abandoned to allow new jungle vegetation to spring up; a succession of new patches being cleared, the burned ones not being burnt and cropped again for fifteen years or so. In the last few centuries the food-economy of shifting cultivation in Africa has been greatly aided by plants originating in the Americas and elsewhere (manioc or cassava from Brazil, maize, tomatoes, etc., and especially the leguminous groundnut: all from South America).

Because of the large area of land needed in proportion to population, and doubtless because of its unfamiliarity, shifting cultivation is usually regarded as wasteful by Westerners, who itch to replace it with tropical crops grown by something more like Western intensive methods. When the Belgians first tried to improve Congo agriculture, they went all-out for 'modern' methods of utilizing the land; but after years of experience in the Congo, they gave up their essentially European notions, and settled for what was little more than a forced systematization of shifting cultivation. Only in limited areas of tropical forest land can continuous cultivation, European-style, be adopted; there is no grass worth the name, and no other crop able to cover the land to shield it from the sun. Tree-agriculture is the best bet; and if that is adopted it compels use of an economic system in which imported food plays a large part if the population is to be fed. Modern methods of mechanization and control of water have little scope. There is a special need for nitrogenous fertilizers to be married to chalk or limestone, which has to be transported over long distances, or imported from abroad, because there is naturally none in the wet regions where the tropical trees are.

Shifting cultivation is the only agricultural system that can directly provide food for the resident population of the tropical forests. If the people supplement their protein with wild animals such as snails and snakes, and are delighted when a white hunter occasionally kills a hippo or a crocodile, who can blame them? They are giving a practical demonstration of the need to work with Nature and not against her. However much the inadequacies of shifting cultivation may be viewed with horror by Westerners, it has—within its climatically-imposed limits—been found to 'work'. It manages soil, vegetation, and water in what seems (ecologically and thermodynamically) to be the only practical way. It is doubtful whether, in like conditions, any Western-imposed scheme of agriculture could pass that pragmatic test.

[M1]   Many irrigation schemes laid out early this century were ruined after a few seasons, and defeated their purpose of producing large crops, because the people responsible for the lay-out forgot the elementary fact that all natural 'water,' except atmospheric precipitation, contains salts. After being led on to the land, the water evaporated, leaving the salts behind to build up a total concentration of salts which was beyond the ability of most crops to tolerate. This may serve as an example of the unfortunate fact that official bodies often appear unable to think of more than one thing at a time (in this instance, of providing extra water as if the water were necessarily pure H_2O)—the name being taken for the thing; it is pertinent to the subject of Chapter 23.

[M2]   Some vegetable crops yield a total of 30 or more tons per acre, but 90% may be water. In general, the seasonal increment of total dry matter in any crop (including trees) seldom exceeds 5 tons per acre in any climate. It is produced by an exchange of mineral acids and alkalies, derived from the soil, chemically equivalent to the reducing effect of some few pounds of hydrogen; that is, to a net chemical turnover, within the plants, of from 30 to 100 pounds of water per acre per annum. *See* the paper by A. D. Hall and N. H. J. Miller, *Proc. Roy. Soc.*, B, 1905, Vol. 77, 1–32.

[M3]   The author of the lines

> 'We plough the fields and scatter
> The good seed on the land'

may have been brought up in Mesopotamia; or else has taken poetic licence in omitting steps which in cooler climates intervene between ploughing and sowing.

[M4]   No pun intended. It will have been noticed that in French the words *labour, -er, -eur* refer exclusively to literal ploughing. Our Old English word (*plow* in American) has remained outdoors, except in metaphorical senses. The 'indoor' compound words in French have dropped the *u* from *labour-*, and English has done likewise.

[M5]   Strictly speaking, the term 'shifting cultivation' should be reserved for the very primitive type of living in which the village is moved frequently as well as the cultivations. What has been outlined in the text refers to cultivation around fixed villages, and is properly called 'land rotation'. I have retained the more familiar term 'shifting cultivation'. Incidentally, it is now accompanied by a local system of transport by lorry and trading to feed neighbouring towns in a complex system of marketing conducted mainly by women that is very little understood by Westerners.

Crop rotation (Chapter 7) consists of growing a succession of different crops on land continuously cultivated.

14

A few tales

'If Dougie wass here he would tell you himsel'.
—Neil Munro: *Para Handy Tales*: Edinburgh, Blackwood

Dougie was the mate, to whom *in absentia* the Captain, Para Handy, would always appeal for verification of one of his more incredible asseverations or excuses. This Chapter is a sort of rag-bag into which have been put some facts, all true, but mostly of the believe-it-or-not class arising out of beliefs connected with food; they may serve to give a lighter relief. Dougie himself sometimes appealed to the 'enchineer'; and so may we, if we consult engineers of high enough cadre —since they are all well founded in thermodynamics.

Belief in nuclear energy as a panacea is illustrated by the legend that has grown up about using it to grow more food by irrigating deserts with water distilled from the sea. The legend about its practicability on a large scale has grown from over-publicized examples of obtaining fresh water from the sea surrounding small tropical islands which are richly productive of oil or natural gas that costs almost nothing at well-head. The water thus obtained is for local use either domestically or for growing crops like fresh vegetables which are otherwise almost or quite unobtainable.

Irrigating large areas of desert is quite another order of things. Even if water is obtainable cheaply from the coast —say as reclaimed sewage of a large city—there are great practical difficulties: because most deserts are high above sea level, serious costs in energy are involved for pumping alone, and miles of piping for distributing the water have to be laid. If there are fuel costs as well, the idea becomes quite impracticable economically. Dr K. C. D. Hickman, an engineer once associated with the United States plans for obtaining fresh water from the sea, estimated that to obtain as much distributable (electric) energy as would suffice for separating all the salts from one ton (220 Imperial gallons) of sea-water it would be necessary to have a ton of water falling from a height of 400 feet, or nearly three times as high as Niagara. To be fair, it is not always necessary to remove all the salts; for irrigation purposes something less than perfectly pure water would do, and that would reduce the cost in fuel or electricity for the water, though still leaving the fixed costs of pumping and distribution.

Supposing that usable water is somehow on its desert site at whatever cost: a depth of about 40 inches of water has to be used for one crop in a season. (In Britain the average rainfall is about 30 inches). One inch of water per acre is 100 tons; so we can reckon on needing 4000 tons per acre, which will feed about one adult for one year. (In British conditions it takes about as much rainfall to produce a couple of bullocks as would float a battleship). The commercial rate at which water is costed in Australia in economic studies of irrigated crops is (in pre-decimal terms) one penny per thousand gallons (a little less than six tons).

Nor is water-supply necessarily the end of the probable requirements apart from fuel for cultivation and fertilizers. Many deserts contain undesirable salts so as to require a soil amendment such as gypsum. Suppose an area of 50,000 square miles of flat, salty, but irrigable land were to be given one dressing of gypsum at the rate of ten tons per acre, the tonnage of gypsum would run into nine figures (like the annual coal output of Britain). All being well, and at an enormous total cost in energy, a desert area the size of England might be induced to provide enough food for 20 million people; and feeding that number would barely touch the increase of world population during one year.

To see only a part of the energy problem of irrigating deserts, we might take a hint from John Tyndall's contribution to an old controversy about the origin of Polar ice. Instead of 40 inches of water per acre, imagine that each acre (of which there are 640 in a square mile) were to be covered with 20,000 tons of cast iron white-hot at its melting-point. The energy for melting the cast iron would be less per unit area than is needed to separate 40 inches' depth of water from its salts in the sea.

If oil were used to distil water from the sea for irrigation purposes, a conservative estimate is that 50 tons of oil per acre per annum would be consumed to feed one adult for one year. However great the reserves of fuel may be, to exchange fuel for water at that rate is unthinkable on a scale that would improve the food situation for the world as a whole.

The cost of nuclear energy in terms of conventional fuels is difficult to compute; it is certainly no bargain, being far more than the chemical equivalent of processed uranium or other nuclear fuel. Pertinent information is lacking: the estimates of money cost of fuelling nuclear reactors for producing electricity sold at about a penny a unit are probably nominal, since the nuclear fuel is virtually a by-product of military production, of which probably only a small fraction is sold off for commercial purposes. There is some indication from the Tennessee Valley and the neighbouring plant at Oak Ridge where nuclear fuel for bombs is produced.

The fuel-and-power situation in the Tennessee Valley has altered dramatically since 1938, when books were being written to extol the Tennessee Valley Authority because it was thought that its formation marked a new era of social progress by co-ordinating effort in several ways, notably in producing 'white coal' from the region's water power. There is no evidence that the output of hydro-electricity has diminished; it may have increased. However, in 1957 it was revealed that the Valley had become dotted with thermic (coal-burning) electricity generating stations. These were reported to be producing nearly three-quarters of all the electricity generated in the Valley, and to have consumed

23,000,000 tons of coal in a year. That was equal to about an eighth of the total British production of coal, for producing roughly three times as much electricity as all the hydro-electric plants of the Valley. The tonnage quoted refers to coal only; it excludes the fuel-equivalent of hydro-electricity.

The umbrella manufactured by 'the bomb' at such a high cost in coal and other fuel and energy has been of inestimable value in warding off the Cuba business, for example; and we in the United Kingdom may be grateful for it. Nevertheless, it is clear (from this and other examples, especially France) that production of 'atomic' fuel is a luxury to which only the biggest nations can aspire with confidence; nor does it seem necessary to rub in the awkward fact that no kind of energy utilizable for any technical purpose can be had without recourse to sulphur and carbonaceous fuels. Solar cooking, for instance, requires metal; and hydro-electric power consumes large amounts of coal in making machinery and concrete. [MI]

If protein were to be extracted from the sea directly, instead of letting the fish do it at a relatively small or no cost in fuel for harvesting them, it would involve enormous amounts of energy. I am not clear whether proposals that have been made for direct harvesting of plankton refer to the total plankton (minute animals and plants) or to the phytoplankton (the microscopic, protein-rich, algae). That has intrinsic difficulties because of possible poisoning; but the energy problem stands out. For example, a factory for recovering bromine from the sea (for making anti-knock for petrol) is practicable because it can obtain about 18 tons of bromine per day by pumping and processing 350,000 tons of sea water daily; that is a volume or weight which contains about one pound of microscopic algae.

Artificial cultivation of fresh-water algae in ponds received much enthusiastic attention in headlines a few years ago, because of the silly claims made for it in fairly exalted quarters. It is a dead duck—as it deserved to be: because of its very heavy demands for energy in various ways; nevertheless, it was claimed to be able to generate energy from sunlight and carbon dioxide 'if all fuel were exhausted'!

This blunder arose because physiologists took up a suggestion by an American (a chemist, I regret to say) who had got his energetics theory sadly wrong. A component of the blunder was overlooking the energy needed to make nitrogenous compounds and other plant-nutrients.

Projects for producing concentrated protein from land sources necessarily depend on fuel. Artificial drying of short young grass as a modern substitute for hay has been widely adopted; it requires as much energy (oil or electricity) as would be produced by burning the whole crop. No balance-sheet is known to me about the energy consumed in milling fresh grass and other sappy greenstuffs to produce protein edible by man that would otherwise be lost or unavailable. That process is one of the most attractive of the proposals for increasing output of protein; but it would surely require much more energy per pound of product than what is theoretically required for merely drying the original material.

There is, in short, absolutely *no* way of getting round, over, or under Nature in respect of energy or anything else. That circumstance make it useless to review here any of the numerous other projects put forward in the hope of getting more food without oxidising fuel. To review a series of chimerical hopes might produce entertaining stories; but those could serve no purpose except as comments on the folly of leaving out of account the thermodynamic accountancy which is the basis of every form of life.

[MI] Proposals for saving fuel (or cow-dung) in tropical countries by distributing cheap 'solar cookers' might have been conceived by woman-haters. The simplest form of such cookers (others require much more fuel in their construction) is a concave metal mirror having the cooking-element at one focus. I would gladly see their inventors condemned to have their faces near a concentrated source of heat while their backs were turned to the blazing sun throughout the period of cooking; at least, they might try to see what it feels like.

15

The maximum size of population

The universe is not hostile, nor yet is it friendly.
It is simply indifferent.
—James Haynes Holland

The maximum size of population that the world is deemed
capable of supporting has been a favourite topic for fanciers
having no science beyond a taste for arithmetic. As I do not
want to waste much space on a critique of the ludicrous I
will say that, in a world of which an increasing proportion
of the population is learning to depend on fossil fuel to support the increase of population, the maximum size attainable
by the population of the world will depend on the size of
the stocks of fuel in conjunction with the choices made of the
ways in which the accessible fuel at any time is apportioned
from this day onwards between food-production and non-
food uses. Those conditions involve several unpredictable
unknowns; and a scientist must refrain from making quantitative predictions on matters not having a factual or scientific
bottoming.

The most that a scientist can say with confidence about the
maximum, is that whatever it is and whenever it is reached,
it must be followed by a decline towards the equilibrium
numbers that can be fed without using fossil fuel to produce
food. About the fancy speculations of the world's maximum
population reaching 4, 8, 20, or 50 thousand millions, the

scientific judgment must be that there is nothing to show that any of them is not possible; but 'it all depends ...' —notably on the ways in which fuel is used, wasted, or conserved.

Looking at 'the bomb'—which is just another weapon, but an exceptionally powerful one for lessening the population—I can from an ecological standpoint suggest that the 'ban-the-bomb'-ers have got their priorities wrong way up. They want to suppress the weapon, or its use; whereas there could hardly be any moral or other argument that would restrain a nation possessing 'the bomb' if it were seriously threatened with starvation and thought 'the bomb' or some other weapon would assist it to get food. Sir Winston Churchill said something much to the point when he spoke at the fiftieth-anniversary celebrations of the Massachusetts Institute of Technology: 'There might be some very sharp disagreement about how the last crust was to be shared.' Fortunately, the wars of the last twenty years have been rather more like the old religious disputes than life-and-death struggles for food.

Population seems to be still on the upward climb towards its maximum. In the absence of a catastrophe, it seems likely that the present world population will be substantially exceeded, and that it will be many years before the maximum is reached.

As to the *time* when the maximum will be reached, scientific caution inhibits any prediction. Like the maximum size of population, the time for reaching it will depend jointly on two unknowns: namely, the *size* of the reserves of fossil fuel and the *rate* at which they are consumed for all purposes.

Two points about 'exhaustion' of fuel seem necessary in addition to the one already made about its exponential decline. Estimation of the size of known and probable deposits of fuel is a matter for engineers that I am content to leave except in the most general way. Estimates of the time during which fuel is expected to last vary considerably up to several thousand years; perhaps something less than a thousand would be a fair average. However, all the estimates of time for world reserves seem to be qualified by a statement like 'at present rates of consumption', a small percentage being added for increase among those nations who are already the heaviest consumers.

That seems to me to make a nonsense of pious aspirations about 'raising the standard of living among the developing peoples'; in short, it looks like leaving them out in the cold. Whatever estimate of duration of fuel is made on a basis of 'Western' consumption, it should be remembered that even without China, the developing nations have about twice the population of those nations already technically advanced; therefore—and all the more if we include China—it would seem prudent to divide most of the current estimates of duration of fossil fuel by three. That would bring the average estimate (for fuel) down to two or three hundred years; and the problem of apportionment of fuel (that is, of peacefully securing anything like fair shares) looms rather menacingly.

New sources of fuel—those lately discovered in Europe, and some others—have been estimated to last decades rather than centuries. The European finds presumably do not have to be shared with other continents, and the estimates may be prudently conservative. Supposing the average estimate of 'life' is 35 or 50 years, for the new finds, we might be still more conservative and multiply them all by four: if only to allow for more finds to come. That would give a total duration of from 150 to 200 years. I put these ideas forward without making a claim for their absolute validity (they can be checked with relevant specialists), but chiefly to put a brake on people who say that 'exhaustion' of fuel cannot happen for hundreds of years, and therefore that there is nothing to worry about, in relation to either machines or people.

Such hebetude is notable among laymen who incline to put faith in the figures of reports like 'A scientific (*sic*) estimate of the world's fuel reserves shows that they may be expected to last x hundred years.' The estimate cannot be scientific; and, if you will believe this scientist a little further, an estimate in such a crude form makes ecological and sociological nonsense.

So, it is seriously supposed that anyone will sit down and wait with folded hands for fuel to be exhausted? In this connexion there is the important point concealed by estimates of total 'world' fuel reserves: namely, that some local shortages can occur, or be threatened, while there is plenty of coal in (say) China, which might not be available to people in (say) the United Kingdom. I need not proceed further with points of detail; nor would I have raised them if there were not reason to think that much unjustified optimism prevails because such points are not always borne in mind.

Arising from the now intimate relations between populations, fuel, and time, the chief risk to population in the near future is the virtual certainty of struggle beginning as soon as it is appreciated that fuel is in danger of becoming insufficient for all purposes. Food need not be uppermost in the minds of those who foresee a threat to their comforts and amenities; the risks are none the less real, and need to be taken seriously.

If we suppose that any nation begins to view seriously a threat to security of its fuel supplies, a grave threat of reduction of population through war could manifest itself long before an overall, global, arithmetically-calculated 'maximum' output of fuel was reached. Accordingly, the estimates of duration sketched above may be much too long. The problem of estimating the duration of over-all, world, fuel supplies may be no more than an engineer's exercise; but it seems reasonable to suppose that a crisis centred on fuel may arise well before the attainment of any maximum of fuel output. A crisis is what matters, not the amount of fuel underground. Problems of reduction of population before the arithmetical 'maximum' output of fuel, may become pressing before very long.

It may not matter very much whether one's grandchildren's prospect is of dying because there are too many people in some overpopulated locality which cannot command enough fuel to feed all its population; or whether the urgency is thought to be to feed machines rather than people; or whether there is no real urgency at all, but a selfish demand for maintaining at all costs a high standard of living to which some community has become accustomed. As a scientist, I can indicate the principles with sufficient accuracy; as a citizen, I may be allowed to point out some possibilities suggested by my reading of the social indications of the principles.

16

Reaching equilibrium of human population. Does Nature cheat?

The consumption of Madeira (B) has been during the past year, zero. After careful calculation I estimate that, if this rate of consumption be steadily maintained, our present stock will last us an infinite number of years. And although there may be something monotonous and dreary in the prospect of such vast cycles spent in drinking second-class Madeira, we may yet cheer ourselves with the thought of how economically it can be done.
—Lewis Carroll or C. L. Dodgson, reporting in his capacity as Curator of the Common Room of Christ Church, Oxford. From *The Life and Letters of Lewis Carroll* by S. D. Collingwood: Nelson, London. 1898

In applying thermodynamic laws (in which I include chemical laws) to animated beings or to an organism of any kind, it may be noted that the physical laws established by Carnot and Clausius were instigated by consideration of boilers and other real or theoretical sources of heat for the working of steam engines. From the outset, thermodynamic theory nevertheless extended far more widely than to the behaviour of steam [M1]. As an example: what is known to physicists as the ideal heat-engine working on the so-called Carnot cycle (it cannot be attached to a moped!) gives the highest theoretical efficiency; but the cycle of operations is not a practicable one for a steam engine. Accordingly, and recognizing the limitations of real machines, engineers adopt 'an ideal Rankine engine' to find what they call the Rankine efficiency [M2] in problems about engines which are obliged, in practice, to work with steam.

Those remarks indicate no departure from the laws of thermodynamics: they are brought in to emphasize the fact that, whilst the laws are infrangible and all-embracing so that no substance or energy is truly lost, in practical applications of chemistry (as by burning fuel) there always are what from a merely human point of view are the sort of 'losses' mentioned in Chapter 5. They arise in transforming substance into energy and possibly another substance: the processes being regarded by Man as 'wasteful' or 'inefficient' because Man does not get out of them more than a fraction of the power or substance he wants.

It is necessary to recognize that exact mathematical definitions and qualifications of meaning may be tedious for a non-mathematical reader; consequently this discussion of entropy will be somewhat loose.

What is entropy? As a part of thermodynamics, the word was introduced by Clausius to mean what can be loosely called disorder. Any organism consists of chemical stuff which even in the simplest one-celled organisms such as bacteria is organized to a very high degree. Multi-celled organisms, like ourselves, have several kinds of organization that normally work in harmony: organization of different kinds of cells into tissues, and organization of tissues into limbs and head, are examples. Since the reigning tendency of Nature is towards randomness and absence of particular pattern and order, it is natural for scientists to ask whether in constructing living matter Nature has in any way departed from thermodynamic principles—has she 'cheated' with entropy?

That question has exercised thought among non-biologists since at least the end of last century. In his 1964 Romanes Lecture, Sir Harold Hartley mentioned that when he was at Oxford he used to discuss it with G. N. Lewis (a physical chemist) and others [M3]. However, it seems that a single complete organism—the egg-and-chick, say—has been taken as the centre-piece of that type of argument. At the other extreme is the use of entropy in discussing the course of generalized biochemical reactions concerned with energy-changes within an organism, where also the type ('the organism') is taken to have a constant chemistry.

Examples familiar to everyone will suggest that disorder is the normal state with inanimate objects. Kenneth Hutton [M4] mentions that 'anyone who has a family of young children will realize that "entropy tends to increase"; in plain language, things get more and more muddled up together.' It is the entropy of the inanimate things that increases. It is only intelligent purposive beings who can make an orderly arrangement (as Mother does when she clears up after the children). The stock example of increase of entropy is that of a monkey let loose in an untended library; more and more of the books are likely to be scattered over the floor but only by a remote chance would the monkey arrange them in their original order.

The disorder of a primeval universe may seem to have *lessened* when the sun and planets were formed: since the earth obviously has structure and arrangement. We are not concerned here with the universe as a whole, but only with our relatively minute, planetary, part of it. To consider how the primitive chemical chaos on the surface of the earth somehow produced organized molecules and systems would require a book about the origins of life. For our purpose we can skip that, while accepting the view that in producing us and other *individual* organisms, Nature may seem to have to have departed from the inflexible thermodynamic principles which she has set for herself and for all of us into the bargain. It may seem that there is a paradox; a contradiction of thermodynamics; it may even look as if there is a chance for us, as an intelligent population, to escape by taking advantage of an oversight. But there is no oversight. . . .

It is the principal purpose of this book to show that there is neither oversight nor contradiction in the present and future existence of Man as a *population*. There is rich variety, and cause for wonder, in the ways in which individual organisms are organized and grow. The hen's egg can become a chick, then a pullet, or another hen (or a cock). The fertile egg of a bird is a wonderful self-contained box of materials and biological tricks, and shows an amazing degree of 'ingenuity' in disposing all the materials (including water) necessary for the chick. For instance, if the solid substances were dissolved in the water, the developing chick would be killed for the same reason as a land plant is killed when it is overdosed with sea-water or fertilizer: too much soluble salts (Chapter 13). Therefore (to consider only the bones) calcium is tucked away in the crystalline calcium carbonate of the shell, from which only as much as is required is *slowly* released; and phosphate is bound up with organic, non-ionized, matter in the yolk.

For me the most appealing example of organization is the process whereby a caterpillar is turned into its butterfly or moth. The caterpillar becomes a pupa or cocoon in which it breaks down into what to the naked eye is a formless creamy liquid mush like pus; from that it is reorganized into the new complexity of the butterfly.

However, by stopping at contemplation of the individual organism or type of organisms, and by taking the general picture of a type (even though that is subject to genetic mutation), we are considering only the organism *per se* with its individual mutations of detail. Whether the organism being thought of is a wild creature or a human being, the 'individual' approach loses sight of the environment (except perhaps as far as cosmic rays or some other external factor may produce mutation). By considering the effect of the supposedly natural environment on a population of one or several species of animals and plants, and the interactions of those species with one another, and with their environment, we are entering the province of classical ecology: for that is traditionally devoted to studying the relations of feral species to each other, and with special reference to their sources of food (if they are animals; correspondingly for plants).

It is a platitude that Man is the only animal having what is worth calling intelligence; it is another platitude that, through his intelligence, Man is learning to modify, or, as some people say, to control, his environment. From those platitudes we can go straight to the heart of the matter: which is not the thermodynamics or chemistry (though it is controlled and limited by natural factors of which those sciences are the human codifications); it is the future of Man himself.

Quite lately in his development, Man has learnt to adapt fossil fuel for his own purposes: not only for food, but for increasing his comfort in ways that are developments of what, some half-million years ago, the caveman did when he learnt to burn wood to keep himself warm and perhaps to split stones.

Man is taking the molecules of fossil fuel out of their assembled order beneath the surface of the earth; and by causing attainable molecules of those deposits to combine more or less purposefully with oxygen, he is breaking up the deposits to rearrange their atoms into carbon dioxide, water, and some sulphur compounds and others of lesser importance. The carbon dioxide, water, and some sulphur dioxide are being scattered throughout the atmosphere, where they take on absolute randomness. Man is acting like the monkey in the library.

The human body is thermodynamically very efficient in using the carbonaceous 'fuel' of its food for doing work. Nevertheless, the internal thermodynamics of the body, considered as an individual member or type of a species, has no relevance to the sociology or ultimate fate of a mass of individuals like ourselves.

A population which relies on fossil fuel to obtain food to keep its numbers above the equilibrium-level of population can take no comfort from considering the high thermodynamic efficiency of each adequately-fed individual. The thermodynamic limit is set by the extra nutrients (for green plants and hence for people) that are obtained by use of fossil fuel. The numerical limits for human population follow from the amount (or, if you prefer to say, the possible energy or entropy) of the combustible material which is available and usable at any instant *either* as food (then we have equilibrium with renewable resources) *or* for procuring extra food (as we do in our present technically-advanced condition by burning fossil fuel).

The definition of 'entropy' in Chambers's Dictionary fits exactly. It is: 'a measure of unavailable energy, energy still existing but lost for purposes of doing work.' Whether the work to which Man expects to put the remaining fuel is to make food or to produce something conducive merely to his comfort, the energy of what has once been burnt is *not available*; and, since the amount of fossil fuel was fixed millions of years ago, its energy for all human purposes is constantly decreasing nowadays.

We might add 'while its entropy or disorder is increasing';

but it is not necessary to word the situation thus learnedly, because ordinary language about 'stocks of fossil fuel decreasing' is quite sufficient for making the point.

The thermodynamic situation having Man on one side and stocks of fossil fuel on the other is clear; it remains the same if we put it in terms of entropy. Therefore, the answer to the problem whether Nature cheats with entropy in regard to Man as a *population* which uses fossil fuel, is definitely and unequivocally that she does not.

The question whether any organism, as an individual that does not use fossil fuel, is subject to the ordinary rules of entropy may be left as a philosophical exercise; it is an argument about the probabilities of initially random molecular arrangements having become organized. The conclusion about entropy in relation to Man as a population—which means nowadays, more or less industrialized people—is a certainty which allows of no hedging and cannot be circumvented except by entering a state in which fossil fuel is not consumed.

And—since science is no more than formalized commonsense—it does not matter in the least whether we use considerations of energy or entropy, or everyday business language like that of Chapter 5, to form a conclusion about the state to which Man is tending, or the state which he must ultimately reach. That ultimate state is the state of balance, or equilibrium, with renewable resources. The condition of the atmosphere when equilibrium has been reached may not be quite the same as it was three or four hundred years ago [M5]; but it is safe to say that few of the people then alive will be bothered by that or worrying about it: they will have to use most of their personal energies just to keep alive.

Where entropy-considerations can help is by defining what is meant by 'equilibrium'. It is: Nature's compromise, or: the limit of disorder. It is a dynamic state of equipoise, in which (for our chosen case) people will always be being born and will constantly be knocking each other on the head or otherwise trying to reduce their numbers to what the surface environment can provide by way of food. That environment will also be in equilibrium: with the daily income of sunlight and the water and salts of sea and soil. On the whole, the population will remain constant, though very much smaller than it now is.

Bearing all this in mind, together with the brutal fact that if an organism does not get enough to eat, it dies (which is the central tenet of any form of ecology), and recalling the meaning of chemical equivalence or balance (or Nothing for Nothing but always 'some substance for another substance'), as explained in Chapter 5 and those immediately following, I offer the following Laws of Human Population: [M6].

I. The first law of population is the classical doctrine of chemical equivalence as it applies to Man and his food.

II. The second law of population is the classical tenet of ecology modified by noting Man's recent adventures with fossil fuels. It is: A population that temporarily rises beyond the level of intrinsic equilibrium with its environment must come down to that natural level unless oxidation-reduction is artificially brought in to assist and enlarge the natural self-equilibrating cycle of food-production.

Also: 'The second law can be put in the form that no population can be maintained above a level of bare subsistence without intelligent use of fuel, and then only for as long as oxidizable (i.e., combustible) materials are obtainable for purposes directly connected with food.' [M6]

On the wisdom with which the remaining stocks of fuel are husbanded will depend the length of time during which technical progress can operate—at first, as at present, on an ascending scale: then in reverse.

Distant fates for Man like those predicted through the cooling of the sun or a perceptible increase in the time of rotation of the earth involve geological periods of time; but virtual exhaustion of fuel may be much more rapid, so as to occupy an almost infinitesimal period on that scale.

Towards the end of last century, after physicists had got used to the idea of entropy as tending to a maximum beyond which no further change was possible, some of them deduced that ultimately life would become extinct when that maximum had been reached. That was pure theorizing; the practical truth is both less fatal and more immediate. Life in any practical sense need never be extinguished because of entropy; but the practical limit of human involution (Chapter 17) of numbers and the sorts of amenity to which we have, in this generation, become accustomed, may not be far distant.

It has been estimated (not by me) that some of the sputniks put up in the period 1957-66 may still be in space after about 10,000 years. If those estimates are approximately correct, some of the earliest artificial satellites are likely to return to a world which will certainly be different from that of to-day—but different in a sense totally unlike what is envisaged by present-day believers in indefinitely-enlarged technical progress. It is possible that the last of the 1957-66 batch of sputniks may crash on a world inhabited by a human population which knows nothing of the technologies by which it was made and detached from our world.

Considering the present rates of consumption of fuel, and the probable course up to the maxima of population and fuel output, it seems unlikely that the period between the reign of little more than subsistence-level of food and amenity (say, medieval times) and the return to a similar domination can be more than a historically brief incident in Man's development.

A retrogression to a technical ability not unlike that of the Egyptian Old Kingdom may occupy less time than has elapsed since the building of the classical Pyramids. Whether mathematics and some other intellectual and cultural acquisitions can survive, at the present or a higher level, throughout social disturbances which look inseparable from adjustment to progressively lower intensities of fuel-use, is a pregnant question. Astronomy will be hampered by lack of instruments; and, if astrology survives, it will be through a persistence of belief in the uncomprehended and mysterious; and because—even then—Man has not learnt that the clue to his fate lay not in the remoter parts of the universe but at a little distance beneath his feet.

Appendix I

This essay is given as an appendix because it touches on outlines of chemical topics with which a layman may not be familiar; Appendix II is still more 'difficult'.

It may be helpful to enlarge upon one of the points left open on page 144. The manifestations of life in all organisms depend intimately on applications within the internal oeconomy [I hesitate to use the ordinary spelling, for fear of being misunderstood] of each and every living thing and cell, of energy used to maintain its organization—quite apart from questions about food-supply for the moment and for maintaining the energy (for walking or breathing, etc.) of the body as a whole. That 'organizational' use of energy by every living cell is directed against entropy, and may be called anti-entropic. [An answer to the other point on page 144—namely, how organized matter arose out of primeval chaos, will not be attempted here]. If the individual living thing or cell did not use energy in that way to maintain its molecular and cellular organization at every point, it would first die, then its materials would became dispersed in the environment against which it is, energetically, fighting while it is whole and alive.

That applies to all living matter without exception. Organisms (it is perhaps easier to think only of animals) in the wholly wild state have no other resource for obtaining and conserving energy than what happens to them (solar heat, say) and what they chance to come upon (in the way of food). Man as a society is 'special' merely, and only, because at a fairly late stage in development he has learnt to use both superficial and deep resources to gain energy for use in various ways. Some of the recently-utilized forms of energy and motion are not connected with food and maintenance of the internal organization of human cells and bodies. No other animal or organism has acquired an ability resembling those uses: either as regards maintenance of its own cells and bodies, or for harnessing energy for purposes of comfort, communication, and other satisfactions external to the naked individual.

A brief discussion of entropy in relation to Man can ignore the 'mechanical' uses of energy, by taking them as read; they are pretty obvious, as is the consumpt of fossil sources of energy that is involved in meeting their demands at the present day and presumably in the near future.

The anti-entropic forces of human bodies—considered as individuals—cannot have significantly changed during a hundred thousand years or more. What has changed the picture for Man, and is constantly altering it, is the proliferation of bodies: otherwise said, the increase of human population during the last two or three hundred years: which demands a greater sum of energy for maintaining the anti-entropic forces of a larger number and mass or weight of bodies and their contained living cells. [That omits consideration of energy required for motion in search of food and otherwise keeping alive; it is restricted to considerations of entropy alone].

Just for the purely biological purposes of keeping people alive in numbers greater than those that could be supported by chance-directed superficial resources upon which a primitive man might happen as he walked over the surface of the earth or plunged into sea or river, it has been necessary to use intelligence. That pursuit of, or by, intelligence has now come to the point where only fossil resources from below the surface can serve to provide enough energy in total to fulfil the biological purposes of nearly all of three thousand million people.

The practical purport of considerations of energy and entropy since the time of Clausius and Darwin has shifted from Man as an individual to Man as a fuel-using population; as Jevons the economist apprehended in 1865 to some extent (Chapter 23, page 243).

Furthermore, in our own century, for a practical and scientific view of Man as an intelligent, tool-using, population, it has become essential to pay keen attention to the conflict between the mechanical and the biological demands for energy derived from burning *substances*: some of which (namely, the fossil reserves) being in strictly limited supply, can only decrease in amount.

Man, as a population, having emerged or 'risen' from the state of being in equilibrium with perpetually-renewable resources, is at present in metastable equilibrium. As an individual, any living organism is in metastable balance with its surroundings; that is why it has to use energy (anti-entropic energy) to prevent its dissolution as a whole, if it is single-celled, say, or because of the failure of some vital part of a more complex organism.

It does not seem necessary to enter deeply into topics of reversible reactions that are so important in organic chemistry; I give them a mention here because they play an essential part in living matter, and in order to suggest that an organism or cell dies when it is no longer able to make essential reactions go both ways. What Mayer was saying in the 1840's (Chapter 2, Note M8) was an early divination of that subject. No organism or organ is static; all tissues —even the solid bones—are, throughout life, undergoing continual replacement of their molecules and atoms: in ways like that so elegantly stated by Tyndall (page 20).

In an individual—a person, say—that kind of renewal of cells can last for only a hundred years or so at the most. As is well known to chemists, artificially-made pure or mixed organic substances, and lifeless residues of once-living matter, are all in a state of metastable equilibrium. That is to say that they have been constrained by the chemist, or by some less sophisticated form of life, to enter into 'un'-natural combinations of atoms into molecules; and, having no life, they have no means of opposing their dissolution into the elements (or simple substances similar to the elements: carbon dioxide for instance) from which they were formed. Energy is released during every such reversion. Examples familiar to laymen are: the fact that explosives require very little encouragement to 'go off'; a slower release of energy from decomposition is shown by 'spontaneous combustion' of damp hay or unventilated stacks of coal; and after a couple of thousand years in the 'ideally' preservative atmosphere of an Egyptian tomb food-grains become unrecognizable as such except by an expert.

Whilst Man and every other organism share in that type of metastability (combated by anti-entropic forces during life) no practical or useful result comes from considering it in application to Man as an individual. The metastability of Man that is important now and henceforth is the state of Man as a population which is conditioned by its relationship to the whole of the environment: which, nowadays, includes the diminishing resources that had accumulated beneath the surface of the earth. Whereas some types of mechanical equilibrium are self-balancing or self-righting (a suitably-designed lifeboat is an example) so as to have positive stability, the metastable equilibrium of the present human population can tend in only one direction—'downhill'—towards the natural equilibrium-level at which there can be virtually no further change in the size of the population, whatever its composition may be or however much it may vary as regards the individuals who compose it at any given time.

[M1] It extended to ideal conditions in engines which are impossible to make: those working without friction, for instance.

[M2] W. J. McQuorn Rankine, the very Scottish Professor of

Engineering in the University of Glasgow, and internationally famous for his studies of the behaviour of steam in engines. By 1868 he had published (in connexion with underwater friction along hulls of ships) the word 'stream-line,' which many Britons believe to be a modern Americanism.

[M3]   Sir Harold Hartley, C.H., G.C.V.O., C.B.E., M.C., F.R.S., was at Balliol from 1901 until 1930. Lewis's best-known work was published in 1921.

[M4]   Kenneth Hutton, 'Chemistry: the conquest of materials,' Pelican Book A 353, Penguin Books Ltd., 3rd edn. 1966.

[M5]   This brings in the matter of the so-called 'heat barrier' associated with Man's burning of fossil and other carbonaceous fuels; the extra carbon dioxide (if not absorbed by the sea) tends to prevent escape of the earth's heat and thus to a slow rise of air temperature. The subject of the 'heat barrier,' having become almost fashionable lately, has attracted some cranks and produced some nonsense. Two Russian scientists were quoted in a newspaper to the effect that when all 'fuel' (presumably carbonaceous fuel was meant) was exhausted, the percentage of carbon dioxide in the atmosphere would be doubled, and Man would therefore be very uncomfortable. If these 'scientists' were reported correctly, they would seem to have been thinking on the lines of 'having your cake and eating it too.' The calculation may or not be correct; it is hardly worth making, because when all (carbonaceous) fuel is 'exhausted' the population will be at the equilibrium-point of mere subsistence and possibly in no condition to spare attention for academic matters such as chemical analysis.

A good discussion of recent and future climate in the light of Man's activities was in the article 'Carbon dioxide and climate' by Gilbert N. Plass, *Scientific American*, July 1959, 8 pp.

[M6]   First published in my article 'The ecology of human population,' *Journal of the Royal Institute of Chemistry*, 1964, Vol. 88, 423-7, 413.

Appendix II

Entropy-aspects of populations

This Appendix makes few concessions to the layman. Part 1 of this Appendix is a condensation of the whole scientific argument of this book. This Appendix 11 is based on a talk, having the same title, given to the Physical Chemistry Section of the Autumn Meeting of the Chemical Society at Brighton, Sussex, 21-22 September, 1966. The Zeroth Law of Population was enunciated on the occasion but does not figure in the mimeographed Abstract C 14 which was circulated before the Meeting.

[Notes to this Appendix are given at the end with the prefix A]

I. Organic compounds exhibit chemical metastability whereby free energy is decreased; living cells differ from dead and non-living organic matter in exerting 'anti-entropic energy' to maintain their separateness from the environment into which their constituents would otherwise merge.

Metastability of protoplasm was divined by Huxley [A1] on chemical grounds, without reference to thermodynamics or to the essential role ascribed by Pasteur [A2] to soil micro-organisms in bottoming the life-cycle. [See Figs. 4 and 5, and discussion on pp. 195-198; also—later in this Appendix—the role of micro-organisms and the C/N ratio in deciding the *rate* of revolution of the life-cycle; and pp. 211-212.]

Pasteur's magnificent words [A2] to the effect that, without the decompositional activities of microbes, death itself would be incomplete, enshrine what is perhaps the most fundamental of his teaching. It is noteworthy that when they were uttered, in 1864, modern microbiology was barely six years old.

Huxley's words [A1] are scarcely less notable:

'Under whatever disguise it takes refuge, whether as microbe or oak, worm or Man, the living protoplasm not only ultimately dies and is resolved into its mineral and lifeless constituents, but is always dying, and, strange as the paradox may sound, could not live unless it died.' [A3]

Recent attention [A4; and see earlier in this Chapter] to thermodynamics of living matter has been mostly 'open-ended'; *i.e.* given to type organisms and organs, without consideration of global quantities of cells or organs on the one hand or to potential limits of quantity of substrate or food on the other. Human populations and effort—called 'progress'—not having been in general considered in accordance with scientific modes, have been assumed to be indefinitely extensible: that view having been formed because the energy- and entropy-aspects of there being only a limited supply of combustible fuel have been left out of consideration. Even by engineers (among whom the concepts and limitations of energy and entropy are well known) fuel-supply is usually taken for granted. Among laymen, too, 'science' has been taken to consist of machines and instruments of which the construction depends on scientific principles, although both construction and operation depend on consumption of (usually fossil) fuel. In thus glorifying 'progress' it has been forgotten that, while much of science indicates what *can* be done by application of ingenuity to knowledge about the behaviour of phenomena, an equally important role of science it to indicate what cannot be done in accordance with the tenets of conservation of energy. [A5]

It does not matter whether the subject of growth-curves and limits of any population is regarded in terms of energy or entropy: necessarily the same conclusion is reached by any scientific approach that takes account of all chemical and thermodynamic factors.

Classical ecology and sociology (including economics) have developed during nearly two centuries without much attention to any kind of physical science; and when industrial history has been considered, it has been mostly in connexion with machines. Thus, it is generally taught that industrial history and its sequential use of fuel started about 1750, with early steam machines powered by use of coal.

Actually, what may be called chemical manufactures—production of glass, bricks, and salt were examples—preceded the 'mechanical' industrial revolution of the XVIIIth century by several hundred years. [A6] Practically all of these 'chemical' manufactures (except for some production of salt by evaporation of sea water along the coasts and based on local outcrops of coal around Newcastle in England and in the Firth of Forth in Scotland: the coal sometimes being carried fairly long distances by coastwise shipping) depended on wood for fuel.

An increase of luxury among aristocrats after about 1400 A.D., and possibly earlier around Toulouse in the south of France (Note M2, Chapter 17), led to extensive devastation of forests to provide bricks, glass and small metal objects for a new many-windowed architecture of grand houses—residences rather than fortresses—

of which Herstmonceux Castle built about 1440 not far from Brighton and now occupied by the Royal Observatory [FRONTISPIECE] is one of many examples surviving in England.

There was also an increase in the demands for metal for weapons, armour, tools, and small fastenings. All this produced local shortages of fuel wherever the total demand for wood outran the natural increment of growth—already threatening to be exceeded, in an age of poor communications, by the requirements for structural timber for ships and (mostly wooden) houses for ordinary people, and for new churches (often brick-built).

The coal-based industrial revolution of the XVIIIth and later centuries was thus not an 'answer to prayer' or a proof of Man's wonderful and growing ability for overcoming and 'mastering' Nature when he was faced with shortages of wood as fuel. Recourse to coal to meet and exceed the supply of energy that could be yielded by wood-fuel, even as supplemented by water-power and wind-power on land, was nothing more than putting back the basic problem— of obtaining a sufficient and flexible supply of external energy— for a few more centuries.

Addition or adoption of petroleum after about 1860, and of nuclear power since 1945, has fundamentally altered nothing at all. In passing, I may note that the Chemistry Department of Glasgow University, through Joseph Black and James Watt (with latent heat [A7] and its sequel the separate condenser [A8] in the XVIIIth century) and Frederick Soddy (with radioactive isotopes) in this century, initiated both the modern power-eras. British historians having had the initial developments of external energy and of fuel and fuel-shortages within their own island, should be the first to point out that *we* (meaning the world) *have been there before*. For those who wish precedent, there is precedent enough.

Archaeologists are fond of following the development and spread of bronze, and later iron, for agricultural tools such as sickles, and thus studying the development of Man through his food-gathering practices. Up to about 1400 A.D. the use of iron and therefore of wood-fuel for food-production was not in serious competition with other uses of the limited supply of wood; at least in Britain [A9]. What is new in our own time is, *firstly*, the growing use of fossil fuel not only for making agricultural and fishing tools and implements and for powering their use, but also for production of fertilizers and other means of directly increasing the output of food at source (and not merely harvesting it after it has been grown by solar energy alone); *secondly*, these uses of fossil fuel for every kind of food-production purpose have come to be greatly overshadowed by a still-increasing use of fossil fuel to produce amenity, luxury, and convenience.

Under that second head the parallel is with the people of Plantagenet times [A10] who, by building beautiful new brick constructions having the amenity of a profusion of glazed windows, accelerated the destruction of forests which yielded the sole source of fuel and material for many other purposes, mostly essential however primitive.

In the light of modern acquaintance with science it will not be difficult to establish chemistry—in which I include thermodynamics —as the empress of the humane sciences.

In spite of the number and diversity of pure substances, chemists are never in doubt that the phenomena displayed by all substances on earth do and will conform to chemical and thermodynamic laws established before 1870. Since food and people consist of chemical substance, quantitative problems of human population follow those same laws; and nothing can alter Man's dependence on chemical equilibria. What chemists can do out of their special and detailed knowledge of the behaviour of matter is to state the choices which lie before the human population in its search for food; and chemists can thus make plain the consequences which flow from each and every choice having a chemical—which is to say in this connexion— a population-and-food-and-fuel-basis. Some people, though not the chemists, may need reminding that 'atomic' energy does not offer exemption from dependence on fossil fuel. Use of 'atomic' power depends on an expensive process of chemical concentration of radioactive isotopes. Even a hydro-electric station puts a heavy demand on fuel for concrete and metals; moreover, like other machinery, it has to be renewed at historically short intervals—perhaps three times in a century. Practically everything we do nowadays involves expenditure of fossil fuel.

Someone (I think it was Kolbe) said: 'Thierchemie ist Schmierchemie'. The idea that animal chemistry is a messy business and isn't capable of being brought within quantitative order may linger among scientists and laymen who haven't seen the over-riding importance of chemistry for population, or the absolute limitations expressed in the Second Law of thermodynamics. About getting food there is a considerable body of folk-lore still being taught as truth: not least in text-books written by people having had various sorts of scientific training. These myths are comparable with the old expectation of sometime achieving perpetual motion; and, like that expectation, they must also become extinct when they are *generally* seen to contradict what, for chemists, are commonplaces of natural law.

Education about what is *called* 'science' seems to have done little more for laymen than convince them increasingly that science is a sort of Aladdin's lamp for getting anything wanted, and without cost. That includes indefinitely maintaining a world population of x thousand millions—where x is greater than 2—thanks to the perpetual bounty of the sun in manipulating the elements, C, H, and O in photosynthesis: aided, of course, by Man's increasing 'command of Nature'. Many such wild beliefs are accepted on every hand: though they fail to take account of either energy or substance. In the absence of taking rightful account of *both* energy and substance, these scientifically unhistorical beliefs culminate—better said, founder—in the upside-down one that Man is a special creation to whom natural laws are ceasing to apply because, by his cleverness, he is well on the way to making the conquest of Nature.

Some of the supposedly supporting fancies are old—like those based on photosynthesis. Others are newer. The fancy that nuclear power or some form of energy yet to come could make an appreciable contribution to food by supplying water to deserts can't be older than 1945—the year of Hiroshima.

The main reference-data

The reference-data to which any population conforms are the ordinary operations of the ordinary laws of thermodynamics, equivalence, and oxidation-reduction: coupled with the fact that if an organism doesn't get enough nourishment of what is for it the correct chemical composition, it dies. It's as simple as that!

For all populations about which one is curious about the fate or the ultimate size, these reference-data need to be linked with the concept of equilibrium with the environment. In the absence of catastrophe (such as, for small animals and plants, the drying-up of a pond) wild populations are always [A11] in equilibrium with their environment, since that is wholly natural if unaffected by Man aided by modern technical resources.

For modern Man the considerations of the first paragraph above apply with exactness; what is wrong in conventional discussions that proceed without proper regard to chemistry is that they do not link the concept of equilibrium with the *whole* of Man's environment. Equilibrium-concepts do not seem to have been taken up by sociology; nor has the idea of environment in relation to Man been taken beyond superficial resources—as a sort of landscaping or park-keeping, in effect. When fossil reserves are discussed, it's usually in relation to industry and economics or money-cost. All of that is inadequate for our own era. Man is a special kind of animal *not* because of the foolish idea that he is on the way to mastering Nature but because he is, and will remain, the only animal whose food-yielding environment demonstrably includes resources lying beneath the surface.

Because Man has adopted techniques of using fossil reserves of combustible material to yield not only much of his food but almost all his amenities, he has bound up his prospects to the duration, under his own hand, of the oxidizable reserves.

In the last ninety years or so, human populations in excess of the maximum numbers that could exist in equilibrium with renewable, surface, resources have been supported by oxidizing fossil carbon and sulphur. That is the most important change that ever happened in Man's relation to his world; yet it's usual to take the novelty for granted, without any sort of scientific scrutiny (other than the merely industrial-technical).

The detail bifurcates and trifurcates over several chemical aspects or planes, in each domain of each habitat [A12]: soil and sea, for instance. Then, there are two fossil fuels to consider. Sulphur has little direct use as source of mechanical or electrical energy; but uses of carbonaceous fuels for energizing operations of farming, fishing, and cooking and transport and preservation of food are made possible by smelting of metals for machinery and other purposes, among which upkeep of fences is important.

Sulphur used for fertilizers has two main purposes. One is to ionize the phosphate of rock phosphate. The principal result of that has been to increase the world mass of leguminous crops having a high percentage of protein (or, if you prefer: a low carbon/nitrogen ratio) on land where the prevailing C/N ratio has been unfavourable to a high density of animal life. The other main purpose is the vital one of providing the makings for the reduced -S-S- linkage in proteins that is essential to all animals.

It's for those and related reasons that leguminous crops are the basis of all perdurable agricultures. All such facts about proteins, legumes, soil chemistry, and so on are interlinked but converge (necessarily) to the same outcome. Witness the enormous flocks and herds of the "new" countries that didn't exist before 1860 because their sustenance had to await employment of phosphatic fertilizers most conveniently made by use of H_2SO_4. (That's the only chemical formula I shall use on this occasion.)

That scamper over about 2^4 factors will indicate the complexities of any purely descriptive treatment of food-production, built on facts of which the linkings multiply by powers of 2 and 3. There is, however, no difficulty at all in referring the phenomena of human food-production and nutrition to first principles: from knowledge and laws already established. The specimens just given are quite enough to suggest how far from reality are the facile assumptions about synthetic nitrogenous fertilizers bringing more food. Sulphur (for example) doesn't come from the air; but making synthetic fertilizers entails a heavy cost in carbon. In the main, synthetic "fixation" of N_2 into fertilizer leads to exchange of fossil carbon for carbon in crops of our own time and henceforth for as long as carbonaceous fuel is available.

Popular ideas about synthetic "nitrogen" form just one part of the mythos about food that is rooted in disrespect of the ways in which plants, animals, and microbes do chemically behave.

A biological analogue for gravitation

This being a talk about energy, entropy, and equilibria, I need not enlarge further on nutritional aspects of food-production. The example of sulphur suggests that food-production has many chemical determinants besides the ratio of carbon to nitrogen; but to take that C/N ratio—again as an example—the distribution of carbon and nitrogen amongst the chemical domains of land and sea, together with the responses of animals, plants, and microbes to values of that ratio (assuming that other needs such as of sulphur and phosphorus are met) suggests the C/N ratio on earth as a biological analogue to universal gravitation.

For one thing, the influence of the C/N ratio can't be shielded, or removed without expenditure of energy (which is to say, fuel); and the present world population is, as it were, travelling in a fire-balloon above the normal equilibrium level to which it must sometime descend: at latest, when heat or energy derived from the fuel runs out; *i.e.*, has itself come to equilibrium.

The C/N ratio in plants and soil cannot be dodged. Reduction of air-nitrogen by carbonaceous fuels to make fertilizers brings about, in general, an increase of protein-poor foodstuffs (as Lawes and Gilbert found before 1900), while decreasing the stock of fossil carbon. Even on the short view, it evidently makes the problems of supply of protein—real food, that is—*more* difficult to solve.

The Zeroth Law of Population

On the principle of *ab uno disce omnes* I am tempted to go back, with apologies, to Joseph Black, and enunciate the Zeroth Law of Population [A13]. It is:

If a belief about food is in conflict with *one* chemical, nutritional, or thermodynamic fact, it is in conflict with all others.

This is no more, or less, than the expression, in food-and-population terms, of the unity of Nature. Or again:

> Once any facet of chemical relationships within the life-cycle has been established, for prediction there is no need to know all the details, because natural laws are consistent and convergent.

I much regret that university chemistry departments long ago withdrew from consideration of biological variables. The last such products were the foundation of microbiology by Pasteur at Lille in 1858, and lesser but still notable achievements at Glasgow and Caen before 1866. The contrast is immense in closeness of academic attention accorded to classical gravitational theory and to chemical ecology of Man.

Development of the C/N ratio in practice

That the life-cycle revolves at all was seen in 1864 by Pasteur to be due to the decompositional activities of microbes in returning once-living materials to circulation. That the *rate* of decomposition —and hence the rate at which the cycle can revolve—depends on the ratio of assimilable carbon to nitrogen was seen by (Sir) Edward Frankland [A14] in his studies of sewage in the 'seventies. The C/N-ratio notion was extended to soils by Robert Warington— son of a founder of the Chemical Society—in the 'eighties [A15]. Though the C/N ratio remains a guiding principle among sewage chemists, it has almost dropped from sight elsewhere. In 1900 Lawes and Gilbert reported that a principal function of nitrogenous fertilizers is to increase the proportion of *non*-nitrogenous constituents of mature non-leguminous crops. In 1926, Woodman and his team at Cambridge showed that young grass could yield over 20% of protein (on dry matter): more than enough to keep animal life going.

Woodman's was the *last* piece of scientific documentation required for a complete chemical appraisal of Man's food-relations with his world. By 1926 there were all the pieces needed to complete the initially random jigsaw of the scientific basis of human population and to bring a clear and unequivocal picture of the relation between people, their food, and fuel. Therefore, publication of a complete summary of the prospects for Man is at least thirty years overdue.

The ultimate limit of human population

The unique energy-entropy ecological relation shown by human populations stems from recent acquisitions of energy through oxidizing subsurface deposits inaccessible to feral consociations and to Man using only primitive techniques. Extra food thereby won has permitted an increase of human (and some animal) populations beyond the limit set by equilibria between current solar energy, green plants, surface stocks of ionizable matter, the microbial population, and—through the microbes—the C/N weight ratio [of noncarbonate carbon to combined nitrogen].

The present-day stock of oxidizable matter may be regarded as a shrinking source of energy, or in entropic terms of its random dispersal, in energy-less compounds, throughout the atmosphere and the seas. A decline of human population is thus foreseeable: to set in, at latest, when maximum output of oxidizable materials has been attained.

There must be a return to equilibrium with surface resources energized by contemporary solar income alone. Human populations are in theory perpetually renewable at some quite low level of subsistence, numbers, and culture. That level is arguably akin to those of about 1600 A.D., on the assumption that the situation differs from those of pre-Columbian times in that surviving "knowhow" about living in approximate balance with the surface environment is equally available all over the world.

The contrast between the avidity for qualitative (Mendelian) and quantitative (entropic) knowledge in relation to Man

A striking instance of educational failure to treat of Man on strict quantitative lines, or to develop the possibility of doing that, is given by the almost exact parallelism of the careers of the geneticist Gregor Mendel and the thermodynamicist Rudolf Julius Emmanuel Clausius; and the utter divergence of interest in the consequences of their respective discoveries. Both men were born in 1822, made their main publications in 1864-6, died within a couple of years of 1886, and had their work practically buried until 1900.

Quantum theory was founded on the virtual re-discovery of entropy by Planck; yet that, as far as the public at large is concerned, has been abandoned to affairs of astrophysics and cosmogony.

The story has often been told of the 'burial' of Mendel's seminal work by his publishing an account of that work only in an obscure Central European scientific periodical: from which several botanists simultaneously and independently 'rescued' it early in 1900, and quickly made their findings known through Europe. The British scientist Bateson is said to have read about it in the train between Cambridge and London on 8th April, 1900. From about that time the pursuit of Mendel's ideas has been continuously active; and nowadays every literate person has at least heard of genes and Mendelian genetics. The minute detail about Bateson's train journey is typical of the wealth of romanticism with which the Mendel story has been treated.

On the other hand, Clausius had first published his ideas in 1850 about what are now known as the First and Second Laws of thermodynamics. He published a major book about them in 1865, and three translations into English of his works were available by 1900 [A16]. If anybody made use of Clausius' ideas before 1900, the outcomes were not made generally known to the educated public; and, as is suggested by Sir Harold Hartley's remarks (page 143 and Note M3 of this Chapter) about the possibility of Nature's 'cheating' about entropy in living organisms, biological aspects of entropy did not make a common topic of even donnish conversation before this century was several years old. Nevertheless, Katchalsky and Curran state [A4]: 'The physical meaning of entropy has intrigued physicists and philosophers since the introduction of entropy by Clausius in 1865.'

Planck used entropy to derive his famous notion of the quantum of energy by the end of 1900 [A17]. After meeting initial reluctance to accept an idea so unprecedented, Planck's energy-quantum quickly came to be accepted for use among theoretical physicists. It was, for instance, the foundation of Einstein's Special Theory of Relativity, published in 1905. Nowadays everyone has heard of that and of more recent developments of relativity and quantum theory in which Clausius' entropy of 1865 is embedded.

Except in such relativistic and essentially philosophical off-shoots having a very remote relation to anything on earth, and excepting some highly specialized applications of entropy by engineers, chemists, and other physical scientists in what are regarded as abstruse branches of their studies, the whole idea of entropy has remained buried; and, unlike what happened to Mendel's ideas about heredity, it has never been resuscitated in any human context or in any manifestation of popular education about science having a human application. Not only was the burial almost complete between 1864 and the virtual re-discovery of entropy by Planck in 1900; but, in matters affecting the public at large or in which some enlightened popularizers might think that the educated public might be interested (as in relativity itself), the idea of entropy has remained completely buried since 1900 also.

Thus, though not a few publications have mentioned that the burning of 'fuel' results in dissipation of carbon dioxide through-

out the air (and the ocean) and thus tends to thermal consequences
by the operation of what is sometimes called the 'heat barrier'
(Note M5 of this Chapter, page 153); the entropic consequences
for human population of that same dissipation have not, to my
knowledge, ever been made plain, or even mentioned. Steinberg's
drawing [A5] is a graphic figure for them.

About Clausius' 100 years of 'burial' there has never been a
'story' written to correspond to those about Mendel's 34 years;
and in the more high-brow books about the history of science or
even in those about thermodynamics, Clausius gets little space. He
seems to have suffered the fate attributed by T. H. Huxley to some
founders of science—namely, of having been so thoroughly incorporated into the foundations of the building that they have been
lost from sight!

In questions centreing on fuel-use and metastability in general,
it is principally entropy that decides the *direction* of change. With
fossil fuel being continuously oxidized by modern technologies, the
direction of human change can only—after the maximum quantity
of combustion has been reached—be downwards.

It is therefore significant for my present purpose (and especially
for Chapter 24 of this book) that Planck's constant, h, has the
dimensions of action.

Meanwhile, an immense amount of attention has been drawn by
popular media to philosophical questions such as those about
whether the cosmological universe is expanding or contracting;
alongside secondary—at least from the point of view of human
effect—but qualitative, 'open-ended', and almost fashionable topics
of Mendelian and other genetics, and speculations about the origin
of life in the distant past, and whether there is life on other planets.
Solid problems about Man on *this* planet here and now go by
default except on rare occasions like the present one.

The most valuable educational lesson would be to make it plain
what quantitative science is *about*. That is, to spread the idea that
the laws of chemistry are useful for indicating the limits of what
is possible and credible about the numbers and progress of Man;
and that the limits of what Man can hope to do, about his own
numbers or anything else, have been known for already a hundred
years.

In face of a draft on combustible reserves that is approaching its
maxima of rate and quantity, it will be seen that people are subject
to two kinds of chemical metastability. One is what Man shares
with all other organisms and organic matter; the other is what he
has brought upon himself by trying to produce more food, together

with a larger population and an enhanced degree of amenity, than are compatible with equilibrium.

One doesn't have to be a chemist to think that the impending involution (Chapter 17) of Man is just about the biggest and most human problem. People *need* help; yet almost nobody has had a chance to get the message that chemistry has social scope and depth in the truest senses.

There's no need to raise moral issues; remembering that in Nature there are neither rewards nor punishments: there are only consequences: and they are ultimately chemical.

II. Mathematical treatment has been sought for population-dynamics of unicellar organisms in artificial culture [A18] substrate-supply by Man being ignored as a limiting factor. In those connexions, terms allied to 'maintenance requirements'—such as 'endogenous metabolism' and 'maintenance energy'—have been freely used [A18] during the last ten years. Ideas of 'maintenance requirements' have been applied in studies of animal nutrition since at least the beginning of the century. It would therefore be unfortunate if any part of the terminology belonging to multicellular nutrition came to be regarded as established, in an attempt to simplify the mathematical considerations, within a corner of biological chemistry while referring only to that part of microbial nutrition that is devoted to combat metastability. It is undesirable to give a restricted meaning to such terms, or indeed to use them at all, in fields of study of unicellular organisms which have only two energy-aspects: (*i*) somatic+heat-producing+[fission-]reproductive, (*ii*) resistance to metastability. [A19]

The term 'anti-entropic energy' (AEE), being unambiguous, and satisfying all canons, is suggested for (*ii*).

[A1]   T. H. Huxley, 'On the physical basis of life' (1868), in 'Lectures and Essays', Macmillan, London. 1902; p. 50. A similar thought in the same lecture, p. 52, is also notable.

[A2]   L. Pasteur, *Rev. cours sci.* [Sorbonne], 1864-5, 199; 'Oeuvres', 2, 648. Masson, Paris. 1922.

[A3]   To modernize the language I have taken the liberty of using 'microbe' for Huxley's 'fungus' and also in Pasteur's wording. The word *microbe* was not coined until 1878, in a tribute to Pasteur: *see* 'Microbes and Us' (Note M5, Chapter 7) for detail about that.

[A4] Typified in the 'difficult' book by A. Katchalsky and P. F. Curran, 'Nonequilibrium thermodynamics in biophysics', Harvard Univ. Press. 1965; London: O.U.P. Most text-books on human biochemistry now have a section on entropy of what Katchalsky and Curran refer to as 'the organism'.

[A5] A readable, instructive, and in places deliberately humorous introduction to chemical equilibria, which does not require overmuch mathematics, is Henry A. Bent's 'The Second Law', Oxford Univ. Press, New York. 1965.

A drawing by Steinberg taken from *The New Yorker Magazine* sets the tone for the book and wordlessly states the entropic impossibilities of the human situation. It shows a little man running away from a heavy ball of material which is chasing him uphill.

[A6] The fall of Byzantium caused manufacture of alum to be established as a Papal monopoly in Italy; before the end of the fifteenth century 'Roman' alum was also made in Spain, Holland, and Germany. Attempts to start its manufacture in the north of England (from coal?) in the Elizabethan period led to the promulgation of perhaps the most terrible and comprehensive curse ever uttered; it was identical with the curse of Ernulphus in *Tristram Shandy*.

[A7] Joseph Black's concept of latent heat and its almost immediate adoption to a practical end by Watt was more than the first application of science to technology: it remained for fully a century the only application of science to industry. Thus, the earliest uses of electricity in metal-plating and telegraphy were empirical and owed nothing to Faraday (whose effects came much later) or any theory (*see* 'Electricity in modern life', by G. W. de Tunzelmann, Scott, London. 1889). Black paid from his own pocket to support Watt's early trials with the separate condenser.

Black's theory of latent heat was derived from William Cullen (1710-90) of Edinburgh and Glasgow. *He* was inspired by 'a Young Gentleman', one of his students, who noticed that a thermometer dipped in alcohol, cooled after it was withdrawn: as was recorded at the beginning of Cullen's paper of 1755 'Of the cold produced by evaporating fluids'. The Young Gentleman who made what David Murray (of *The Scotsman*) called the Lucky Dip has been identified by Murray as Matthew Dobson, an Englishman from Bolton (*see* also correspondence in *The Times*, 1956, 11th Aug. *et seq.*) For detail about Cullen, Black, and their scientific era *see* 'An eighteenth century lectureship in chemistry', *ed.* Andrew Kent, Jackson: Glasgow. 1950.

Of Black's M.D. thesis on *magnesia alba* it has been remarked (D.N.B., London, 1886, 5 *sub voce*; and Kent's book *supra*) 'there is, perhaps, no other instance of a graduation thesis so weighted with significant novelty.' Times, or maybe examiners, change; or perhaps there is much to be said for the advantage of hindsight; anyway, it is interesting to compare this with the reception of the thesis of Arrhenius (page 240).

[A8]   Black's theoretical advance with latent heat was practically confined to *use* of steam. Nevertheless, his interest in heat laid the basis of the Zeroth Law of thermodynamics [A13]. Carnot's concern with heat, which led him to enunciate the principle of the First Law in 1824, was triggered by consideration of the rule-of-thumb 'English' methods of *raising* steam; that is, his concern was with fuel economy.

[A9]   It is beyond the province of this book to do more than allude to developments of architecture and metallurgy in their relations to fuels. I need not do more than mention the well-known examples of devastation of forests in Dalmatia, Spain, and elsewhere for timber primarily for ship-building; but since an unarmed vessel in the era of the rise of Portugal, Spain and Venice was exceptional, the demands on wood for making guns must have become considerable by the times of the later Plantagenets (after, say, the time of Joan of Arc).

[A10]   The Plantagenet period of England extended from 1154 until 1485. Hampton Court Palace, of which the earliest part was built of brick just after Plantagenet times, is a well-known example of luxurious ostentation.

[A11]   'Always' is not meant to have eternal exactness. The time of attaining balance with the superficial environment and with other species may be years or shorter periods; with soil microbes, at least, responses to pabulum, aeration, wetness, etc. can be very rapid and may be almost instantaneous both as regards numbers and species.

[A12]   By *domain* is meant a chemical, or metabolic, group of mutually dependent organisms which may live in the same habitat. In the sea, which constitutes (broadly) one habitat, there is only one domain if the large seaweeds are left out of account. Accordingly, for all dwellers in the sea—from the microscopic up to the largest, and including the birds which exclusively eat marine fish—there is no problem about protein supply : for that is 'automatically' adjusted within the domain and within the limits set by climatic changes. (In the absence of technically-advanced Man, understood. The example of guano-accumulations of ancient Peru, and of the decline of the sea-birds, together with the guano they furnish, under the influence of power-fishing for export of dried fish-meal by Peru during the last 15 years, is instructive (Chap. 6, Note M4). If the large seaweeds are included, they form a separate and rather peculiar domain, since, while they are growing they serve directly for the nutrition of few kinds of large animals; *i.e.*, while alive, they apparently do not contribute much to the life-cycle).

On land—which also, very broadly, forms one habitat (sub-divisions can be recognized according to altitude, climate, and hence tree-cover and so on)—the principal domains besides those of the soil-dwelling microbes and small animals are: large animals, non-leguminous plants, leguminous plants.

Further elaboration does not seem germane for this outline; but it would be useful if the idea of the C/N and similar chemical biotic ratios were pursued in detail.

[A13]   The Zeroth Law of thermodynamics was so named in recent years by the English thermodynamicist E. A. Guggenheim, on the grounds that it should have been called the First—but the first two places were already taken before Black's most prime (if the expression be permitted) contribution to thermodynamics in the XVIIIth century was recognized as such. The primacy of Joseph Black is fully recognized in the books by Katchalsky and Curran [A4] and Bent [A5]; though in the latter Black is set down as English. The contributors to Kent's book [A7] did not specifically refer to Black's originality in thermodynamics.

This completes the thermodynamic analogy for Laws of Population: the first two having been stated on page 148 of this Chapter. There seems no possibility of a biological analogue for the Third Law. The C/N-ratio analogy for the Law of Gravitation could be carried a good deal further than has been attempted here.

[A14]   Edward Frankland (1825-99): the same who is said to have introduced the concept of valency into pure chemistry. In 1866 he collaborated with Wislicenus and Fick in being the first to show that muscle energy is derived from carbohydrate, and not from actual consumption of blood or muscle tissue. That was in the so-called 'Faulhorn experiment'.

Recalling also the classical cases of Pascal (page 262), Pasteur, and others in going ever higher to make some point of science, there seems to be room for an essay on the role of Swiss and French mountains in the advancement of science; even if geological achievements such as those of Agassiz are left out. Tyndall's calculations (page 134) seem to have been founded on Swiss mountains.

[A15]   A documented history of early developments of the C/N ratio (except for the work of Frankland) up to about 1915 was given under the title 'Carbon-nitrogen and other ratios' (*Anon., Soils and Fertilizers,* 1945, 8, 135-7). Politics crept in; the Viennese bacteriologist Kaserer, presumably very conscious of the *Anschluss,* claimed in 1941 a retrospective *German* origin for the ratio. He alleged that it had been first used in 1911-15 in papers published (in unmistakably Viennese journals) by three of his students.

See also pages 89 and 217 of this book.

[A15]   Clausius was made a Foreign Member of the Royal Society in 1868, and was awarded the Society's Copley Medal in 1879. His book 'Abhandlungen über die mechanische Wärmetheorie' was published 1864-7; a translation into English by T. A. Hirst was published 1867; a translation as 'The mechanical theory of heat' was published by W. R. Browne 1879. His original paper of 1850 was translated and edited under the title 'On the motive power of heat' by R. Magie in his book 'The Second Law of thermodynamics' (Harper: New York, 1899). That title clearly matches that of Carnot's 'Reflections on the motive power of fire' (Paris. 1824), translated and edited by R. Mendoza (Dover Books: New York. 1960; London: Constable): which includes translations of papers on the Second Law by Clausius and E. Clapeyron. Clausius' biography by E. Rieck was published, in German, 1889.

Entropy was not Clausius' only contribution to the biological sciences underlying food and population. In 1857 he made a suggestion about the behaviour of electricity (or of electrons and ions as we would now say) in aqueous solutions of salts and other electrolytes. The suggestion was, after much delay, taken up by Svante Arrhenius and others; it was, in Arrhenius' modification, the basis in 1884 of his theory of electrolytic dissociation or ionization: "ionic theory" for short.

Since plants take up their nutrients as ions of what is dissolved in their external media, and the behaviour of soils, blood, and all other aqueous media of life is determined by ions (Chaps. 19 and 22, pages 193 and 235), this physico-chemical theory has potentially, and to some extent actually, been of enormous importance for biology.

Possibly no corpus of theory that is widely spoken of in all branches of pure and applied chemistry has excited more violent opposition in its early years or has suffered more travesty or neglect, in some branches of applied chemistry that claim to use it, than ideas of ionization in water. Neglect to make use of the full biological potentialities of modern ionic theory is especially evident in agriculture and physiology; Chapters 9 and 22 give some examples of that.

[A17] Max Planck's own account of how he was brought to introduce entropy into quantum mechanics is given (in English) on pp. 141-2 of Bent's book [A5]; and Planck's first reactions to Clausius' ideas are given on pp. 50-1 of that book.

[A18] *See*, for example, the review by J. S. Hough and D. A. J. Wase in their article 'Continuous culture: theory and applications', *Process Biochemistry*, 1966, 1, 77-83 (82 refs.).

[A19] Credit for introducing the concept of metastability in a form useful for study of massed micro-organisms in artificial culture seems to be due to the English microbiologist D. Herbert since 1956; but he is not responsible for initiating use, in relation to microbial cultures, of the terms criticized. Those seem to have been used some years before 1956 by another microbiologist whose knowledge of biology (and/or his concern with use of language) seems to have been unduly narrow.

The main philosophical implication of Herbert's introduction of the idea of metastability into study of microbial growth-curves is that it has greatly helped to weaken the former classical idea that such growth (of pure species) is normally exponential.

Whether microbes have a sexual stage or not, it will be clear (even to the layman who happens to read this) that their needs of energy for maintenance and reproduction differ widely in character from those of a multicellular organism such as a mammal, which has organs and cells specially adapted to each reproductive, somatic, and metabolic function. Consequently the same language cannot be justifiably used for the non-entropic energy-requirements of microbes and multicellular organisms; nor can the meanings of terms be 'crossed' in respect of, say, milk-production in a cow and the anti-entropic requirements of microbes.

In the present state of knowledge the term 'anti-entropic energy' will serve exactly to say what it means for all organisms.

Without this, we may be witnessing formation of another cultural 'ox-bow' through inattention to what happens along the mainstream of biology, and of a type similar to those mentioned on page 242, Note M2.

17

The size of the equilibrium population: the involution of Man

As many lines close in the dial's centre
So may a thousand actions, once afoot
End in one purpose.
—William Shakespeare: *King Henry V*, Act 1, Sc. 11

A working estimate of the size of the population which the world can support after fossil fuel has been 'exhausted' [M1] can be made by anyone in possession of the facts about the ways our present existence is governed. Since there will be virtually no fuel except what is provided by the annual increment of wood and other vegetable fuels, there will be little industry to which chemical and thermodynamic considerations can usefully be applied; there will be no advanced industry or technology, and what manufacture there is will differ little from what is implied by the original literal meaning of the word.

The lower practical limit set by the laws of Nature to the works of Man will have been reached; and presumably— though the consequence is not infused with the same foreseeable necessity—the upper limit to the numbers of Man that is set by conditions of natural equilibrium will be reached and maintained.

The only scientific concept about this miserable state that needs to be invoked to-day is the idea of equilibrium with the surface resources accessible to Man by use of muscles unaided by steam or other motive-power based on fossil fuel. This suggests that the equilibrium population will be of the same order of size as existed before the primitive equilibrium was disturbed, and will be a necessary reversion to such numbers of people.

For reasons similar to those mentioned in considering the possible sizes of the maximum population of the earth, and the time when the maximum might be reached (Chapter 15), the situation in different parts of the world may not be uniform, nor may similar situations in different places be reached at the same time. In view of the inherent imprecisions, it may suffice to consider only the order of size of the world population, assuming the whole world to have reverted to a technology not unlike that which prevailed in Europe and continental Asia before recourse was had to fossil fuels for industry. Use of sulphur (for gunpowder) can be conceded, since the surface deposits of volcanic sulphur can be assumed big enough for an annual consumption rather larger than that of, say, 1500 A D.; and it may be assumed at the outset that enough iron is available and can be smelted by use of wood-charcoal to provide a modicum of guns (for hunting) and small implements like ploughs and fastenings for fishing vessels [M2].

With these somewhat favourable assumptions, and assuming also that some technological know-how is preserved for adaptation to a wood-fuelled community; and assuming furthermore that that knowledge has been spread over the whole world, the average density of population may be about the same as what existed in humid climates of Europe and Africa five or six centuries ago. That approach would give a total world population not exceeding two thousand millions; and probably much less. (Fig. 3.)

Another approach would be to consider what world population is reliably estimated to have been in a period when there was little use of iron: if we take that period as being about 1400 A.D., the equilibrium population would be at most one thousand million.

A population of the order of 1-2 thousand million could be supported for ever. If the reader proposes to add 'short of catastrophe', it will be remembered that there can be no 'bomb' (unless unused ones have been preserved); so a major catastrophe must be of purely natural origin.

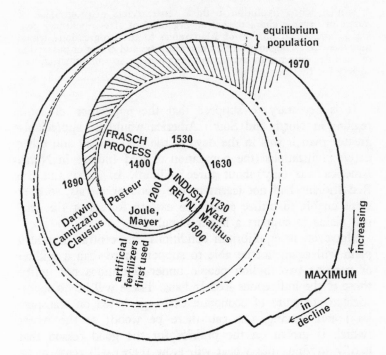

Fig. 3. The involution of Man.

The course of world human population is suggested from an indefinite date about 1000 A.D. to attainment of the equilibrium population in balance with renewable resources. For simplicity, the population is taken to be constant up to about 1700 A.D., after which a significant expansion of population is indicated by separation of the two full lines. Notable use of fossil fuel (for all purposes) is indicated by the narrow band of which one border is dotted. When equilibrium with renewable resources is approached, this band again becomes too narrow to show.

The size of population is roughly indicated by the radial distance between divergent (or convergent) full lines. The serrations near the bottom diagrammatically express disturbances at about the time when the maximum population has been reached (they may also occur earlier); and violent changes of course in the full and dotted lines express possible sudden (catastrophic) falls in population and in use of fossil fuel.

The shaded area shows times between about 1880 and the present, while the population was coming to rely increasingly on fossil fuel for food without being generally aware of that growing dependence. The time-scale is pseudo-logarithmic to avoid any appearance of prophecy.

Involution is not here an antonym for evolution in the Darwinian or similar sense. Evolution in those senses refers to progression of innate or organic characters of an organism or class (including geological strata); involution of Man refers to the progression—which may likewise be negative—of human numbers and extent of possession of facilities external to the human organism as an individual and its society for the time being.

It is necessary to suppose that the population of some regions in North and South America would be appreciably greater than it was in the days of the Red Indian and other native civilizations (the population of Red Indians in North America was only about three million). In 1400 A.D. the Red Indians had not learnt to use wood or metals, so they were unable to utilize either the eastern forests or the central plains to support a larger population.

However, in equilibrium conditions, the central American plain will again not be able to support more than a million or perhaps two million people under conditions not unlike those of the indigenous Red Indians. There will be no sophisticated structure of economic exchange based on transport [M3] and fencing, nor can there be wood; so the wheat (which is grown on the prairies for the good reason that hardly anything but wheat will grow there) will cease to be important; so will animals for food beyond that needed by a subsistence level of human population.

Somewhere, no doubt, there will be islands of intellectual culture (of the kinds that can be enjoyed with not much more than medieval facilities) in small aristocracies able somehow to shield themselves from the prevailing scrabble for enough food to maintain the majority of people at the bare subsistence level that is consonant with equilibrium with perpetually-renewable resources alone.

A pseudo-religious innovation appears to have accompanied the modern faith in the sun as the never-failing provider of all things. It seems that among many people—whether or not they believe in some kind of personal life after death—there has sprung up a belief in a sort of corporate, technically-based, immortality. This metaphysical novelty extends not only to the existence of Man himself but even more strongly to his intellectual and technological progress. These beliefs are so formless that it is difficult to express them concisely; but (tempered by fears of catastrophe that centre on 'the bomb') they amount to expecting an eternally increasing number of people on earth, blessed by boundless 'command of Nature'. Another way of expressing the same unnatural faith is to say that, socially though not individually, it looks as if belief in eternal 'command of Nature' is replacing 'defeat of Death' as the predominant item of the creed of a large number of people who live in the technologically-advanced countries.

As a short essay on human equilibrium in relation to *all* natural resources this Chapter has probably contained enough to suggest that any form of 'progress'—whether in size of population or in technological development—can go backwards as well as uninterruptedly forward. Because all 'progress' in any modernistic sense depends on command of fossil fuel—the word 'command' being here meant in the economic logistic sense—what is called 'progress' must, sooner or later and probably to unequal extents in different countries, go backward towards the equilibrium levels for Man. The arrogant idea that Man can or will ever be in 'command of *Nature*' (even for a historically short time) is totally vain and without foundation. It is a gross misunderstanding of the facts of life.

[M1] In this Chapter the word 'exhausted' is used for brevity to mean that little or no fossil fuel is accessible for technological use. There will still be fuel (*see* Chapter 4, Note [M3]) but if it lies deep there may not be enough metal to provide the necessary deep-mining equipment, etc.

[M2] These and other uses for iron and wood necessarily cannot exceed, in total, the annual increment of wood produced by unaided growth of timber: with which the total use of fuel and metals (except gold) will (by definition) have to be in equilibrium.

In England, the first fuel-crisis (departure of human use of timber from equilibrium with annual growth of trees) occurred during late Plantagenet and early Tudor times owing to increase of amenity, or technological evolvement above primitive conditions, by adoption of a new architecture which involved glass and brick. Building in brick seems to have been introduced from France, if one may judge by the English involvement in Aquitaine from 1152 until 1453, and by the numerous ancient brick buildings in, for example, Pamiers (Ariège). *See* Notes [A9] and [A10] of Appendix II, Chapter 16.

The Royal Greenwich Observatory occupies Herstmonceux Castle, Sussex, where a large portion of the original brick wall remains, built about 1440. [FRONTISPIECE]

[M3] Communities which keep up a high standard of living from monoculture or the growing of one or two crops (including animals; the crops need not be of food plants) must depend on a complex system of transport and exchange that includes banking and other commercial facilities. As examples are the monoculture of wheat (of which no quantity, however large, can by itself feed the people who produce it) on the American prairies, and ranching in North and South America. Animal production can feed a population directly, because it supplies protein and fat; and an excess of protein is not harmful—most cattle-raising communities eat much more meat than the minimum nutritional requirement. However, the problems of the whole standard of amenity remain for a population which has no other plenitude than either flesh foods or vegetable protein.

Continental North America shows textbook examples of the dependence of agricultural populations on transport and other aids to exchange. A much simpler example is presented by Hawaii. That State has a very limited domestic production of food and fish. Its only commercial crops of importance are sugar and pineapples—which (like wheat) are not foods in the sense of being able to sustain life. The sugar and pineapples are exported to the mainland United States, and thence to other parts of the world. Practically all food needed for the resident and tourist population of Hawaii is imported, in exchange for sugar and pineapples, from the mainland United States.

Though perhaps not the best example of use of fuel to maintain a high density of human population at numbers well above the equilibrium level—Britain, Japan, and several Western European countries are probably better examples of that—Hawaii is the clearest example of use of fuel (mainly in transport) to maintain a very high level of amenity from domestic agricultural products. New Zealand is a good second. Though her agricultural industry also depends greatly on ocean transport, the fuel most important to her agriculture is sulphur. As a consequence, New Zealand has the world's highest per capita consumption of sulphuric acid: nearly all of it being used to make fertilizer to produce proteins in clover, mutton, wool and cheese. The sulphur is all imported.

18

Choice and Chance

'There is, however, a time to speak in the flowery terms of poetical allusion and a time to be distressingly explicit. Descending to the latter plane for one concise moment ...'
—Ernest Bramah: *Kai Lung unrolls his mat*, London: Richards Press. 1928 (also Penguin Books Ltd.)

With governmental encouragement, attempts are being made by economists in the United Kingdom (and no doubt elsewhere) to assess the net economic export value of contemporary science and technology with a view to evaluating their net monetary effect on the balance of payments. Since the aim of these attempts is to interpret values in financial terms, it is natural that economists should make them; the question whether scientists are the best persons to assess 'values' of any kind is beside the point. What is obfuscating to science and scientists is that 'science and technology' are lumped together in such exercises: to mean actual and potential technology and other applied science seen by laymen as capable of yielding some concrete exportable result: such as a machine which can be constructed and sold, or a process or patent that can be licensed for money—in a word, technology.

Cognate but distinct is the problem of how much money and effort can be justifiably spent on advanced experimental physics. That is known to everyone to be a costly enterprise. This problem is distinct from the foregoing because it relates to the domain of pure science, and also because it involves heavy and complicated equipment so that its pursuit is virtually a branch of financially unremunerative engineering which may produce prestige but is unlikely to improve any nation's balance of payments.

If we leave military and aerospace subjects out of account from a monetary point of view (they cannot be left out of thought if one is thinking in terms of fuel and population), most of these expensive projects are for furtherance of particle physics, stellar exploration, and geophysics—the last being typified by a 'Mohole' bored to investigate the Mohorovičić discontinuity. Contemplation of the often very high costs in money and of their apportionment between several nations (since the cost of one such project may be more than any one European nation can well afford), together with the supposition that these branches of physics are—if not the only kind of pure (*i.e.*, peaceful and unmercenary) science—almost the only excitingly mentionable branch of science, and thus are the most frequently-mentioned variety of science, can hardly fail to deepen a popular impression that pure science and scientists are expensive luxuries: however much they intensify the process of wresting secrets from Nature by venturing ever further into the unknown.

As a corrective to false ideas about what constitutes real science, it is salutary to recall that all the money spent on supporting the lead-directing thoughts and researches of a few dozen people like Carnot, Cannizzaro, Pasteur, the Curies, and Soddy—which have had immensely beneficial and the most practical outcomes—would, even if capitalized at to-day's monetary values, have been hardly more than the cost of a powerful radio-telescope, and would be only a small fraction of the cost of a big atom-smasher.

It is a common plaint among those, including ordinary taxpayers, who have anything to do with budgets for what is grandly and indiscriminately called 'scientific research' that 'science' is constantly becoming more expensive: largely because some kinds of equipment have become very complicated. But the real question is not a comparison of money costs of research nowadays with those of last century; the real question, as always for any proposed project whether it is scientific or not, is: 'What do you hope to *do* by embarking on this new course of action or enquiry?'

The thermodynamic and chemical laws discovered in the period before 1870 have had, and continue to carry, enormous practical value (in money or other terms) as principles deciding how to go straight to such goals as improving efficiency of machines and of processes; besides avoiding waste of effort in what, without those principles, would become empirical attempts at doing the impossible. More recent fundamental rules—for example, those about isotopes discovered up to about 1916—have been helpful in stimulating new kinds of technical knowledge and control. Those have been notable in medicine and industry; but they have not added anything new to knowledge about the ways in which the prime forces of Nature behave or can be harnessed.

In designing an 'atomic' power station, for instance, thermodynamic considerations are paramount after safety considerations have been attended to. It is thanks to new knowledge about the properties of the earth's envelope that the experience of Marconi (mentioned in Chapter 3) is now understood; the new knowledge can be directed to furthering achievement and research in many ways besides telecommunications; but it is a phenomenon, not a principle, which has become better understood and can be utilized. No fresh laws of practical importance about the behaviour of mundane matter have emerged since 1870.

The laws of Nature that impose limits to human manipulation of matter and energy might be called the laws of fixed odds. They may be looked on like that, because they neither have, nor allow to Man, any latitude whatsoever in applying them. The rules governing production of food are in that statistical category. However, since world population has for many years ceased to be in equilibrium with renewable resources, and has adopted the device of using diminishing resources, the practical limits to its future numbers will be the phenomenon that it is the total amount of fuel that is fixed. That phenomenon will be decisive for Man's future welfare; but whatever Man does with his fixed resources will be limited and bound by the 'fixed-odds' laws—because Man cannot escape their operation.

There is another kind of odds: the variable odds. Those are particularly evident in biology. The 'variable-odds' laws are not a substitute for the 'fixed-odds' ones. The two require separate discussion because they are different in kind —the variable odds operating within the limits and conditions set by the fixed-odds laws which dominate all organisms.

In contrast to the almost incredibly vast numbers of 'units' (molecules or atoms) present in small samples of solids, liquids, and gases, the numbers in biological samples have only a few 'units' (plants or animals, for example); but each animal or other 'unit' is exposed to widely variable and essentially unknown conditions.

Therefore, scientific understanding of biological variables needs what is superficially a quite different discipline from what has grown up in everyday physics and chemistry. The two disciplines of dealing with 'fixed odds' and 'variable odds' have ultimately the same philosophical basis; but to discuss that proposition would take us far beyond the problem of food.

Suffice it to suggest that in chemical and engineering excises like calculating how much food or other substance can be made from any other substances, or in calculating the efficiency of a boiler or machine, all the terms are known or ascertainable with some precision: whereas in comparing such things as effects of fertilizers (of known composition) on yields of (variable) plants grown on (variable) soil, the only valid approach is the mathematical one of calculating probabilities of matters wherein nothing is known with exactness about behaviour of any of the components when in contact with the others.

The mathematical theory of probabilities is at least three hundred years old. It began because players at games like cards and dice, wanting to evaluate their chances in terms of cash, sought the aid of mathematicians; mathematicians then became interested in the calculation of probabilities for their own sake, and so there was founded a new branch of mathematics. However, until the early nineteenth century, the chances were of the types associated with distributions known in advance; such as with hands dealt from a pack of cards, and throws of dice. The theory of probabilities later became associated with matters like cash values of life expectancy for endowment and assurance policies; then with biometry (*e.g.*, probable heights or weights of a sample of people).

Calculation of random probabilities is called mathematical statistics. It should not be confused with the older meaning of statistics in the sense of collection of numerical data. A virtually new branch of mathematical statistics was evolved by (Sir) Ronald A. Fisher (1890-1959) to deal with problems of genetics. This expanded vastly in the 1920's to give an entirely new conception: namely, the design of experiments. These new ideas brought the possibility of calculation of the probability that a given set of experimental findings would be unlikely to be a result of chance and might therefore be reasonably accepted as a real outcome of the treatments to which the variable experimental material had been subjected [MI].

That was a new idea which upset most previous ideas about experimentation. For instance, it rejected (except for any but the simplest types of demonstration-experiment in classical physics and chemistry) the notion of 'altering only one treatment at a time', which some people still regard as the essence of the ideal experiment. It founded a completely new *philosophy* of experimentation. By doing that, it extended the *scope* of experimentation, and made it feasible to draw impersonal deductions from numerical data which had previously been open to only subjective conclusions and review (Chapter 3 and 23). As if that were not enough, the almost brand-new mathematical-statistical approach gave rise to operational research, which soon applied itself to industrial and other problems.

The first application of the new mathematical probe was in 1922 (*ref.* page 41) to a problem in soil bacteriology being studied by Dr (now Sir) Henry G. Thornton in the James Mason Laboratory at Rothamsted Experimental Station in England. The laboratory had been the result of a private benefaction. The fact that the first application of mathematical statistics in a modern sense was to a problem about soil bacteria is of interest from a food-and-agricultural point of view; but the main purpose of giving this brief sketch of the rise of a new experimental philosophy and the effective birth of operational research out of a concern with biological kinds of variability is to point out that it betokened a vast extension of pure science of which the knowledge and use spread rapidly, after about 1940, throughout the English-speaking world [M2].

The money cost of its gestation was small; its technique became available at little more than the price of text-books; so, while being a major contribution from British science, its export value was almost negligible in money terms. How, then, would its value be assessed? Would the economists currently engaged (at the behest of politicians) to put values on what politicians call 'science and technology' pay much attention to something as intangible as the development of new mathematical techniques, which brings forth no material or saleable product (unless books)?

The very expensive projects like those for cyclotrons and the Mohole will extend knowledge of *phenomena*. Whatever *principles* they reveal can apply to matters of only intellectual content (as about behaviour of sub-atomic particles, for instance). It is not conceivable that knowledge gained from new adventures in experimental physics will have fresh importance for any of Man's practical interests in food or amenity.

That apparently sweeping statement—which some laymen may regard as unworthy of a scientist—is based on nothing but science.

The reader can see that this is so when, for example, he reflects that should a Mohole open up a vista of tapping the interior heat of the earth, or should nuclear fusion bring to actuality the dream of lighting a whole city by power derived from the atomic nuclei in a cupful of water, those, and like projections of fancy upon knowledge or theory about phenomena, relate solely to energy obtained as heat and electricity: which have no nutrient value and must incur a heavy cost in fuel to win them. So far from their making a contribution to food-gathering, the fuel spent in realizing them will have subtracted from stocks of fuel potentially available for producing food later.

That is not 'my' principle or law; nor does it resemble the incautious opinions about the future that are freely bandied about without scientific justification. It is the most elementary deduction from what has been known since a century ago, and has been in constant test and approved use for a century and more.

Consequently, the question about the social value of the more expensive outlays of effort and money for extending experimental physics is the commonsense one of how much a nation can afford in the way of devoting brains, equipment, and fuel (as well as money) to gain little more than the intellectually aesthetic satisfaction of putting new frills on to the existing coat of academic knowledge. That is not, in the main, a question for scientists to answer. What a scientist can and should do is to assist laymen to see what the question really is.

Whatever is now attempted—Mohole or anything else—and whether it is done for 'practical' purposes (like building more machines or making more aeroplanes), or is done with the aim of 'extending the frontiers of knowledge'—can be done *only* by means of some machinery and equipment built to operate in accordance with laws already known and by use of some of the remaining fuel. It will be mortgaging the future of Man.

It should therefore be attempted as a deliberate choice, made with full knowledge of what science indicates as the consequences of the working of natural laws of thermodynamics and chemistry. Once those laws become sufficiently widely known to be a basis for social policy, the moral and social values of past and present and future discoveries in science, and of their application to technology, will not require scientists for their interpretation.

An instance can be imagined in connexion with planetary exploration. It is already possible—at a considerable cost in fuel—to send a vehicle to the environs of Mars. The physiological and other problems of sending a man to Mars remain for the present unresolved; though they are probably getting attention of the kind which is an extension of what has been given to manning earth-orbiting artificial satellites. The solution of the problems may not be obtained for years or possibly decades; but by the time it becomes technically feasible and safe to send a couple of human beings to Mars, the fuel situation may be such that it will be a question whether enough fuel can be spared on Earth to get a Mars-bound vehicle off the ground. It is possible that that may then be seen as a question of prestige rather than of prudence about the remaining fuel. What the priorities will then have become it is now impossible to foresee. The possibility looks odd to me. . . .

Everyman

'Well, perhaps your feeling may be different,' said Alice; 'all I know is, it would feel very odd to *me*.'

'You!' said the Caterpillar with scorn. 'Who are *you*?'

Which brought them back again to the beginning of the talk.

[MI] The wording of the sentence after the word 'calculation' may seem awkward if not downright clumsy. It is difficult to word the concept briefly for a layman in mathematics and science. The engaging little book by Warren Weaver, 'Lady Luck: the theory of probability' (New York: Anchor Books, Doubleday & Company, Inc. 1963) is an introduction in popular language to the ideas of probability and gaming.

The wording of page 181 was adopted to avoid the reader's falling into the trap of supposing that statistical calculation of probability of error gives a measure of the 'truth' of the results obtained from any experiment or set of numerical observations (such as observation of an industrial process).

A statistical calculation, when properly performed on the data of a suitably-designed trial or experiment, does give an indication of confidence which may be placed in a conclusion as a basis for action; but, because mathematical statistics deals with uncertain inference, what it measures might be called *un*confidence: *i.e.*, the possibility that the observed result could have been attained by the operations or happenings of pure chance. The calculation does not otherwise give an index of the extent that the result is a 'real' one. To make a true judgment about variables is still as much beyond human capacity as it was in Pontius Pilate's time.

It is about naturally *invariant* rules on 'fixed odds' lines (page 179; and previous Chapters *passim*) that we have acquired knowledge sufficiently complete and reliable in itself for making confident predictions which, as a matter of practice and policy, we can be sure will not be contravened. Predictions based on rules such as the laws of thermodynamics will give us no cause for surprise; they must infallibly 'work out' and come true.

An analogy for appeal to that kind of fixity of behaviour in Nature would come from measurement of something which does not vary; say, the length of a side of this book. Once in possession of the appropriate relational information that one inch $= 2\frac{1}{2}$, or 2.54, centimetres, we can measure the length with any solid wooden or metal ruler graduated in inches, and then be quite sure what the length measured by any solid ruler graduated in centimetres will be found to be. There is no room for opinions or inference.

In connexion with food it is of passing interest that Fisher's pioneering book 'The Design of Experiments' (Edinburgh: Oliver & Boyd, various editions) started with the example of a lady who declares that she can tell from tasting a cup of milky tea whether the milk has been added before (English style) or after (Scottish style) the tea was poured. The first experiment in the book, which is virtually the starting-point of all operational research and other modern experimental enquiry into variable odds, is the model of a design to test whether her belief can reasonably be accepted as valid.

[M2]   Like other ideas which contravene the rigid Marxian dialectic that Communist Man will be able to control the whole of his environment and circumstances, mathematical statistics has been proscribed in the U.S.S.R. Soviet industry must be labouring under a severe, self-imposed, handicap if the banned techniques are indeed never used; they appear not to be used in genetics or biology generally, but it is possible that some use of them is made *sub rosa* elsewhere. It is noticeable that the fields of 'scientific' (read: technological) achievement in which the U.S.S.R. has made the most evident and most publicized advances are some forms of engineering to which the established 'fixed odds' laws and the mathematics of invariables are applicable without modification; whereas Russian development of computers and other instruments which depend on principles of randomization has not gone very far.

19

An approach by chemical first principles

'Why one to come and one to go?'
'Don't I tell you?' the King repeated impatiently.
'I must have *two*—to fetch and carry. One to fetch, and one to carry.'
—Lewis Carroll: *Through the Looking-glass*

If a nutritionist were to make a detailed exposition of human energy it would be necessary to follow several paths and make several differences clear; as between the nutritional values of carbohydrates and proteins and what the body does with each in different conditions of the body (pregnant or not, and so forth). However, such nutritional differences are inbuilt; in presenting the chemistry basic to *production* of food (which is also basic to its utilization in the body) it is not necessary to account for them. We can take the fundamental chemistry as a set of a very few facts, and then look simply and radically to the laws which are obeyed in every manifestation of those facts.

Explanation of the body's peculiar needs, and its method of dealing with them—once it is given sufficient of the right kinds of nutrients, minerals, and water—belong to nutritional and physiological science. All that needs to be added in that connexion in order to make an accurate judgment of prospects for population is the proposition that five units (the unit being an average person, or a million or a thousand million people) require five times as much food as does one of those units.

The overall chemical argument is not more difficult than

that. The chief difficulty for some readers will come from an unfamiliarity with the chemical terms. These go in pairs, like 'positive' and 'negative'. That is for the good reason that the chemistry, being ultimately electrical, also has two, and only two, aspects. Those are 'on' or 'off'; plus or minus; presence or absence; 1 or 0: with no intermediate. Nowadays it may be helpful to invert a familiar comparison and to say that the chemistry of feeding any number of human beings operates on the same principle, and for the same reason, as a computer or 'artificial brain': they all depend on 1 and 0. Those are the two possible states of electricity, because electrons are electrically charged and are present or absent; and chemistry operates by gain or loss of electrons.

That is true in an animal body, a plant, or anywhere else. Therefore the soil and the fertilizers added to it to produce more food are examples of the operation of electronic phenomena in relatively simple substances. In view of the excitement and intensity of interest that have been provoked in recent years by 'artificial brains' and computers and all those kinds of machines, it seems a pity that attention to the origins of food has not become more fashionable—since the management of electrons in boxes does not differ in any fundamental way from the management of media which produce food. The practical difference is that the one can be manipulated by pressing buttons (given an original source of electrical power, of course) while management of farming and fishing is not nearly as simple. However, if you believe that computers are more important than people, you can accept the analogy without going any further.

There is one big difference between a human brain and any sort of artificial electronic machine. That is, that the machine, once it has been built, can be operated by electricity alone as long as the supply lasts. Though a human brain (or body) can be stimulated by electricity, it has to have some substance (food of the right kinds and quantity) in order to keep it going. That substance cannot be produced or substituted by electricity; because what is essential to produce food from the salts of soil and sea are chemical, or electronic, *transformations* of one substance into another. To make food it is always necessary to have suitable substances to start with; and electricity, sunlight, and other electro-magnetic forces are not substance. They cannot *produce* food.

A discussion of prospects for food and population can be made on sound chemical lines by jumping off from part of the conventional presentation of the life cycle. The usual pre-sentation is confined to the fate of carbon and oxygen; and that will do as the start of a chemical argument. It is desir-able—indeed essential—to bring nitrogen and earthy com-ponents of food, as well as the role of soil microbes, into the picture; but as a start the usual, bare, presentation of the circulation of carbon and oxygen will do.

According to the traditional life-cycle, green plants take in carbon dioxide from the air, and liberate oxygen. The oxygen comes from water; oxygen is taken in by animal res-piration to burn up assimilated food; in that process more carbon dioxide is set free into the atmosphere; and so the cycle goes on. The better versions of the story [MI] bring in carbon dioxide from volcanoes, industrial processes, and plant and microbial respiration. But the barest version is enough for our present purpose—provided it is understood that the free oxygen comes from water.

The decomposition of water in photosynthesis provides free oxygen—which we breathe—and hydrogen which is not set free as gas but combines within the plant with carbon dioxide to form carbohydrates (as is well known). Respira-tion involves the process of combining with free oxygen by *oxidation*. The term *reduction* for the process of combining with hydrogen is not so well known; but we need both *oxidation* and *reduction* to make an incontrovertible approach to the problem of food and population. 'Reduction' is an old term that chemists keep for convenience, although the word has other meanings; *hydrogenation* may be used instead of 'reduction' if that is thought more logical; but whichever term is used, or if none of them is used, an acquaintance

with the main chemical facts on which food depends is
essential for a full understanding of population.

Biological chemistry depends on two primeval chemical
facts. One is that all life depends on water; the other is that
oxidation and reduction are inseparable—as with the two
sides of a coin or banknote, there cannot be one without
the other [M2]. Not only are they inseparable, but the
effect of one is equal and opposite to the effect of the other.
If any substance is reduced, something else is oxidised to
an equal and opposite extent. That applies throughout the
whole of Nature (not only in questions of food and photosynthesis).

That fact brings in the concept of *equivalence,* which is
the chemical way of expressing Nature's invariable observ-
ance of exact balance and equilibrium: we are back at the
general proposition of 'nothing for nothing, but always something for its exact chemical equivalent'—whatever the currency of exchange and transfer may be (in energy or chemical
substance or anything else).

A layman may sensibly ask: 'If it is "an equivalent", what
is it equivalent *to?*' So suppose we put it another way, and
say that a chemical equivalent is a measure of the amount of
chemical, or electrical, or any other kind of work that can
be got out of a given weight of a substance. To that, there
is a definite limit, always. It does not need to be put into
chemical terms what the limit is; you already know that a
lump of coal will not give out more than a certain amount
of heat, and that if you want more heat, you have to use
more coal.

In burning completely, the coal will have combined with
its equivalent weight of oxygen from the air. The carbon of
the coal will have been oxidized, and will have formed carbon
dioxide. The weights of carbon, oxygen, and carbon dioxide
will all be exactly equivalent (chemically) to each other; and
so on for any chemical substance or transformation whatever. To paraphrase the quotation at the head of Chapter 5,
Nature will have seen to that.

Really of course, the idea of any equivalent being equal
to any other equivalent is Man's way of saying that the

chemical work or change that any substance can be induced to perform is the same as the (measured) equivalent for any other substance. Chemists have to be more specific if they want to make calculations; and I will give only one example. To make water, or when water is decomposed, the union is made, or broken, between two atoms of hydrogen and one atom of oxygen. The weight of the hydrogen atom being taken as 1, on that chemical scale the weight of an oxygen atom being 16, the equivalent of hydrogen is 1 and the equivalent of oxygen is 8. Then 8 parts of weight of oxygen will combine with, or replace, just so much and no more of any other substance as *its* equivalent (by weight). The equivalent of carbon being known to be 3, we know that (say) 6 pounds of carbon will combine with a maximum of 16 pounds of oxygen to give 22 pounds of carbon dioxide (and will also give out, in the process, a fixed equivalent of heat). Fixed and knowable quantities like that are what we all have to work with all our lives, whether we are using a coal fire to heat the room, running a hurdle race, making or letting off an explosive, or trying to produce (say) a synthetic fat. It is always known in advance what the maximum is that can be obtained; for the limits have been fixed by Nature and the result of the calculation will be (as a maximum) the same however the operation of making something is conducted—by a green plant, a sheep, or a Professor of Chemistry or Botany. In practice there are always losses in conversion (page 45); but, again, it is impossible to get *more* food, or anything else, than the equivalent of what is already in, or is put into, the mill for it to work on.

Now, a clarification to avoid possible misconceptions; they are dreadfully easy for a non-chemist to fall into. The fact that 'all life depends on water' is a fundamental, rock-bottom assertion about the chemical exchanges that govern all life, always within the thermodynamic limitations set by energy changes. Because food, living organisms, soil, sea and so forth are composed of substance, it is of no practical use to deal only with energy: because energy by itself cannot *produce* food, although the limits of food and population are set by chemical energy. Saying that life depends on water thus goes more deeply than thinking that fish swim while land animals and birds have legs or wings; to go into these sorts of consideration is to leave fundamentals behind and to begin to specialize.

Only a small fraction of the world's water enters at any one time into chemical changes like those involved in forming plants and animals. There is a vast excess—not only of water—but of many other substances—as well as of sunlight; but in purely natural conditions (by which I mean those not influenced by the activities of any but the most primitive people) the limits to growth of plants and animals and microbes are the limits of the quantities of mineral substances around them that plants and microbes can usefully build up into their living material (assuming an adequacy of water).

If any *one* of those inorganic, mineral substances—say the ammonia and nitrate or the phosphate of soil and sea, or one or more trace elements—is lacking or in insufficient supply: the plants will not start, or, will be able to proceed only as far as is permitted by the totality of plant nutrients.

Both the *extent* of the circulation of nutrients, and the rapidity or *rate* at which the life-cycle turns, are controlled by the mineral, purely inorganic, plant nutrients that are in shortest supply. That implies that the possible mass of plants at any place on the land or in the sea is limited by the essential elements which happen to be already in, or about to enter, the cycle at any moment; the fact that some materials (like salt in the sea or iron compounds in the soil) may be superabundant does not matter from the point of view of nutrition and the activities of plants and microbes in their accustomed environments [M3].

In agriculture, whether fertilizers are used or not, nutrients are conserved, or added to from outside the cycle, so as to remove the purely natural limits and to expand the plant-microbial cycle for a while so as to have more people and domestic animals than the cycle would naturally support. Theoretically, the life-cycle would seem to be able to go round quite well without any kind of animals; and what the role of the human animal is, is very difficult to see. However, here we are; that, too, is a fact which has to be considered —but always within the rigid framework of chemical and thermodynamic laws to which human ingenuity can add nothing.

Solar energy has to be taken into account chiefly because another limitation is climate (air and soil temperatures, rain or snow, and so forth). Within climatic limitations, the sun can be relied on to produce the maximum natural amount of plant and microbial mass that is permitted by the nutrients locally available. By increasing the local stock of one or more 'major' nutrients and trace elements, fertilizers and manures temporarily raise the plant-nutrient limits; and if the crops are edible crops, more animals can then walk about on two legs or four—for a time.

For reasons connected with the balance, or ratio, of carbon and nitrogen in *soils* and their microbes, nitrogenous fertilizers have a special importance in enabling the life-cycle to turn a little faster. That is a matter of *rate*.

For similar reasons connected with the balance of carbon and nitrogen *within* green *plants,* nitrogenous fertilizers— in conjunction with earthy materials, especially potassium salts—assist in increasing the *extent* of photosynthesis and of plant growth as a whole.

Nitrogenous fertilizers—always in conjunction with earthy materials—represent the chief means by which more than the natural amount of photosynthesis is, and can be, achieved; for as long as fossil fuel lasts. This subject of increase of photosynthesis and of plant growth is discussed in greater detail in Chapter 21. For the present, it will suffice to bear in mind that an increase of photosynthesis and of green-plant mass on land is attained not by the sciolistic route of increasing the efficiency of absorption of everyday solar energy by plants, but by having recourse to fossil fuel which is the product of plant growth of long ago. It is the capital of substance, not the income of solar energy, that has to be utilized to obtain greater growth of green plants to-day and in the future. The ordinary operations of chemistry (and of thermodynamics, if you like) insist that that must be so.

It has not been found practicable to use fertilizers economically in the sea, and it seems unlikely that means can be found for doing so.

So far, we have considered only one of the ways in which water can chemically split its molecule. If the formula of water is written

HOH or HHO

(both of which are legitimate) it can be seen that every water-molecule can split in two ways. The splitting into two atoms of (reducing) hydrogen and one atom of (oxidizing) oxygen —chemically opposite and equivalent—is the basis of all chemical operations, including photosynthesis.

But water splits also into the groups H and OH, each of which carries an electrical charge: the H being positive and the OH, or HO, being negative, so that we write them as H^+ and OH'. That is to show that when considering the electrically-charged hydrogen we do not mean 'chemical' hydrogen gas (which consists of pairs of atoms of hydrogen, is electrically neutral, and has the formula H_2); also, there is no substance having the formula OH or HO. The formulae H^+ and OH' indicate charged particles or groups called *ions*. [M4]

It is only a very small fraction of pure water which splits into ions (ionizes); but because the electrical charges of the ions of water are opposite and equivalent, water is electrically and chemically neutral. More ions are produced spontaneously whenever a salt, an acid, or an alkali is dissolved in water. Some of these ions—positive and negative, again—come from the dissolved substance. If the substance is one like common salt which is not acid or alkaline but neutral, there are, in a watery solution of that substance, only the ions of the salt, plus the ions of the small fraction of the water that is always ionized; but if an acid or an alkali is added to water, it upsets the balance between H^+ and OH', causing more H^+ ions, or more OH' ions, (respectively) to be formed from the water than are normally present.

Water is thus the source of all acidity and alkalinity: depending on what is dissolved in it. An acid is a substance which can induce water to yield extra H^+, and an alkali is a substance which induces water to produce more OH'. Those two ions—H^+ and OH'—are the real 'principles' (to use old-fashioned language) of acidity and alkalinity, respectively; they come from water when its H^+—OH' balance is disturbed; and there is not really any 'acid' or 'alkaline' substance—only substances which have the property, when dissolved in water, of provoking more H^+ than OH' (or the other way round) to be formed from the *water*.

Ions of water, and ions from salts, acids, and alkalies dissolved in water, invariably occur in pairs: each member having an opposite charge (positive or negative). It is convenient to call the positive ions cations (pronounced cat-ions), and the negative ones anions. H^+ is a cation and OH' is an anion. It is not necessary to go further into ionic chemistry beyond saying that water gives rise to the effective cations and anions of fertilizers, as well as of the soil itself.

Water has many other chemical and physical functions. There is material for a book in its relations with fertilizers alone. All fertilizers, manures, and soil amendments without exception become ionized in the soil water. Plants cannot derive benefit from taking in any substance (except water and gases dissolved in water) which is not completely ionized —by means of water in which it has dissolved. Manures and fertilizers of all kinds are effective towards growth and activity of plants (through their roots) and towards soil microbes and the soil itself, only to the extent to which they are ionized at any time. Sometimes the ionization of fertilizers is almost immediately complete as soon as the fertilizer comes into contact wth the soil water; soluble fertilizers like nitrate of soda and ammonium sulphate act like that. Sometimes the process of becoming ionized is prolonged, and the substance therefore has a correspondingly protracted and less intense effect on soil and the living things in it: as happens with lime and farmyard manure and most 'organics'.

It should not be overlooked that the organic substances which take part in the life-cycle include (a) residues of existing plants, of which the finer roots are continually being shed; (b) recent residues of the last generations of plants and animals (big roots, fallen leaves, animal excreta, bodies of animals of all sizes); (c) living and dead cells of the soil microbes that effect the decomposition of all these effete animal and plant products, by oxidizing them and splitting their components again into carbon dioxide and ions which the plant roots can absorb. The soil water also ionises: in conjunction with the salts and colloids present in, or added to, the soil, it gives a controllable degree of acidity.

Water and oxygen from the soil air are essential; so are the soil microbes which act through a chain of biological and chemical processes to keep the cycle turning. Pasteur's greatest thought about bacteria and other microbes was (in modern language) that, without the soil microbes, death itself would be incomplete, because the earth would soon be cluttered up with undecomposed dead things allowing no future.

Photosynthesis is definitely not 'the most important chemical reaction' as some writers would have us believe; it is not half of the life cycle. If we assume that what they mean by 'photosynthesis' is 'the whole of plant growth and metabolism', that is wrong not merely because it misuses words (and about a subject which they believe to be so important, too) but because plant growth may be looked upon as being concerned almost wholly with *reduction*: and the other half of living processes—namely, *oxidation* by microbial processes and animal and plant respiration—is lost from sight. So is the exact balance of life, and any pretension to balance in the argument.

Nor is photosynthesis the 'centre' of all biological processes. Solar energy keeps the whole life-cycle turning by activating plants *and* microbes. Energy from the sun is the sole source of direct and indirect energy for all biological processes; but it is, so to speak, part of the circumference of the cycle; it operates by pushing on the rim; but almost half of the cycle is occupied by soil microbes, a small part being allotted to animals. It is often convenient to represent the life-cycle by a triangle, of which the soil microbes form the 'floor' or base (Figs. 4 and 5) as they do of our life. Photosynthesis forms at most one side.

The activity of bacteria, fungi, and other microscopically

small organisms in soil can be judged by the fact that in a reasonably good soil, like that of any British field, the weight of these soil microbes is about the same as that of the farm livestock walking over it or supported by its produce: say, a small cow per acre.

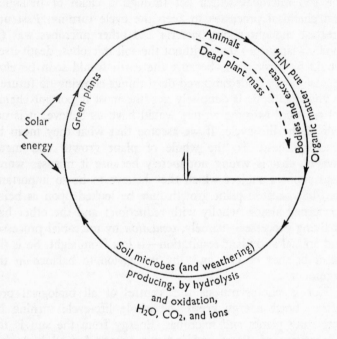

Fig. 4. The natural life-cycle in simple form, for soil. Gains and losses of nitrogen are not shown.

The horizontal line indicates the limit of production of ionized matter from organic matter and by weathering of earthy material. It is roughly the upper limit of the volume of the soil and surface litter in which the soil microbes are active, and is conceptually near the soil surface. Its level rises and falls (as is indicated by the double arrow) according to climate and season. The extremes are: in tropical forests the chemical stock and biological activity are mostly on and above the soil surface; in deserts they are normally confined below it.

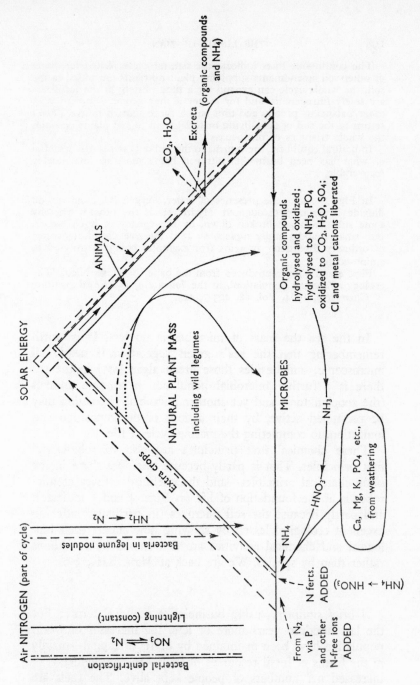

Fig. 5. The soil-based life-cycle more completely indicated than in Fig. 4.

The continuous lines indicate the natural cycle. When fertilizers or other soil amendments supplying plant nutrients are added to the soil, the whole cycle can expand for a time: briefly if the fertilizers are solely nitrogenous, and for longer if they promote formation of more 'balancing' protein and thus enable more animals to live. Direct return to the soil of once-living material from rooted plants occupies the whole triangles of plant-mass.

In natural equilibria, fire returns to the soil only the earthy material of what has been burnt—its nitrogen being more or less quickly recoverable.

In Figs. 4 and 5 the presence of water, oxygen (O_2), and carbon dioxide is assumed throughout. Hydrolysis is the process whereby some substances are broken down, by the agency of liquid water, into smaller and simpler molecules. It is the sole chemical process of ordinary digestion: proteins (for example) being hydrolysed to amino-acids.

Figs. 4 and 5 are reproduced from the paper by Hugh Nicol, 'The ecology of human population', in the *Journal of the Royal Institute of Chemistry*, 1964, Vol. 88, 423-7, 413.

In the sea the mass of microbes is no less. It is worth remembering that the sea's green vegetation is nearly all microscopic; and besides those green algae [M5] in the sea there is a further microbial population of minute animals (the zooplankton); and yet another microbial population may be presumed active, by their actions of decomposition and ionization, in completing the marine cycle of life.

These chemical first principles are also microbiological first principles. That is partly because microbes share in the same chemical principles—and the chemical activity of microbes is at the foundation of life (as Figs. 4 and 5 indicate); and partly because the soil microbes (in particular) offer an excellent ecological lesson by showing how closely their biological and chemical activities are determined by *conditions* rather than by species. We are back at *Matt.* XIII, 3-9.

A brief summary, using businesslike chemical terms: For the last hundred years more or less, the increases of world population have been maintained by drafts of capital—mainly in the forms of fossil resources of fuels—to pay dividends of increased net numbers of people kept alive. The fuels are reducing substances: by which it is meant not that their amounts are constantly becoming smaller (though that is true!) but that they are able to produce energy for chemical transformations by being oxidized when burnt in air so as to combine with some of its oxygen. Among the chemical transformations brought about by use of fuel to make fertilizers is an extra growth of food-producing plants; extra, that is, to food that would have been obtained if Man had relied solely on the world's income of energy and substance from surface resources alone.

There has been no instance of 'command' (in any intellectual sense) of Nature. The laws of oxidation-reduction and of every other natural exchange of one substance with another, and of substance for energy, have never changed. Man is, on balance, very much an oxidizing animal whose sole source of personal energy comes from having the right sorts of partly-reduced chemical compounds (food) to put between his teeth. There is no likelihood that anything will change as regards the amounts or kinds of food needed per head for the next million years.

The facts about the chemistry concerned in growing and eating food demand that fuel should be oxidized to produce more food then the equilibrium quantity which is consistent with renewable resources. The amount of fuel used in mechanical cultivation, transport, cooking, canning, refrigeration etc., makes a further call on irreplaceable resources. But the major pressure on fuel and population of the future is being exerted by uses of fuel that have no connexion with food; these uses may be called luxury consumption, or luxurious oxidation.

So long as some part of the world is able to live on the capital of stored oxidizable fuels applied to production of food, Nature's accountancy may appear not to be working; and indeed hitherto it has been overlooked. Some day the call for a sober stock-taking and general reckoning will become insistent.

[MI]   *Petit Larousse* (art. *Carbone, cycle du*): Larousse, Paris, 1963; G. N. Plass, *Scientific American*, July 1959.

[M2]   Some readers who have recollections of school chemistry in which substances were classed as 'oxidizing' or 'reducing' agents may be disturbed by this statement. Chlorine, hydrogen peroxide, and permanganates (for example) may have been classed as 'oxidizing' whilst sulphur dioxide, carbon monoxide, and sulphuretted hydrogen were classed as 'reducing'. That is terribly illogical and misleading for beginners, it being impossible for any substance to oxidize (or reduce) unless another substance (or a group of substances) is correspondingly reduced (or oxidized) to the exact extent of the chemical equivalent of each. The substance mentioned as oxidized in a elementary chemical description of a process may not have been regarded as important: thus, in a school-book account of iron manufacture it may have been said that carbon monoxide reduces the iron from its oxide, without mentioning the carbon dioxide infallibly formed by oxidation. If iron ore is reduced by hydrogen gas in a laboratory experiment, the other product is water (hydrogen oxide).

The distinction was based on practical, not scientific, considerations. In technological treatises or patent specifications it is legitimate to list certain substances or groups of substances as 'suitable oxidizing agents' while excluding others and without mentioning the corresponding reduction; and conversely. Lists of that sort are meant for people who have completed their apprenticeship in chemistry.

In the light of the caution given in this Note, readers will allow such statements as that on page 195 about plants being concerned mainly with reduction and animals mainly with oxidation. They lead up, in this Chapter's Summary, to fuels being called reducing substances.

[M3]   If the total osmotic pressure is not too high, and if other physical factors (including acidity and the balance by weight, of cations and anions, *infra*) are tolerable for a given species of plant.

[M4]   Ions also occur in gases; this discussion is concerned solely with ions in water and aqueous solutions; it is not concerned with gaseous ions beyond mentioning that they also are electrically charged.

[M5]   A reader alert (it may be hoped) for contradictions will have noted the statement on page 135 that 350,000 tons of sea-water would in one day be expected to contain only about a pound of phytoplankton. The explanation of the seeming contradiction is that one day's pumping is only a snap sample from which the algae were supposed to have been harvested artificially and completely removed from their normal cycle. If the green algae were left in the body of the sea, and if they doubled their numbers by reproducing only once a day throughout the year, each 350,000 tons of surface water would yield a pound of green food to enter the marine food-chain every day, and another pound of green algae would be formed. Thus, the entire marine biological, or biotic, equilibrium would be maintained; but it would be subject to seasonal fluctuations—least marked, perhaps, in the larger animals and fish.

It will be remembered that the 'small cow' is a product of (say) a year's growth. You cannot have a cow every day from one acre. Compare Note M2, Chapter 13.

20

The story of green-plant photosynthesis

The full written papers dealing with the matter are in the Hall of
Public Reference at Pekin, and can be seen by any person on the
payment of a few taels to everyone connected with the establishment.
—Ernest Bramah: *The Wallet of Kai Lung*, London: Grant
Richards. 1900. Also Penguin Books Ltd. 1936

It is not really necessary to bribe everyone in a public
library in order to find a book, books, or original scientific
papers devoted to some aspect of photosynthesis in green
plants; but, as has happened with other treatments by biologists of the simpler truths of energy and inorganic chemistry,
the subject has been so much clouded with errors and misunderstandings that it is difficult—if not impossible—to pro-
cure an account of the relations of modern Man to green-plant
photosynthesis that is both short and accurate: however many
taels are paid to anyone except Messrs Constable and Company
Ltd.

For example, one of the best-known writers about
scientific aspects of photosynthesis, having mentioned photosynthesis which occurred in the times when carbonaceous
fossil fuel was being laid down, wrote that indeed photosynthesis is the source of all energy requirements of modern
civilization 'except those met by water-power and nuclear
disintegrations.' One may suppose that by 'water-power' he
did not mean a wooden water-wheel with fastenings and
machinery of iron smelted by use of timber, but was referring to hydro-electricity. He was thus wrong about both his
exceptions—even if (and it is a big 'if')—we allow that noth-

ing but photosynthesis goes to producing green plants—or ever did so.

Photosynthesis is not restricted to green plants or indeed to the vegetable kingdom; but because Nature can be induced to produce human food only as a *consequence* of past and present photosynthesis in green plants, the discussion will be confined to green-plant photosynthesis after clearing up a few points. First, a definition: Green-plant photosynthesis is the process by which electro-magnetic radiation (from the sun) is induced, by the agency of pigments called chlorophylls, to transform carbon dioxide and water into organic compounds consisting of carbon, hydrogen, and oxygen; and to release free oxygen gas from the water. [MI]

Photosynthesis, of any kind, is a process whereby electromagnetic energy transforms some substances into others. It does not make anything; but (for green plants) it changes the chemical combination in which carbon, oxygen, and hydrogen exist in water and carbon dioxide. Water and carbon dioxide are the end-products of complete oxidation of hydrogen and carbon respectively: whether by straightforward burning in air (a forest fire, say) or by the oxidative operations of an animal body on food. Being completely oxidized, water and carbon dioxide have no energy, nor can they yield any. In photosynthesis, some energy derived from sunlight is imparted to their carbon and hydrogen anew, so that they become capable of being oxidized again and to yield up more energy in being oxidized.

The amount of energy that is gained by photosynthesis of a given weight of carbon dioxide and water is limited; it is, in theory, exactly equal to the amount of energy that can be yielded by burning the photosynthetic products. The weights of carbon dioxide, water, and photosynthetic products, and the amounts of the energy involved, are known: they are all the photochemical equivalents (Chapter 19) of each other. In practice, of course, there is some loss of substance and energy available to Man from burning or eating the products of photosynthesis; but never more can be taken out of the photosynthetic mill than goes into it either as energy or substance.

It is most important not to confuse photosynthesis—which is a process strictly limited as described above, and directly concerns only the elements carbon, hydrogen, and oxygen —with green-plant growth and metabolism as a whole. That confusion is a vulgar error which is at the root of many misunderstandings about the origins of food today and about food and population for the future. Sunlight, through photosynthesis, supplies the energy which makes green plants grow; but their growth is possible only if the plants have enough of other substances besides carbon dioxide and water to support that growth.

The author whose words are quoted just above did not seem to be making the distinction between plant growth and photosynthesis clear, though he is an authority on photosynthesis proper. Muddling up photosynthesis (in green plants, understood) with all the other processes of plant growth is practically endemic among writers about food and about sources of energy for what they are pleased to call civilization [M2].

When food is made synthetically from natural gas or coal, the appeal is to fossil fuel directly; that is to plant, animal, bacterial and other microbial residues from past ages; and thus to the inorganic and organic matter utilized in plant growth—*not* simply the photosynthesis—of those times. Herschel was unlikely to have known much of this, but his wording, quoted and discussed in Chapter 2, remains unassailable. It is to be wished that caution like Herschel's had prevailed since 1833 about the effects of solar energy.

The distinction between photosynthesis and plant growth (with the consequences of plant growth for animal and microbial populations) is not just an academic one or a matter of words only: for, without appreciating the reality of the distinction between them, it is not possible to understand the present and future problems of human population.

Besides familiar green plants, and less familiar green plants of which the most notable are the microscopic marine algae which are the ultimate food of nearly all the animal denizens of the sea, there are photosynthetic 'sulphur' bacteria. These contain and employ chlorophylls much as all green plants do (including the large algae which are the well-known sea-weeds). It is not necessary to go into the chemical differences between the various kinds of chlorophyll, because they are all so broadly alike, and fulfil broadly the same chemical function, that the word 'chlorophyll' may serve for all these greenish pigments. However, there are differences which are important for specialized biological studies and are suggestive about the course of evolution of ordinary green plants. Though the photosynthetic sulphur bacteria are not known to have any direct importance as food-producers, a few words about them will not be amiss, if only because their chemistry links up with—even by sometimes being sharply different from—that of green plants of land and sea.

Green plants require oxidizing conditions; so their watery external medium—soil, river, or sea—must be well aerated; also, they give off free oxygen in photosynthesis. The photosynthetic bacteria belong to the large class of microbes denoted anaerobic because they cannot tolerate the presence of air or free oxygen: they obtain their respiratory oxygen from what is chemically combined in oxygen-rich substances such as glucose, nitrates, and sulphates. The photosynthetic bacteria use sulphur to substitute some of the oxygen of water; as all living things do, they require water in excess of their purely chemical requirements, so it will be illustrative of their unusual metabolism if I mention that some photosynthetic bacteria secrete solid sulphur instead of gaseous oxygen as a terminus of their photosynthetic process. They also have different, and possibly simpler, mechanisms for transferring energy from light than those possessed by green plants.

All living cells transfer energy (whether gained from light or from internal metabolism) by means of a phosphate-rich substance called adenosine triphosphate (ATP for short); but green plants also require another phosphatic substance known as nicotinamide-adenine-dinucleotide, or NAD, which takes part in transferring hydrogen and oxygen from water so as to assist in maintaining the balance of oxidation and reduction on which all life depends. One may guess that the sulphur bacteria were among the earliest forms of life and did not need NAD; but such speculation in detail would take us beyond the scope of this book. One more matter can be justifiably mentioned here: it is that whereas some sulphur bacteria can obtain their carbon (for photosynthesing) from acetic acid and other organic compounds as well as from carbon dioxide, green plants (having lost, or never acquired, that facility) depend on carbon dioxide exclusively as source of carbon.

It is from the partly-reduced carbon compounds formed in green-plant photosynthesis that all organisms which do not contain chlorophyll derive all their energy; those organisms include all animals, most microbes, and saprophytic plants (the leafless dodder is an example; also yeasts and mushrooms). It is thus that they obtain their metabolic energy, and also derive carbonaceous substance with which to build up the non-nitrogenous matter of their cells and tissues. We are parasitic upon green plants; and the mammalian embryo is parasitic on its mother; both as embryo and while sucking, it depends on green plants.

Nitrogen does not enter into green-plant photosynthetic reactions at all, nor does any other element except carbon, oxygen, and hydrogen [M3].

Other elements are used, notably magnesium to make chlorophyll and other catalysts of the reaction; but they remain outwith the photosynthetic reaction itself; as does the very important phosphorus (as phosphate) which is an essential constituent of ATP and NAD. Phosphorus occurs in the first known carbonaceous compound formed by photosynthesis: glyceryl monophosphate or phospho-glyceric acid; it has three carbon atoms (from three molecules of carbon dioxide).

Photosynthesis reduces or hydrogenates the carbon dioxide while oxidizing or dehydrogenating the water to an equal and opposite extent. The products are (*i*) reduced carbon compounds which still contain some oxygen; (*ii*) free oxygen given off into the air. No hydrogen is set free; and the oxygen which is set free comes entirely from the water. The water is what is in the plant and in moist air; a 'dry' photosynthesis is inconceivable. The carbon dioxide all comes from the air. It does not react as carbon dioxide gas, but indirectly: the gas first combines with water to form the electrically (negatively) charged bicarbonate *ion*.

The ultimate end-products of photosynthesis are sugars and other carbohydrates [M4]. These are compounds of the elements carbon, hydrogen, and oxygen only. They owe their names to an old idea that they were hydrates of carbon, that is, merely compounds of carbon with water. That is nearly correct since carbohydrates have compositions which can be represented as several atoms of carbon united to several molecules of water; but their structure (arrangement of atoms) is complicated and the structure undergoes apparently spontaneous rearrangement within several of the sugars. That lability is the chemical key to the extraordinary versatility and biological importance of the sugars, because their entry into energy-changes in animal metabolism with the aid of phosphates is of the utmost importance.

In talking about energy changes in animals which have ingested soluble carbohydrate, not all the importance should be accorded to the carbohydrate; for though the actual energy comes from oxidation of their contained carbon (the hydrogen, being already sated so to speak with its equivalent of oxygen, in effect cancels out) the phosphate combined as sugar phosphates and as ATP and NAD is indispensable in getting the energy-production to work *in vivo*.

After the phosphoglyceric acid, or whatever is the first product of photosynthesis, has been transported away from the illuminated zone where it was formed, it enters into further chemical changes to form sugars, starches, fats, proteins and all the other substances the plant requires for growth and reproduction: some of them we require as food. *But,* when those changes within the plant begin to happen, photosynthesis has been left behind. In considering such

changes we enter into looking at plant growth and metabolism—with which photosynthesis has no more than an indirect and philosophically remote connexion.

For one thing, most of the substances employed in plant
growth, metabolism, and reproduction contain elements
other than the carbon, hydrogen, and oxygen that were captured in photosynthesis. Hence—and most importantly for a
discussion of the relation of green plants to food and population—all but three of the elements needed by any green
plant for its internal affairs, like the rest of the elements in
compounds (*e.g.*, proteins) for which we look to green plants
when we rely on them for food—must, and do, come from
the soil [M5].

Of these 'extra' elements indispensable for our food, but
not entering into photosynthesis nor excreted by normal
animal, plant, or microbial respiration into the air, the chief
are nitrogen [M3], sulphur, phosphorus [M6], calcium, magnesium, and iron and some other trace elements. The fact
can be accepted that proteins and other organic compounds
are formed within the green plant with the aid of what it can
obtain from the soil; but by the time when we come to consider the formation, within green plants, of nutrients other
than carbohydrates that are valuable to us and other sapro-
phytes (Man to mushroom, to put it fairly comprehensively),
photosynthesis has been left far behind.

I may seem to be labouring that point. I stress it because
the relation between Man and green plants has been and
generally is so badly taught that it seems very important to
have, and to keep, a definite and clear distinction between
photosynthesis and the rest of plant metabolism. A good
image for any green plant is a tall slender column of which
photosynthesis is the capital (in an architectural, not financial,
sense) while most of the rest of the plant is in the base,
separated from the top by an appreciable operative distance.
It may be still more helpful to think of a typical tall palm,
wherein the photosynthesis is indeed done at the top—the
stem serving mainly as a transport system upwards and
downwards between leaves and soil: though its functions
for storage and support are not neglible.

After recalling that the typical element of photosynthesis is carbon, and that the typical element (among all the other elements) required by any plant, animal, or microbe is nitrogen, we are equipped to go on to the entire life-cycle. The operations of Nature on earth are always circular. Simply for the reason that in no discussion can we usefully consider much more than the relations of one subject at a time (and in biological matters a selection of subjects for discussion must always be arbitrary, because the subjects ramify and interrelate so extensively) we can justifiably leave some things for another place. This Chapter will therefore be devoted to some aspects of photosynthesis alone.

The odd history of photosynthesis

The history of photosynthesis has been philosophically odd for more than the last hundred years. It did not take long for successive observers to piece the observed phenomena together between 1772, when the Englishman Joseph Priestley excitedly observed the evolution of oxygen, and 1804 when the Swiss Nicolas Théodore de Saussure, by stressing that water was necessary, capped the findings of the Austrian Jan Ingen-Housz that photosynthesis is performed by light acting on green leaves and stems, and of another Swiss, Jean Senebier, in 1782 that carbon dioxide was necessary. In 1845 the German, Julius Robert Mayer, who was also noted for his introducing the concept of conservation of energy into animal feeding and metabolism [Chap. 2, M8] brought in the idea that the energy of sunlight is the force driving photosynthesis. Others had remarked that sunlight was necessary; but it was Mayer who took hold of the ideas about force and energy or power that were floating about at that time—mostly in connexion with machines—but not well distinguished from each other. Mayer applied them for the first time to living organisms.

By de Saussure's observations of 1804, knowledge of the involvement in photosynthesis of the simple chemical compounds and elements was completed. The chemical dance of those substances had, by 1804, been uncovered as far as was possible with the knowledge available then and for well over a hundred years to come. Even without Mayer the chemical knowledge was correct as far as it went.

In the absence of any means for deciding the source of the oxygen, by 1804 the hypothesis was accepted that it came from splitting up the carbon dioxide to release oxygen, while the carbon—not as black elemental carbon, of course —was retained in the plant to build up its carbonaceous tissues. That was a perfectly reasonable hypothesis or guess; nor can de Saussure and his predecessors in the study of photosynthesis be blamed for adopting it. Theoretically, and with the present advantage of hindsight, it may look as if they might have considered the role of the water as well; but apparently they thought of water as an indecomposable menstruum because not much was known about methods of decomposing water artificially before about 1810.

The sheer ineptitude that accrued to teaching the supposedly fundamental chemistry of what was often called (and still is called by many) 'the most important chemical reaction in Nature' (meaning photosynthesis) is shown by the circumstance that for almost 150 years this guess about the origin of photosynthetic oxygen was everywhere taught as a fact. It was not until the early twentieth century that it began to be thought that at least some of the oxygen might come from water. Mild suggestions to that effect did not influence teaching about the chemistry of photosynthesis; and chemical formulae representing oxygen as being detached from the carbon dioxide occupied a hallowed place in books that dealt with photosynthesis.

In 1941 a team of three American chemists (S. Rubin, M. Kamen, and H. A. Barker) applied the new technique of isotopic analysis to prove conclusively that all the oxygen came from water and none of it from carbon dioxide; and therefore that the carbon dioxide was taken integrally into the green plant to be reduced by hydrogen derived entirely from the water.

By the 1950's this new and solid information made some progress in botanical and horticultural teaching; and the old guess began to be finally discarded. That guess is now a matter of history and has ceased to be taught uncritically as a fact, instead of as the working hypothesis that it was for scientists who had had to make do with eighteenth-century ideas. Surely 'the most important part of Nature's chemistry' —if it was worth singling out as that, in the face of what was learnt about soil microbiology after 1864; alleged, moreover, to be important by providing food for Man (which it never did)—has deserved better attention than the casual treatment it has everywhere, and almost continuously, received as part of the food problem?

It would not be difficult to compile a long list of oversights about the true facts of human existence; but just one more almost incredible instance of one-sidedness must suffice here. It is all the more remarkable that it starts from the chemical equation, showing formation of sugars and free oxygen from carbon dioxide and water, which is given in almost every exposition of photosynthesis in its supposed relation to the cycle of life. In its modern form that familiar equation can be accepted (provided it is understood to be limited to participation of its three chemical elements: its extension to the whole of the life-cycle is unjustified, as already said). However, some authors go on to point out— by way of emphasizing the alleged prime importance of the photosynthetic reaction—that it is thanks to photosynthesis that we need never fear a deficiency of oxygen in the air we breathe.

The other side of the argument goes unnoticed: although the authors have their own equation in front of them, and 'as every schoolboy knows' every equation has two sides which must balance. It is odd that the other, balancing, side to the equation and the discussion has seldom been noticed. The Dutch microbiologist A. J. Kluyver and his pupil C. B. Van Niel [M7] mentioned in 1956 that owing to uptake of carbon dioxide in photosynthesis there could be a deficiency of that gas. Kluyver and Van Niel pointed out that because microbes constitute almost half the protoplasm on land, they are quantitatively more important than the mammals. If it were not for the respiration of microbes (they continued), the atmosphere would, by utilization of carbon dioxide in photosynthesis, be depleted of that gas within 30 years; or

—recalling that there is at least 50 times as much carbon dioxide gas in the sea as there is in the atmosphere—photosynthesis could use up the whole stock of free carbon dioxide within a historical span of time.

Those calculations are hypothetical, since life is, in fact, a circular and circulating process. Life as we know it does depend on continuance of the exact balances of carbon, nitrogen, and other elements that are maintained between plants, animals, microbes, atmosphere, soil, and sea. The calculations are nonetheless useful because they supply a corrective sense of proportion to much of the nonsense that is written and said about photosynthesis, chemically and otherwise. They provide a graphic reminder of the enormous importance of microbes for our own life. The importance of microbes is so nearly equal to that of the green plants of the land that if, to a first approximation, we ignore all mammals (including ourselves), green plants are no more important than the microbes which complete the cycle of life. If we then restore mammals into our thoughts, photosynthesis is put into its proper and natural perspective as a method of capturing energy which would quickly run down, to become unserviceable to us, if it were not for the microbes. That was what Pasteur was saying in 1864.

The converse of photosynthesis

Once again: at whatever point a start is made in considering the cycle of life, and whatever the means or the route that is adopted (provided that it is guided by science and not by fancy or half-knowledge) the same immutable conclusion is reached.

The converse of photosynthesis is shown also with the aid of microbes, even though they work in tanks constructed by man. It has been studied by (the late) A. J. Kluyver; but much more by the United States engineer, (the late) A. M. Buswell, who was chiefly interested in producing fuel gas from waste materials [M8].

If miscellaneous plant material is fermented in a closed tank anaerobically (without air but with added water) a mixture of carbon dioxide and methane is produced; the mixture can be burnt to yield energy. The mixed gases are almost free from nitrogen compounds. Substantially all the nitrogen of the plant material, and some of the original carbon, go to form a sludge of microbial cells which have used some of the organic matter for energy and growth. A full study shows that some of the water actually takes part in these processes; but, ignoring that, and regarding the original water as cancelling out, the equation may be written

$$CO_2 + CH_4 \text{ [methane]} = 2C + 2H_2O = C, H_2O + C, H_2O$$

This suggests that the average net effect of plant growth, as far as the elements which take part in photosynthesis are concerned, is to combine carbon with water.

[M1]   Recent editions of leading encyclopaedias have perpetuated gross mistakes about photosynthesis. One has stated that carbon dioxide is decomposed to yield oxygen. Another made cautious mention of possibilities expected from artificial culture of green algae (see Chapter 14) and supplied a reference to the American book of 1953 about it—instead of dismissing the subject as unworthy of serious consideration on energy grounds.

[M2]   The term 'civilization' is often used as a synonym for technological advancement of 'Western' type. Hindus and the classical Greeks are examples of possessors of civilization though without technology in a modern sense.

[M3]   Nitrogen in food gives no energy; indeed, after eating of protein, some of the potentially oxidizable carbon and hydrogen of food that has been assimilated is lost through the occurrence in urine of ammonia (NH_3) and organic nitrogenous substances, of which urea, $CO(NH_2)_2$, is the chief.

[M4]   The word 'carbohydrate' is here used in the broadest possible sense to include glycerol and other higher alcohols such as mannitol, as well as the sugars, starches, and cellulose.

[M5]   Plants can absorb nutrients through the leaves; but nutrients thus taken in are carried to the leaves mainly as dust, which has come from soil (or volcanoes). Pure fats consist only of carbon, hydrogen, and a small proportion of oxygen; but modified fats (lecithins) containing phosphorus and nitrogen are important in plants and animals.

No animal can digest the carbohydrate, cellulose. The peculiar ability of ruminants such as cows and sheep to deal with that constituent of green plants is derived from microbes in the rumen wherein the food is fermented; any ruminant is thus a walking compostheap and vinegar factory. Ruminant metabolism is specially adapted to deal with the acetic acid and other products of rumen fermentation; apart from that, the ruminant, as animal, has no special digestive juices or other means for digesting cellulose.

[M6] Phosphorus (the element), and its oxidized acid-radical or ion phosphate, amount to the same thing biologically, because phosphate appears to go through whole biological and geological cycles without ever being reduced or further oxidized. The unique biological properties of phosphate—notably as intermediate in transfers of energy—may be connected with that. Compared with the importance of phosphorus or phosphate in facilitating energy-transfer within every cell, formation of bone phosphate in a limited class of vertebrates is secondary.

One may suspect that, in the anaerobic conditions of deep marshes, traces of phosphate are reduced to a spontaneously-inflammable compound (? P_2H_4) which sets fire to marsh gas (methane) derived from an anaerobic fermentation of vegetable matter (*cf.* Buswell's work), to form a will-o'-the-wisp. This is difficult to prove: first catch your (unburnt) will-o'-the-wisp!

[M7] Van Niel has been especially associated with study of photosynthesizing sulphur bacteria.

[M8] The papers of Buswell and associates were published mostly in *Industrial and Engineering Chemistry* around 1930. Their data were collected, with a review of earlier work on the subject, in a booklet of 193 pages which is difficult to obtain but will repay reading by specialists in its rather obscure nominal subject: *Bull.* 32, *Illinois State Division of Water Survey*, Urbana, Ill.; not dated. 1936.

When pure organic compounds are anaerobically fermented after addition of water and inorganic nitrogen and mineral salts, the recovery of carbon in the gases is the theoretical within small experimental error. If a substance like oxalic acid, having an 'excess' of oxygen, is thus fermented, the gases produced are still only carbon dioxide and methane—showing that water has entered into the reaction to supply hydrogen.

21

How the capital of life is turned over by plants

At its own level, biology may well be found to have laws of its own, which are irrelevant to anything in the inorganic world ... The existence of biological laws at one level is quite compatible with biological happenings begin entirely covered—at another level—by our physical and chemical theories.
—G. J. Goodfield: *The Growth of Scientific Physiology;* London, Hutchinson. 1960

The wood in which things have no name is in fact the universe itself, as it is apart from symbol-manipulating creatures who label portions of it . . . The realization that the world by itself contains no signs— that there is no connection whatever between things and their names except by way of a mind that finds the tags useful—is by no means a trivial philosophic insight.
—Martin Gardner: *The Annotated Alice,* Penguin Books Ltd. 1965; Clarkson N. Potter Inc. (U.S.A.). 1960.

The over-all efficiency of photosynthesis in the field does not seem likely to be increased by anything Man can do; indeed there are good biological and thermodynamic reasons why it should not change appreciably in human time; although it must have altered in mode and extent during evolutionary time [MI].

An obvious way of increasing the efficiency of photosynthesis goes on the lines of illuminating green leaves with light of the special wave-lengths which operate the process, instead of relying on the mixture of radiations that constitutes ordinary white light; but that implies much contrivance, and therefore expenditure of energy, so perhaps it is really a method of increasing the extent of photosynthesis, albeit on a limited scale.

The known methods of increasing the extent of photosynthesis, and simultaneously of plant growth are:
  (*i*) to supply extra carbon dioxide to plants receiving adequate nitrogenous and other nutrients; and
  (*ii*) to supply nitrogenous fertilizers (along with mineral fertilizers as necessary).

Scheme (*i*) implies building closed chambers (greenhouses) at relatively great expenditure of energy, as well as providing fertilizers and a supply of carbon dioxide which can, in practice, come only from fuel.

Scheme (*ii*) is the one most usually adopted. There is, under Scheme (*ii*), the special case of encouraging nodulated leguminous plants—which fix their own nitrogen directly from the air—by use of non-nitrogenous fertilizers providing principally phosphate, calcium, sulphate, and some trace elements of which boron is the chief.

The previous two Chapters, by bringing the importance of the miscellaneous microbes of soil into prominence equally with growth of green plants in general, gave a hint towards seeing that Nature's motto about life is the same as the exhortation of the French policeman: *'Circulez, circulez!'*: in English, a shade less appositely: 'Keep moving!'

The chief nutritive elements with which we are concerned in showing how life goes on, whether under completely natural conditions, or with fossil fuel brought in to increase, for a while, the output of food plants and therefore of viable human beings, are carbon and nitrogen. There are others not less important (remembering the fable of 'the stomach and the members') but because it is impracticable to deal in short space with all the various 'element' cycles, the cycle of carbon and nitrogen will be taken as typical: it being understood that all the rest follow the same general Big Wheel course alongside the carbon and nitrogen in the life-cycle as a whole. There is no need to make a special distinction between food plants and other vegetation. There is, fortunately, one simplification; for in the sea all the microscopic green algae are food-plants for the marine animals, and for Man only to a minor extent; so it is feasible to concentrate on the life-cycle on land.

On land, the plant nutrients are constantly being added to by the non-biological processes collectively called weathering, whereby the rocks are slowly broken down and made soluble and ionized. But, since under natural conditions the soil and the plants, animals, and microbes which the soil bears or houses are all in equilibrium, weathering does not do more than make good the losses of solid matter that are inflicted by rain and other agencies which transport soil and soil-matter down to the sea; so, the average picture at any one place and over a few seasons is remarkably constant (unless there is a geological upheaval or the like, which we may leave out of account).

The rock-material contains only earthy substance; it does not contain or bring nitrogen compounds (though clay colloids help to store some nitrogenous compounds which have reached the soil, principally from plant and animal dejecta).

Nitrogen is 'special' because it is the only nutrient element that can be brought down from the air by natural processes to add to the soil's stock.

Keeping still to the equilibrium state, and it being given that the total stock of any one element in circulation is constant, it will be seen that, in the total mass of living and dead organic matter, the ratio of total organic carbon to combined nitrogen, by weight, is a constant. From observations like those of Buswell, it is known that the average ratio of oxygen to hydrogen in plants, or the O/H ratio, is the same as that of the elements in water, namely 8. Similarly, the ratio of organic carbon (excluding carbonates in soil) to the organically-combined nitrogen (or the total combined nitrogen, since the normal proportions of ammonia and nitrate are small) may be referred to as the C/N ratio. In most topsoils, after the roots have been removed, the C/N ratio is fairly constant round about 10, ranging from 6 to 14 or 15, roughly.

An average or ratio by itself is no more than a very rough guide; it hides information rather than giving it, unless one knows something about the quantity of either or both its terms. So, to state that an average C/N ratio in mature crops is about 18 for clover hay, 20 in grass hay (containing some clover), 24 in cereal grain, 40 in cereal crops, and 100 in whole trees, does not help at all unless we can find a lot more facts to tie up such figures with.

Average protein has about 60% of carbon, and 16% of nitrogen; so the fact that the C/N ratio of protein is about 4 does suggest that any animal will experience difficulty in obtaining, from most kinds of ripe vegetation, enough pro-

H

tein to raise the proportion of protein in its diet to about a sixth (or 16% of the dry matter). (That difficulty does not exist for marine animals, all of which are as it were 'automatically' provided *ab initio* with protein-rich food.)

The difficulty is a real one for all land animals even if, like the ruminants, they can utilize the cellulose which helps to raise the C/N ratio in mature plants. The problem is solved by human beings only on the lines of having recourse to pulses, young vegetation, or meat foods: the last meaning living on other animals which have solved their form of the problem. In these classes of human food the C/N ratio is low.

That supplies an explanation for there being only two main sources of 'balancing' protein, listed in Chapter 12. For everyday dietetic purposes it is sufficient to know that a food is 'rich' (or, poor) in protein reckoned on dry weight [M2].

Something has been said in Chapter 11 and elsewhere about leguminous crops as suppliers of protein for human diets; but before saying a little more about C/N ratios, something more should be said about wild and cultivated legumes, because both in the wild state, and cultivated, they are the principal agents for replacing losses of nitrogen from soil, as well as being the principal agents of supply of extra, or balancing, protein to animals.

Cultivated—as crops and trees—legumes suitably fertilized are able to increase the percentage of nitrogen in the soil; and, in a rotation of crops which includes a legume (Chapter 7) extra nitrogen becomes available to the other crops.

Natural additions of nitrogen to soil are brought down by rain (as nitrate) after atmospheric nitrogen has been burnt by lightning discharges and has had some of its nitrogen oxidized. Rain is virtually the only means by which plant-available nitrogen in added to the sea, wherein there are no legumes. Coastal waters receive compounds of nitrogen, washed out from soil, brought down by rivers. On land, some air-nitrogen is fixed by bacteria which live free in the soil; but the total contribution from these and from rain is small (per acre). In some marshy soils, wherein the C/N ratio is high, and nitrogen and other elements needed for plant growth are at a premium, plants like alder and bog myrtle develop, on their roots, nodules colonized by microbes resembling bacteria (their exact type is not known) which are able to fix nitrogen from the air. In some situations there are plants which capture and digest insects and benefit from the nitrogen combined in their bodies. Some nitrogen is directly returned—as free nitrogen gas—to the atmosphere by bacteria able to decompose nitrates; the process is called denitrification. Figure 5 gives an outline of several of these changes. (Chapter 19).

Leguminous crop plants all bear outgrowths, called legume nodules or simply nodules, on their roots. The nodules—which can be easily seen by the naked eye—are colonized by a special group of bacteria called legume-nodule bacteria. These bacteria are unable to fix nitrogen while they are free in bare soil; but they invade the roots of suitable legumes and cause the formation of nodules within which they fix nitrogen from the air into compounds which the host-plant can build up into protein. Almost nothing is known about the mechanisms by which nitrogen is fixed by any of the nitrogen-fixing microbes; nor is it known how, in a nodulated legume, the nitrogen fixed by the bacteria is exchanged for sugar (or whatever it is) which supplies the relatively large amount of energy always required (in nodules or fertilizer factories alike) for nitrogen-fixation.

In warm climates a high percentage of wild trees of the forest are leguminous. Their leaf-fall is a form of manuring similar to what is agriculturally called 'green-manuring' or 'catch-cropping': in which a crop (usually a legume) is grown for a short period and is ploughed into the soil before it is ripe. Sometimes a temporary crop also serves other purposes, such as preventing soil erosion. In England crimson clover (*Trifolium incarnatum*) is grown almost solely as a catch crop; it should not be confused with ordinary red clovers but has much brighter flowers and provides one of the most beautiful of English late-summer country sights. Around tea gardens, leguminous trees called shade-trees are grown, apparently more for their manurial leaf-fall than for shading.

Indigo wastes as green manure have been mentioned in an earlier Chapter.

Some books state, or at least leave the student with the impression, that the richness in nitrogen, and hence in protein, of the non-woody legumes at any stage of growth is owed to the activity of the bacteria in the nodules. This looks like a blunder; for hundred of researchers (*dont je suis du nombre*) have grown quite normal plants like clovers and alfalfa in greenhouses without the intervention of any kind of microbe [M3].

My former chief, Sir Henry G. Thornton, F.R.S., has been prominent in showing that if legume seedlings are grown—with the appropriate nodule bacteria round their roots—in a medium well supplied with nitrogen combined as ammonia or nitrate, the nodules either do not form, or, if they do form and are invaded by the bacteria, little or no nitrogen is fixed; though the plants otherwise develop normally. It is doubtful whether Le Chatelier had heard of nodule bacteria before 1888, and certainly they have never heard of him; but this behaviour of both the plants and their normally symbiotic bacteria provides yet another illustration of the fact that thermodynamic laws extend everywhere.

In actual farming it is recognized that it is usually uneconomic to buy nitrogenous fertilizers to be given to leguminous crops: except for special purposes such as obtaining very early crops of green peas, or for *dis*couraging growth of clovers on a very clovery sward (or on a lawn or tennis-court). The nodule bacteria are not killed by the fertilizer; they and their nodules are simply rendered ineffective; also, on lawns and the like, the clover plants tend to be smothered by a more vigorous growth of grasses, as has been suggested in Chapter 8.

The evidence suggests that the superiority in percentage of protein and the unusually small C/N ratio possessed by non-woody legumes as compared with what is contained in non-legumes at similar late stages of growth is an inherent characteristic of those legumes. In normal practice the temperate crop-legumes are grown in soils not abnormally rich in nitrates and ammonium salts; thus the evolutionary de-

velopment of nodulated legumes (not all legumes are nodulated) seems to have been a natural mode of providing extra
nitrogen for soils : and, for animals, extra protein and other
food beyond what had been at the disposal of their predecessors. Sir Henry mentioned to me that the development of
leguminous and other flowering plants of modern type was
roughly contemporary with the rise of mammals. That evolutionary theme cannot be pursued here beyond recalling Note
MI, and mentioning two other points. The mode of transfer
of nitrogen from nodulated leguminous plants to non-legumes
(grasses and other flowering plants) growing near them occurs
partly by leaf-fall and decay of the above-ground parts of the
legumes, and partly by decay of the nodules and roots. Since
the total stock, and the ratio, of carbon and nitrogen in plants
may be assumed to have been constant at any one period of
geological time, the rise of leguminous plants will have been
accompanied by extra carbonaceous matter in the non-
legumes; possibly by a larger proportion of starchy grain in
the grasses.

Our modern food situation depends very little on being
able to increase the stock of nitrogen circulating in the whole
green-plant mass, or even what is in the much smaller mass
of non-leguminous crop plants. We now possess the ability
to bring down atmospheric nitrogen in factories; nevertheless,
the tonnage of nitrogen that could be thus fixed, even with
a consumption of fossil fuel much greater than what is annually devoted to synthetic nitrogen-fixation, would be insignificant in comparison with the weight of the world's crop
vegetation, or of its carbon.

What is most important about the C/N ratio, in soils and
plants, for agriculture and the prospects for food, is not the
ratio itself, but small changes of that ratio in the immediate
environment of roots of land- and fresh-water plants. The
absolute value of the ratio does not matter (so long as it is,
for soil, within the usual range around 10 mentioned near
the beginning of this Chapter).

What happens is like this:

If we apply a dressing of inorganic nitrogenous fertilizer, alone or in mixture with other fertilizers, to cropped soil, the extra nitrogen in the compounds which have 'come from above' will locally lower the soil's C/N ratio (*i.e.*, make the ratio smaller); the plant will take up some of this added nitrogen, and the C/N ratio of its sap and circulating constituents will also be lowered (the carbon in cellulose and other more or less static materials not being immediately affected). Thus, the plant will be impelled to restore what I may call its 'metabolic' or 'circulating' C/N ratio to what it was before [M4]. That metabolic ratio can be restored only by the plant's performing more photosynthesis. In field conditions (and assuming that the plant is not a legume) that can be done only through formation of a larger area, and bulk, of chlorophyll-bearing stem and leaf: up to the limit of new growth permitted by the supply of earthy nutrients (phosphate, potassium, magnesium, etc.) that are needed for the additional growth not only of the aerial parts but of roots which the plant will put out to match the new green growth [M5].

In that way, the internal balances of carbon, nitrogen, and other elements are restored; and gradually the extra nitrogen around the roots will disappear as the soil's C/N ratio tends to return to what it was before and to what is customary in that soil's equilibrium.

This is not a complete picture since it leaves out the soil microbes and the effects which the extra nitrogen will have on them as well as on the green plants; but the simple picture explains why 'a principal function of nitrogenous fertilizers is to increase the output of sugar, starches, fibre, and oil' (to paraphrase the words of Lawes-&-Gilbert's principle quoted on page 88). It also fits the nutrient actions of farmyard manure, composts, and green manures; the good physical effects of such as these on the structure of soil do not directly depend on their nitrogen and other nutrients they supply, but rather on their bringing slowly-decomposable recent residues of plants.

If the fertilizer is an organic one which does not contain

plant remains, like fresh or dried blood (having a very small C/N ratio) its effect will depend on its speed of decomposition: that is, of involvement with soil microbes near the roots. If the blood is fresh, the effect may be catastrophic for the green plants. Dried blood offers a relatively slow release of its nutrients for microbes and green plants, yet, horticulturists know that its use demands caution.

If the manure has a very high C/N ratio (as straw, raw sugars, and starches and sawdust have) the effects—in temperate climates at least—are bad because, in attempting to revert to its natural C/N ratio consistent with equilibrium, the soil 'locks up' nitrogen and the green plants are deprived of much of it, while undesirable microbes (mostly fungi) increase; nor do those microbes quickly decompose to release the nitrogen which they had seized upon and abstracted from the soil to build their own tissues abundantly. It may be weeks or months before the normal microbial equilibrium and C/N ratio are again in force.

As far as the *soil* is concerned, the damage foreseen from incorporating a carbon-rich material like straw can be avoided by applying, at the same time as the straw, a highly-nitrogenous inorganic fertilizer such as sulphate of ammonia *together with* lime or chalk. That is composting *in situ*. Or the straw and other plant wastes may be composted in the ordinary way above-ground with added nitrogenous matter (and alkaline material if necessary): as is done in making farmyard manure.

Thus, if the urine and dung of animals is insufficient to compost all the straw produced by cereals ('white crops', the farmers call them) and if the excess straw or stubble is ploughed-in beyond a quantity which fits the over-all ratio of carbon to nitrogen in straw *plus* soil, the next non-leguminous crop is likely to have its growth delayed until the soil is again fit to give at least a normal crop; and artificial nitrogenous fertilizer (=fuel) will have been used solely for the purpose of keeping the soil's C/N ratio right [M6]. The same will hold when a poor crop of grass, having no or sparse clovers (say), is ploughed up. Any nitrogenous fertilizer used to increase *yield* of the following crop will in such cases be additional to what is required to lower a high C/N ratio of the soil.

This apparently discursive exposition of what may, at first sight, look like a set of problems for farmers and market-gardeners to worry about, illuminates a subject which has the greatest importance for understanding prospects for food.

For one thing, it indicates that the usefulness of nitrogenous fertilizers—and, by correct implications, all other fertilizers—cannot from any practical point of view be regarded simply as suppliers of nutrients for crops. Their effects on the soil, and on the soil's population of microbes, have to be considered in the round, and in the way Nature actually works with soil and plant chemistry.

We possess all the needful knowledge; but that knowledge has not yet been widely enough disseminated to prevent fancies for the future being published and believed, though they have no warrant in reality. If fancies were translated into action for a short time (it could not be for long, or we should all be speedily dead) they would show that it cannot pay to operate against Nature. It is better to try to operate with Nature.

The idea of 'increasing the efficiency of photosynthesis' —possibly after undertaking more research in what is plainly a vain chase—is one of the fancies from which impossibilities are fondly expected. Some aspects of it have been dealt with earlier, including the major stop that if it were achieved without corresponding amounts of nitrogenous fertilizer having been found from somewhere, the result would be an increase of sugars and starch and cellulose and fats only; and those are not food for man or beast. A similar set of effects is produced by applying nitrogenous fertilizer to cereals and other non-leguminous crops intended to be harvested mature; the result from that is not quite identical but comes to much the same thing in practice; *i.e.*, no additional effective food. That is Lawes-and-Gilbert's principle of 1900, re-stated.

It is not possible to bring about the dream of increasing the uptake of only carbon dioxide and water by plants, and to produce food that way. The dream has been often promulgated, sometimes by people who should know better. Whether the proposition is looked at from the standpoints of carbon/nitrogen ratio, of thermodynamics, or microbiology, or any other way, the conclusion is the same. Possibly the reader will agree by now that that same single endpoint of impossibility is reached *necessarily*.

An ideal experiment

Increase of uptake of nothing more than carbon dioxide from the air without expenditure of fossil fuel is impossible. It could be done—though the consequences would be very bad for us if it were done—only by waving a magic wand.

However, we may borrow an idea from the theoretical physicists, who are fond of constructing 'ideal' experiments and demonstrations : by 'ideal' they mean an apparatus which could not conceivably be built as a real model, but can be thought about for demonstrating a cycle or a *reductio ad absurdum*. In that way the physicists question their own purely theoretical ideas, in order to see where the snag is and what has to be added or done to make the cycle workable and make it satisfy (if it can) the most abstract line of consistent thought. Probably the reader will agree that if the best thought is needed in problems of astronomical physical enquiry, it is not less needed about prospects for people.

Having, then, constructed the ideal experiment whereby green plants of every kind on the land and in the sea are made to take up, say, twice as much carbon dioxide as they now do (any other multiple will serve instead of twice, the effects being less the smaller the multiplier) but nothing else—that is, without any cost or effort except that of waving a magic wand—all the nitrogen and protein would be diluted with extra carbonaceous matter. That would have two main effects :

(*i*) Quite soon, very nearly all the people living then would starve; because all the edible leafy and other vegetable tissue of the kinds which feed people and their meat-

producing animals would have its average percentage
of nitrogen halved. It would be very difficult to find
enough protein to balance the diet of all but a few
people and some land animals. (The human population as a whole is already just poised on the edge of
protein sufficiency).

(ii) Within a few seasons, the C/N ratio of soils would be
doubled as the carbon-enriched plant remains returned
to the soil; the consequence of that would be (as the
example of manuring with untreated straw shows) a
general slowing-down of the activity of the oxidizing
microbes: consequently of the green-plant activity: so
that what is now one season's crop could be grown
about every other season. The impediment to oxidation
would make the sea, lakes, and rivers stink. Some of
the effect on the C/N ratio of the soil would, for a
few years, be offset by the much larger number of
bodies of animals dead from protein insufficiency. But
it is necessary to elaborate further?

Yet there are people who idly suppose that a solution to
problems of food might come from instigating 'research' into
increasing the efficiency of utilization of solar energy in
photosynthesis. Sometimes that is thought of as being done
by living green plants; sometimes by an artificial process in
a factory. The second alternative probably arises from preoccupation with chemical technology, and from some un-
considered analogy with synthetic fixation of nitrogen.

An important conclusion from consideration of the carbon/
nitrogen ratio is that synthetic nitrogen-fixation is itself largely a route to increase of photosynthetic activity. Since
synthetic nitrogen-fixation is almost entirely performed with
the aid of carbonaceous fuel, its performance amounts to
hardly more than exchanging fossil carbon for green-plant
carbonaceous matter insofar as the synthetic nitrogenous fertilizer is used for crops producing mainly sugar, starch, and
oil.

Whatever form the idea of increasing photosynthetic efficiency may assume, it is a non-starter in fact. It is best left
to novels like Mr E. C. Large's 'Sugar in the Air': a book

which does not pretend to be more than a fantasy and an amusing skit [M7].

The history of the C/N ratio

Some account of the history of the C/N ratio may be of interest. It was first used as a practical guide to action by (Sir) Edward Frankland, a celebrated English chemist who adopted it for work with sewage. That was in the 'seventies; but in the 'fifties (Sir) Thomas Dyke Acland, of a famous political family from the West of England, had pointed out the differing proportions of carbon and nitrogen in the crops of a four-course rotation [M8]. The principal user of the ratio for soils was Robert Warington (1838-1907) [M9] at Rothamsted Experimental Station; like all the members of the Rothamsted team last century, he was keenly interested in problems centreing on nitrogen in soils and crops.

After about 1905 interest in the C/N ratio of soil decreased to almost nothing among soil chemists, while the utility of the ratio was vigorously examined by sewage chemists in the United States and elsewhere. C/N ratios are basic thinking among sewage chemists, since they understand the conditions for success in the process of sewage purification. In that limited field the primacy of microbes and of nitrogen-supply in relation to carbon is fully understood; but elsewhere—as examples mentioned in this book will, it may be hoped, have made plain—the decisive role of microbes in setting the biological conditions for production of food from the land is far from having obtained full recognition.

The C/N ratio as the biological analogue of gravitation

The carbon/nitrogen ratio applies only to the living matter (and its recent products) on and just below the surface of the earth and sea: not to the whole cosmic universe; but if we regard the soil biosphere (roughly: all plants and large animals above the surface; the roots, small animals, and microbes in the soil) down to a few feet or a couple of metres below the surface, as a universe; the astronomical analogy is close. It remains close when extended to masses of different circulating types on the soil and in the sea. The stocks of organic carbon, and of nitrogen, are constant; therefore their ratio is constant, though differently distributed among different groups (legumes, non-legumes, animals, etc.) and different habitats such as soil and sea.

Very different are the quality and intensity of thought given to the astronomical universe and to the operations of the nearer biotic universe with which the immediate future of Man is directly concerned.

That disparity can be particularly referred to the newness of science in comparison with the antiquity of interest in the stars and the regular motions exhibited by the solar system. The motions exhibited by the solar system, though variable in one sense, are of a type amenable to visual observation and traditional mathematical treatment; and their study has long been agreeable to human intellect. Investigation of non-biological types of variable, and the discernment that they too are governed by fixed laws, is about as old as physics and chemistry, and thus an affair of barely two hundred years. Investigation of variation in biology (including palaeontology) is hardly more than a hundred years old; and methods for quantitative interpretation of balance between variables are still so new that they they have scarcely begun to seep into public thought except for a recent awareness of randomicity in sampling of opinions. Moreover, during the present century the concept of biological balance between variables in those sciences and techniques which are based on chemistry (with the exception of sewage treatment) has become almost atrophied. Some examples have been given in Chapter 9; others follow in the next Chapter.

It seems legitimate to suggest that this shrinking has followed from the fact that chemical language has come within the purview of many thousands of people not equipped philosophically to look further than to a simplification of the bare terminology. The simplication would thus be purely man-made, without reflecting back on Nature herself. It would not tend towards uncovering generalizations able to mirror the background simplicity of natural laws. The manifestations of those laws are widely various, as in settling the outcomes of biological equilibria; but they cannot be more intractable than the manifestations of heat must have seemed in the early years of the steam engine.

For the matter of food-and-population the whole set of definite guide-lines was laid bare more than forty years ago. We moderns have thus been offered the fresh start postulated on page 2. The mental effort we have to exercise (under very stern penalties for non-compliance) is to work out *methods* for following the indications of known laws and phenomena, and for keeping ourselves within the limits they portray.

The C/N ratio points a difficulty about food

The C/N ratio has been used in this Chapter partly because that ratio indicates a difficulty in general terms about human food, and partly because the idea of the ratio is useful by reason of its being independent of weights (of diet or population); and, within its limits—land and marine vegetation not being alike—it applies to all animals and their food. However, in order to make the generalization it has been necessary to import the assumption that the typical cover of land vegetation has a fairly constant, but low, average of protein percentage or weight per unit of land area. That, again, is roughly true; and where it has not been possible to replace trees, or other indigenous plants such as prairie grass, with protein-rich vegetable crops directly or indirectly edible by the human population of a settled area, it has been necessary to adopt elaborate and roundabout methods for supporting the local population. Thus, it is not enough to grow wheat and protein-poor crops (as has been done on the former American prairies and in Hawaii); but it is necessary to exchange them for meat and other protein-rich foods wherever the 'balancing' protein could be obtained: often at a considerable distance.

Use of the carbon/nitrogen ratio in this Chapter may look like a cumbrous and roundabout means to an end: especially to those—and they are the great majority—to whom the C/N ratio is an unfamiliar concept. It will have served a useful purpose if it has indicated the complexity of the practical difficulty of securing balanced diets for everyone in

all climatic circumstances; it has incidentally thrown some
light on North American history.

If it were possible to grow grain-yielding legumes everywhere, the world's dietary problem would, on the face of
it, come within sight of solution: though the nitrogen/
phosphorus and other important relationships have not been
even touched upon. It would still be necessary, as the minimum requirement for obtaining more protein, to use fossil
fuel to make phosphate fertilizers and to distribute and
supply them and other earthy materials.

[M1]   During short geological periods (of the order of 10 million
years) the modes of photosynthesis and the extent of plant growth
have probably been sensibly constant. Even an emission of carbon
dioxide by volcanic action on a scale like that of the last great
volcanic activity might not produce a marked change in flora and
fauna unless it led to chemical changes in the soil situation as
great as those which accompanied the emergence of chalk in the
Cretaceous. That rise brought the soil's anion-cation ratio [M4, below]
for apparently the first time close to 2.5 (its present usual value in
good farm soil) and thus compatible with the emerging modern types
of land vegetation like those on which we chiefly rely for food.

[M2]   Fresh milk contains only about 3-3½% of protein and might
be regarded as a poor source of protein, unless it is recalled that
the milk contains some 87% of water; the effective protein percentage is about 25.

[M3]   Some non-leguminous trees and other plants require to have
their roots infected with fungi (mycorrhiza) to assist intake of
nitrogenous and other nutrients from the soil solution. Apparently
all common crop plants, with the possible exception of orchids, can
be grown artificially without intervention of any kind of microbe.
The only food-product derived from an orchid is vanilla.

[M4]   Thomas C. Fletcher, in a critically-written book 'Scientific
Farming made Easy' (London: Routledge, 1st edn. 1860, 2nd edn.
1861) suggested that 'the sap of all plants, like the blood of all
animals' was virtually identical. There is little information about
the composition of the sap of plants; but the available information
suggests that in all internal fluids of all animals the ratio, by weight,
of all anions to all cations is close to 1.7; that ratio for ocean water
is 1.73.

Fletcher suggested recovery of ammonia (then wasted) from coke-oven gas. Of necessity he had little to say about potash, beyond estimating the quantity wasted by the London daily papers in washing printers' formes, and giving a little more space to the subject of human urine at railway stations.

[M5]   It does not seem to be widely known that the development of the 'feeding' roots of plants (all roots of soft non-woody plants; but the big 'supporting' and 'buttress' roots of trees excluded) closely balances the development of the above-ground parts. Thus, trimming the leaves also 'trims' the extent of the roots, to balance the amount of green top. For that reason, a closely-cut lawn is not well adapted to resist a prolonged drought; the roots are also short and mostly in the dry topsoil: there being few roots long enough to reach down to the damper layers below, and to find enough moisture there.

[M6]   There is some evidence that straw added to soil can increase nitrogen-fixation of nodulated legumes well supplied with phosphate. That would be another aspect of C/N ratio, for which the N is supplied biologically. The role of fuel then would be to supply non-nitrogenous fertilizer.

[M7]   'Sugar in the Air: a Romance,' London: Cape. 1937.

[M8]   In a book 'Meat, Milk, and Wheat' (London: Ridgway. 1857). (Sir) Thomas Dyke Acland was an active educationist in other spheres besides farming. The family motto is apt: Inébranlable.

[M9]   The name is pronounced 'Warrington'. He was an English chemist who became the father of the young lady botanist who first demonstrated the essentiality of trace elements (page 84, Chapter 9).

22

Some variables disregarded in agriculture and biology

Perhaps the most important single contribution ever made to physiology and biochemistry was the discovery in the early 1880's by Sydney Ringer that simple solutions of the chlorides of sodium, potassium, and calcium can maintain the action of the perfused hearts of frogs and tortoises.

—Ernest Baldwin: *Dynamic aspects of biochemistry*; Cambridge Univ. Press, 3rd edn. 1959

The ratio of carbon to nitrogen is only one of the many possible ratios between the constituents of organisms and of the media in which they grow. Special attention has been given to the C/N ratio because it is one of the most typical for understanding the equilibria that subsist between plants, microbes, soil, and human food.

Plants never stand still; they grow; and the relationships of their constituents to each other and to those of the nutrient medium are constantly altering during growth. It would be impossible to apply conventional methods to analyse even one crop for all organic and inorganic constituents (including trace elements) at every few moments throughout its life; but it would be possible to take representative samples of leaves, stems, fruit, and roots of several crop plants at intervals of a few weeks. That is one aspect of beginning to understand the course of the variables on which our life depends. Insofar as such analyses have been made for plants, I will use the term 'partitional analysis' for lack of a better term.

The first partitional analyses were made by a young Dutchman (on potatoes) and a young American student, John Pitkin Norton, both working under the auspices of J. F. W.

Johnston in the Edinburgh laboratory of the Agricultural Chemistry Association, in 1845-7. The crop about which Norton sought information was oats. Wheat and turnips grown at Kirkintilloch about 1859-60 were the subjects of partitional analyses performed by Professor William Anderson at Glasgow; and wheat was the subject of a series of analyses—the most extensive analyses ever made of a crop —carried out by Professor J. Isidore Pierre of the University of Caen around 1866. If we add the foundation of microbiology by Pasteur at the University of Lille in 1858, this list includes all the major contributions made by University chemical departments to study of biological variables. Subsequent years have produced no further substantial contribution to knowledge about all the interrelated constituents of crops at various stages of growth. No partitional analysis has been made in America; and the analyses of oats made by Norton around 1846 and those of turnips by Anderson around 1860 remain the sole source of published knowledge about the chemical dynamics of those two crops. [MI]

The ethos of organic chemistry—which embraces all the carbon compounds (except carbon dioxide) of which living matter is composed and includes many thousands of artificial compounds—is concerned with exact characterization of single organic compounds. The prime aim of organic chemistry is to determine the relationships of different kinds of atoms, and therefore the structure, of each single molecule of a substance; although it does not neglect lability within molecules (as in glucose), the aim is essentially static and is fulfilled when the whole structure has been conceptually unravelled, reassembled, and displayed. The laws peculiar to organic chemistry are thus those according to which the atoms or characteristic groups of atoms behave within the molecule. The very complicated but already familiar examples of nucleo-proteins able to transmit genetic information illustrate recent triumphs of organic chemistry in the field of what is known on molecular biology.

There is an absence of interest, among most chemists, in macroscopic biological variables; and it is probably not an exaggeration to say that most organic chemists do not understand what ecology is; *a fortiori,* few chemists have any conception of the part played by simple inorganic chemistry as the basis of the variables and chemical equilibria that regulate such things as growth of plants and the procurement of food. On the other hand, most biologists and physiologists, though extensive users of chemistry, are not chemists and have not been exposed to enough training in appropriate facets of inorganic chemistry. That makes one reason why accounting for the inorganic equilibria that are at the bottom of all life has not often been attempted since the 1880's; and, with the eminent exception of the classical work of Sydney Ringer, most of the attempts made have been jejune. Unchemical, often subjective, explanations have become embedded in teaching after biologists have escaped from the influence of strict early training in chemistry departments ('first-year medical' and the like).

Students of the philosophy of science will find a rich field in the treatment of inorganic ionic theory throughout agricultural and physiological science; it may be the more interesting to them because agriculture is usually neglected by academic historians of science, and because elementary inorganic chemistry has been for nearly a century regarded as *vieux jeu* and therefore unworthy of scrutiny by biologists.

Now that physiology and biochemistry have risen to the status of independent sciences, there is no longer a reason for university departments of chemistry to be especially concerned to do research with biological variables; but being the custodians of the academic tradition of pure chemistry, university chemists have cause for concern about the paraphrases of inorganic chemistry, borrowing chemical terminology, that practitioners of these modern biological sciences have accepted as genuinely chemical thinking during the whole of the present century.

These paraphrases (simulacra might not be too strong a word) have handicapped modern biological thought about equilibria between salts, and have probably obscured advances which might have been made in several branches of science. The subject is too technical to be discussed in detail here; but, since this book is concerned with biological equilibria up to the highest level, a few illustrative subjects can be mentioned here without chemical chapter and verse. If specific examples are required they can be found in almost any text-book about animal or plant physiology.

One of the commonest perversions of chemistry can be illustrated by translating the allusion to salts, quoted at the head of this Chapter, into current medical and physiological jargon. The effects of salts—not only in an isolated frog's heart, but throughout discussions of the human body in health and disease—would then be attributed to sodium, potassium, and calcium: or to some simple arithmetical ratio between these and other cations. The anion (chloride) is certainly *there* and must produce some effect on the equilibrium; but it is conventional to ignore it—possibly because no specific physiological function has been attributed to chloride in the animal body that is comparable to what calcium and phosphate do in forming the solid structure of bone.

This pseudo-chemistry about single ions (species of ions, understood), or small groups of ions, is standard in animal physiology. It often takes the form of attributing specific effects to single ions. Ions can never occur, and can never exert an effect, as single species. In aqueous media an ionic effect is always due to the totality of ions present; there is no way, consistent with chemistry, of conceptually isolating the effects of any group of them fewer than the total.

Ideas to the contrary seem to have originated from a twist imparted to Ringer's findings ever since physiology took up ionic theory. The famous dictum of Claude Bernard (made about 1865) about the constancy of the internal medium has not been developed by those who have failed to do their homework about Ringer and ionic theory jointly. Insofar as inorganic chemistry has been deserted or misapplied in favour of home-grown doctrines lacking the groundwork of fundamental science, no radical enlightenment can come, and explanation of observed phenomena which depend upon ionic balances must limp.

As one example: whatever the pathological features may be that are associated with having or administering an excess of common salt (sodium chloride) in the diet, their ionic origins can certainly not be attributed to the 'sodium' alone. That, however, is the medical fashion: in default of looking to the ionic equilibrium as a whole in the light of chemical ideas appropriate to dynamic consideration of balance.

In plant physiology the confusion about ions is even worse: it being common to call constituents 'ions' when they are not ions at all. As the instance of 'nutrient theory' (Chapter 9) shows, in agricultural sciences little regard is paid to ions or even to salts, though those are at the bottom of fertilizer science, and hence of modern food-production.

In the biological disciplines there is a marked preference for dealing with the cations only; but sometimes that is abandoned (especially in horticultural science) to make the chloride anion the 'nigger in the wood-pile' and to attribute toxicity (most unnaturally!) to it. This reigning preference for cations and its occasional erratic abandonment show that physiology tolerates a strong element of subjectivity. That is philosophically deplorable; and defeats the object when realistic explanations of natural phenomena are being sought.

Great advances have lately been made in understanding conduction of impulses by nerves. The electrical phenomena invoked have, however, been of fundamental types identical with those understood in physics: and in no wise esoteric like the inorganic 'chemistry' which physiology has attempted to apply to equilibrium-problems in circulating fluids and biotic environments.

Physiology seems to have adopted its peculiar version of inorganic chemistry by its own free choice; the fossilization of its ionic jargon, and of some chemical notions (such as an insistence on calculating in equivalents) which are themselves sound but ill-adapted to fluid equilibria has been aided by the voluntary separation, since about 1900, of the physiological sciences from strict chemical influence. [M2]

In the governance of research in agriculture and food-production an insistence on 'practical' results has for almost a century tended to smother investigation of types regarded as normal in other branches of physical applied science. Enquiry by agricultural scientists directed to gaining knowledge that is fresh from a fundamental point of view is put at a discount; if it is done at all in Britain it has to be conducted after a manner not unlike that in which a Russian might use theory which had originated in the West.

In many other fields, this kind of restriction does not seem to apply. Astronomy and theoretical physics are examples; and a botanist may spend his life classifying hopelessly uneconomic groups of plants without its being suggested that he is wasting public money. In agricultural spheres it is necessary to establish an *a priori* case that a proposed experiment is likely to produce ultimate profit for someone; otherwise no grant comes forth. Official notice of astronomy was first taken for practical reasons of safety of navigation; but that pragmatic stage, though not neglected in astronomy, has merged—approximately since R. Bunsen and G. Kirchhoff developed spectroscopy at Heidelberg about 1860—into highly theoretical studies freely pursued. The contrast with the agricultural sciences dragging a heavy chariot of practical expectations instead of riding a scientific Pegasus could hardly be greater. In some quarters it is not sufficiently realized that it is fundamental enquiry which most surely brings practical results: even though the enquiry may not lead to immediate economic gain.

The technique of dating historic objects by use of carbon-14 rests on a biological basis, since it depends on growth of plants. It could have been conceived in an agricultural laboratory. We owe it to the American nuclear chemist W. F. Libby and to those American foundations which supported its development, not simply with apparatus but (at a later stage) by making it possible to buy vintage wines as sources of water of known age for comparative purposes. If the idea had occurred to a member of an agricultural laboratory in Britain, it is fairly certain that he would have given up as hopeless from the start any expectation of getting a grant for a purpose showing no early prospect of being profitable to anyone; and to 'sell' the idea of buying wine with public money for a scientific purpose would, we may be sure, have required more than an ordinary skill in advocacy if official scepticism were to be overcome. The financial case was hopeless anyhow if it were to be judged by the standards applied to agricultural chemistry in Britain: if the innovator had looked rather far ahead and had suggested that his novel technique might some day enable the Government to ensure that money spent on buying art treasures was not being spent on fakes, he would have incurred the reminder that that sort of thing was none of his business: let him stick to making agriculture more profitable, and put away thoughts of doing anything less down-to-earth.

But—of course—any advance that still can be made in applying theory to practical purposes in any aspect of food must come in the guise of developments of fundamental theory made by scientists who have been able to follow lines of thought inspired by nothing more than scientific curiosity. For an example, we have to go back to last century and to Lawes-and-Gilbert. Though Lawes made a fortune out of superphosphate, his abiding interest for sixty years lay in the circulation of nitrogen in soils and crops: to that he devoted most of his money and practically all his thought. He had no financial interest in nitrogen fertilizers, but he and his team had abounding curiosity, from which sprang principles still having much potential benefit.

Imagine, if you will, that the physicist J. J. Thomson had had to appear before a lay committee (a Civil Servant being Chairman) in order to justify spending a few hundred pounds on equipment for what he intended to do. He would have a weak case. He would say that he wanted to investigate the properties of electrons; he would have to admit that they were figments of a shadowy concept about which his ideas were not at all clear (that is why he wanted to study their behaviour more closely). He could not call other people to have their heads counted in support—since all colleagues would say that their ideas about electrons were not clear either. Electrons were something to do with electricity.... One member of the committee might ask whether the applicant proposed to do anything to make it cheaper to generate electricity; the horsey member would ask whether Mr Thomson's invention (*sic*; there has to be a lot of misunderstanding, or the committee will not be typical) would speed up the delivery of telegrams; and another member might say facetiously that since the point about telegrams had been raised, did the applicant expect to be able to send telegrams overseas without wires of any sort?

A member better informed than the majority says that he has carefully perused the applicant's letter but has failed to find any mention of the electric light-giving ray, mentioned in an article he has just read, but about which Mr Thomson must be aware (Mr Thomson nods). Does the candidate not think he would do better to apply his undoubted skill in scientific matters to finding a method for lighting shops?

The outcome of such an interview may be guessed. Fortunately, Thomson had a laboratory founded by a private benefactor (the Duke of Devonshire) and having a tradition of fundamental enquiry; and Lawes was never a poor man.

The physical sciences underlying agriculture have been almost continuously in the doldrums since the end of last century with a recent exception in soil physics; whereas 1900 was a banner year for pure physics, which has been continuously vigorous in enquiry into questions of universal scope.

There is irony in the situation that for well over a hundred years the most percipient thought—like that of the physicists and chemists Maxwell, Le Chatelier, J. J. Thomson, Soddy, and Rutherford—has been devoted, on the world scale (so that British scientists have been prominent while having numerous colleagues and competitors abroad), to progressive establishment of principles which have found their most practical application to machines; while, outside the mathematical sphere and with some other few noteworthy exceptions, what has been done to establish quantitative principles validly referring to production and maintenance of food and population, has been done sporadically under largely amateur auspices like the Rothamsted team of last century, and by members of fringing professions, like Ringer and chemists engaged in brewing and sewage purification. Such generalizations as have been established on a sound observational basis uniting chemistry and several biological sciences have largely dropped out of sight or suffered a worse fate.

There is a cognate reluctance to seek information from agricultural sources about scientific and technical development. Chemists sometimes claim that Edinburgh had the first chemical society, but there are few to point out that Edinburgh has at least as good a claim to have been the seat of the first Agricultural Chemical Society (mentioned above). The much-esteemed Professor James Kendall wrote a book entitled 'Great Discoveries by Young Chemists' [M3] which contains, among other good things, an enthralling 'detective-story' of efforts to trace documents for re-establishing the reputation of a man from Kirkintilloch whose achievement as a pioneer in chemical theory had been obscured by a chain of circumstance; it also tells the odd story of the introduction of ionic theory by the Swede Svante Arrhenius (1859-1927) and its reception at the hands of the examiners of the University of Uppsala. Young Arrhenius was wise enough to realise that if he presented his thesis too starkly he would be failed, because 'what examiners don't know isn't knowledge'; having judiciously wrapped up his meaning, he obtained a Fourth Class for what inorganic chemists regard as a major help in their studies of salts.

Ionic theory must have been born under contrary planets, because its biological history has been persistently of misunderstanding and neglect, except lately among pure chemists and by a Danish brewery scientist who happened to be also an oceanographer. To those might be added the Englishman famous for deriving ionic relations in biological chemistry, who is said to have been warned against making too much of that aspect when standing as candidate for the Royal Society. Fascinating as its stories are, Kendall's book does not mention people like Norton, Lawes, or the first Sir George Wilson, whose claims for notice as young pioneers are indisputable.

Nor have the mechanical foundations of sociology been better seen. George Stephenson's daring in casting the road for the Liverpool & Manchester Railway across the unstable Chat Moss has been often applauded; but I have never known it to be suggested that he had been perceptive enough to take a hint from the tramway which had been built for draining part of the Moss, nor have I found a modern allusion to the tramway itself; though there is an engraving of it. Nor do sociologists seem to know that the first suggestion for nationalization of railways was made by a Scot in the eighteenth century on the grounds of benefits expected for agriculture. Need it be said that the sources for these and similarly surprising statements are in agricultural literature?

Inattention to what has been occurring in the practices of food-production must also be the reason for the huge oversight by ecologists and historians about last century's introduction of fossil fuel as the factor which now dominates our existence as a population.

That the velocity of advance of science differs considerably in various directions according to the fashionableness, or directness, of its appeal to laymen is only another way of saying that for some scientific branches the purse-strings are loosely held, while scientists in other branches are expected to combine scientific insight with unusual doggedness outside their laboratories, high skill in persuasion and exposition, and financial acumen—a combination of a sort not normally expected in a member of any other profession or indeed in all scientific directors.

Among laymen the appeal of science seems to have little relation to its value for human existence.

One might say that $V = me^{\frac{1}{2}}$, where V is the velocity of advance, and e the intensity of education about science among the mass m of the public. e is large for some branches (Polar exploration, archaeology, and astronomy, for instance). For the sciences concerned with food and population it approaches zero. m is now almost constant as measured by censuses, TAM ratings, and the like; but, as the equation shows, the magnitude of m is bound up with both V and e.

[MI]   Agricultural chemistry and chemical ecology should not be confused with the chemistry of natural plant products. That is an active branch of organic chemistry that looks upon plants as a sort of quarry for isolated materials to be investigated either because of their economic value (drugs etc.) or from some point of view of interest for chemical theory. An outstanding example of chemistry of natural plant products came from the collaboration of the English chemist H. G. Smith with an Australian botanist, R. P. Baker, in investigating the oils of eucalypts. This was continental in scope, and occupied the years 1895-1921, during which many correlations between chemistry and botany were revealed not only among the 300 species of *Eucalyptus* but among other Australian native trees. Smith is probably the only person to receive a botanical name (or nickname): Eucalyptus Smithii.

[M2]   The phenomenon recalls the linguistic one that a language transplanted into another climate conserves forms which come to be regarded as old-fashioned or incorrect by speakers of the parent language. Examples are the spellings connoisseur and espionage in English—the latter being commonly given a French pronunciation in the belief that it is a French word. Canadian French and U.S. English offer examples of retention of forms after separation by geography and custom.

[M3]   London: Nelson. 1952.

23

Opinions and Suggestions

I. As it seems to me

The pieces are the phenomena of the universe; the rules of the game are what we call the laws of Nature. The player on the other side is hidden from us. We know that his play is always fair, just, and patient. But also we know, to our cost, that he never overlooks a mistake, or makes the smallest allowance for ignorance.
—T. H. Huxley: *Lay Sermons: III. A liberal education.* London. 1870

In 1865 the economist Stanley Jevons published a book 'The Coal Question' [M1] about the alleged impending exhaustion of our coal deposits. It attracted a good deal of attention. In 1866 a gentleman signing himself 'Optimist' wrote an article in *Punch* forecasting that if coal ever ran out something equivalent to it would doubtless turn up or down. In 1872 Winwood Reade published 'The Martyrdom of Man' [M2] in which he forecast the discovery of a motive force to take the place of steam 'with its cumbrous fuel of oil or coal', secondly the invention of aerial locomotion which would transport labour at a trifling cost of money and time to any part of the planet (he may have been reading Hans Andersen!); and thirdly 'the manufacture of flesh and flour from the elements by a chemical process.... Food will then be manufactured in unlimited quantities at trifling expense.'; and more to a similar effect.

It may be noted that no creator of any such technical or moral Utopia, from More to Wells and our own time, seems to have given the least thought to creating a physical basis for either food or mechanical energy in the ways Jules Verne (1828-1905) did in several of his books written about 1870.

How far have we advanced in the last hundred years?

Professor R. V. Jones has made a survey (reference at head of the next Chapter) of official appreciation of formal technical and scientific education; so it may suffice to consider here the broad lines of some products of such education about scientific matters as had been given, or received, during the formative period of the leaders of thought and national action during the time from the beginning of the First World War.

As with the suggestions made in the next Chapter, these examples are merely indicative. If the examples were chosen, and the comments made, by a layman in science he might claim that it was done 'objectively'—meaning that the discussion was about 'objects' or concrete matters, and that he was trying to be fair and as detached as possible about a wide-ranging and controversial field. While trying to be fair—though the selection of topics is personal—I wish to avoid the misapprehension that the discussion is 'scientific': it is about matters of science, and by a scientist; that is all.

It can be suggested that if a thorough-going enquiry were to be made into the extent to which scientific thinking, as a basis for action, had penetrated any government or population, one part of the enquiry would concern itself with the media by which attention is or is not drawn to a science-based problem. Another part is of the type *quis custodiet*: namely, who decides the nature and quality of the knowledge with which the subject is discussed when it is brought to official notice.

Since the media of popular instruction—serious newspapers, television, and radio alike—seem to be conducted almost entirely by journalists without much bottoming in science, while Ministries and political institutions are conducted by another class also little affected by science (except that they are dependent on the first for most of their ideas of what science is), the two parts are scarcely separable. The duality is perhaps more apparent than real.

Matthew Arnold, the poet and Inspector of Schools (1822-88) wrote [M3]: 'The humanists themselves suffer so much from the ignorance of physical facts and laws, and from the inadequate conception of Nature and of Man as a part of

Nature. . . .' That might not matter nationally if it were only the humanists who suffered in an isolation of their own choice; but that cannot be, since we are no longer in the eighteenth century, or even in the nineteenth: and some, rather unskilled, attention is currently being given to the twenty-first. Arnold went on: 'The conduct of human affairs suffers so much from the same cause'; and suggested the ideal of a general, liberal, training 'to carry us to a knowledge of ourselves and the world.' That may sound like one of the more noble-minded platitudes which spring up from time to time; but in Man's present relation with his world it expresses an indubitable need. If government is conducted out of 'ignorance of physical facts' and from an inadequate conception of Man as a *part* of Nature—through its acolytes being 'tumbled up and down in their own conceits' (Bacon), we shall all suffer.

It is probably not by formal channels of education that the majority of literate people have come to know the difference between gorgonzola and Botticelli; so, in considering the areas of ignorance that constantly produce *gaffes* far more serious than conversational ones made at a dinner-table, it may suffice in a preliminary canter to confine the discussion to such bodies as Ministries, the British Broadcasting Corporation, and the more influential newspapers. These are among the principal repositories and sources of the general kinds of information affecting the public weal; but the particularism given to science is usually of a different kind from that accorded to the arts.

That contrast may be illustrated by suggesting that an arts critic would not last long (supposing he were engaged at all) if he thought or wrote—even once—on the lines that Don Quixote was a great Portuguese dramatist; yet—apart from occasional specialist articles on often abstruse topics that do not manage to convey a coherent image of scientific endeavour and philosophy—it is difficult to avoid the impression that basically scientific questions of potential social importance get haphazard treatment, and that it is a matter of chance whether they are ventilated with scientific insight. The view of science given by the better articles can be likened to a townscape drowned by the sea; the tall towers and a few spires stand out, but the relationship between them and the life that imbued them is hidden.

We may put aside the sort of mistakes that can easily occur in the rush of publication of news, and to detect which would need specialized knowledge beyond what could be expected from an enlightened journalist or other member of the general public. Two examples of amusing venialities may suffice. President Kennedy was reported from New York as opening the Seattle Exhibition by pressing a key in Florida that actuated, in Seattle, a mechanism set in motion by light 'bounced off' a star 10,000 light-years away. The year of that Exhibition is not material; since, if the report be correct, it would not be opened for another twenty millenia. Something seems to have gone wrong along a line of hurried communication of an item meant to underline the marvels of science!

In the early months of the First World War a British M.P. asked in Parliament whether the Government would restrict the imports of fats into neutral countries (from which the fats could reach Germany) because it had 'recently' been discovered that glycerine for explosives could be extracted from fats. That glycerine is a component of fats has been known since 1830. I would not pillory that Member for not knowing about the history of the fact he volunteered for the assistance of Government in more rigorous prosecution of the war; he was doing his best (though the seeming neglect to check a chemical fact with a chemist is suggestive). In any event technical matters should not be left to the chance knowledge possessed by members of the public; the facts, and the relations between them, should be known or access- ible to the executive branches of government. As it hap- pened, official British ignorance about explosives in 1914 was far more grave [M4].

A sort of analysis

A list of some deviations from scientific modes of thinking may be useful; at least, I have never known anything of the sort to be attempted, so this may serve as a start to consideration of mental burdens that hamper official and semi-official bodies confronted with science-based problems.

I select five:

(a) inability to recognize that there is a problem, or to see that a problem has a scientific nexus; and therefore failing to pursue appropriate action or to obtain advice that is appropriate;

(b) looking on an evident problem as one of *matériel*: the *matériel* being obvious to the lay administrator, who therefore becomes confident that he can deal with a scientifically-based problem by calling on what seem to him to be the right authorities; this a really a special case of (a);

(c) faith in 'authorities'—adjudged to be such by the layman;

(d) categorization (best illustrated by examples);

(e) the backwardness of political thought and imagery.

These all overlap; they all boil down (except perhaps (e)) to lack of information among administrators (including Ministers and civil servants and their equivalents in the B.B.C. and the more serious journalism) about the modern scope of science. Allied to them is the lack of information about how and where to get information—when it exists [M5].

Mistakes under (b) are probably less frequent than they were before 'operational research' became a term of educated general knowledge. The whole subject is clouded by the confusion between technology and science proper.

The net result

The net result of failures and aberrations of these and related kinds is that when a layman is confronted with a problem having a scientific nexus for which the resolution is not provided for by 'the usual channels', the scientific *quality* and the *relevance* of the answer (or action) are both decided in advance, or set, by the *layman*: according to his perception, if any, of the scientific nub of the matter, and accordingly by his selection of 'authorities' (if any) to whom he will submit the problem.

A layman will not attempt to design or construct a power station, for that is recognized as a 'scientific' matter and a subject for discussion with specialist engineers and contractors: as is exemplified by the B.B.C., which has a host of competent engineers for dealing with technical matters of transmission and the like but appears to have only one qualified scientific adviser on the programmes side (and he cannot be everywhere).

Some examples presented and discussed

As part of one of two articles by A Special Correspondent, *The Times* [M6] quoted a passage from *Esso Magazine* which alleged that some deposits of oil contain more than enough 'to take us [mankind] beyond the next century and into a world where new technologies will doubtless provide sources of energy and patterns of energy consumption as yet undreamed of.' This flight of fancy slipped through several chances of being dismissed as scientific nonsense; at no point can it have caused editorial eyebrows to rise to the point of asking anyone whether he really believed that Don Quixote was a Portuguese, or a dramatist. The Esso organization is known to have hundreds of scientists; but their influence did not extend to the house magazine. The passage may have originated in some journalistic optimism in the United States; it was taken to be meaningful by the Special Correspondent—who must have been regarded as an authority (on what?)—by *The Times*, whose editorial staff did not expunge it in proof, so that it gained fresh circulation (and probably fresh 'authority' for laymen). It was an expression of belief that some form of magic might arise to relieve human miseries when all fuels had been exhausted. It is not easy to see who could gain from publishing or reading such a visionary belief: certainly not the oil interests or anyone concerned with practical matters.

A preoccupation with *matériel* shows itself in many ways. The Chairman of the London Traffic Board was the late Sir Henry Maybury, a distinguished civil engineer; though it may be doubted whether his qualifications included objective analysis of traffic flow. It would seem better to have an advisory scientist as chairman, with other scientists on the Board to assist him; and to call in a civil engineer to build roads and works when their necessity and location had been decided by methods appropriate to a problem essentially not static but of variables. A geneticist might have made a good chairman; he would have had at least one important qualification for such a post.

Preoccupation with what was obvious to laymen who relied on opinions and selected their own 'authorities' must have lost the United Kingdom millions of tons of shipping during both World Wars. The problem was the effectiveness of convoying. In both wars the opinions of admirals were chiefly sought, because convoying meant warships, and admirals were clearly the proper people to consult because they knew all about navigation and warships. In the first war there was no practical alternative to taking the opinions of admirals; but by 1938 (say) a technique had emerged for assessing variables (including such uncertainties as those posed by the German Navy) that left no sure place for opinions. Nevertheless, mere opinions from the British Navy were allowed to decide practice for about two years, while many merchant ships were sunk. After that expensive initial period the adoption of mathematical techniques for dealing with probabilities was imposed with the help of knowledgeable civilians; and although ships were still sunk, objective scientific method—newly applied to the organization of ships and modes of combat—had paid off. It might go without saying that these probabilistic techniques had not entered into the training of the admirals or of the peace-time civilians who had controlled them.

A war-time experience with food illustrates several points. It also suggests that lay officials must have been satisfied that they had done the right thing in seeking 'scientific' (in reality, technical) advice. A large bulk of grain was being imported into Britain on behalf of the domestic poultry producing eggs, which were scarce. Somebody asked a poultry expert (the scientist) how much grain went to producing a pound of eggs; and, on receiving the answer 'five pounds' (or whatever it was) said, in effect, 'Good heavens! This must stop. We would do better to import the eggs and save shipping space.' So far, so good; and it was decided 'as an experiment' to load two or three ships with fresh eggs. On account of delays on the sea and unusual congestion, due to the war, at the docks, the eggs arrived in doubtful condition and went very bad at the dockside. That caused another problem. . . .

The main point is that the laymen who conceived the 'experiment' should have asked for scientific advice in designing an experiment which would have been capable of giving a reasonable answer to the right question: which was, whether it was feasible, in wartime conditions, to bring fresh eggs in bulk across the Atlantic and to distribute the eggs in eatable condition. That was not seen to be the real question; and, as with the well-documented fiasco of the African ground-nuts scheme initiated in 1948, no scientific advice was sought about it. At the bottom of that scheme was the assumption that Nature could be bull-dozed into complying with the fancies of a set of laymen. About the feasibility of importing eggs in bulk across the Atlantic, sufficient information (that is, a sufficient answer to the real question) could have been obtained from a properly-designed experiment using a few hundred cases of eggs; and at much less cost in money and vexation than was ultimately paid in freighting shiploads of bad eggs.

For the ground-nuts scheme the 'authorities' seem to have been mainly financial. Both in that and the egg 'experiment' success was assumed beforehand. They were instances of the backwardness of politicians and the like about the meaning of common scientific terms like 'balance' and 'experiment'. In the lay conception of 'experiment' a subjective element of extracting satisfaction seems to be inherent; there is also a lack of comparison, which is the essence of even the crudest experiment [M7]. Scales or balances must be among the oldest instruments for obtaining a quantitative measure; that is the way they have been used by business men for possibly six thousand years as a sensitive means of obtaining equivalence of one thing against another; but the politician often prefers to reject any pretension to measurement, and uses his 'balance' to show that one side goes down with a bump.

Categorization is best illustrated by examples. Accuracy about religious topics is regarded as important. Partly because of fear of offending religious elements of a population, and partly because lay writers mistrust their own competence to discuss specialities of religion, appropriate priests and clergy are sought as writers and advisers. Religious categories are plainly labelled by denomination; so a mistake cannot be made by a layman. Somewhat similarly, archaeologists are invited as speakers and reviewers about archaeology, astronomers about astronomy, and so on wherever the category is apparent to ordinary general knowledge. It is in the sciences fringing on biology that laymen make erratic choices about their 'authority'.

General knowledge associates medically-trained people with what are really medical specialities (*e.g.*, pathogenic microbiology); so that, to expound almost any bacteriological subject, medical people are likely to be the first choice even though their experience may not in fact have been more than nominally suitable. Imprecise categorization is an aspect of reliance on a layman's choice of authority, which may lead to important subjects being omitted from public ventilation: for example, the subject of evolution may be confined to evolution of vertebrates because medical interest hardly extends beyond them; and to problems about food being shared between nutritionists and physiologists on the one side and economists on the other. Population-problems in general seem to be allotted to medical men (by the B.B.C. especially) apparently on the grounds that doctors deal with people, population is a lot of people, *ergo*. . . . As accuracy about religion is regarded as important, so is accuracy about machines; it can usually be secured without much difficulty, because categories of engineers are sufficiently differentiated. Serious consideration of human ecology is at the other end of the scale, there having been no recognizable category.

A disability to which governmental bodies seem especially prone is inability to connect intention with fact; it might be described as an inability to think of more than one thing at

*I

a time (and thus to put into action something which depends on colligating two or more ideas): apart from balancing political chances, at which politicians are astute. The Antwerp business of Note M4 was a major example. A minor example was the decision of the Northern Ireland Government that everybody should carry a personal photograph; it was then found that there was not enough sensitized paper.

Such minor absurdities form possibly the commonest class of examples of publicized 'official blundering'. Their existence does not suggest confidence that government as at present organized at local and higher levels is well adapted for what is sometimes called 'this increasingly complicated technological age'. Nor does it seem that 'planning'—in the sense usually comprehended by that term—can be an answer unless the machinery of government is first integrated to deal effectively with complex variables. The root of conventional planning is static, being akin to 'providing a chart for navigating unknown seas'. That expression indicates another limitation of the political mind: it being assumed that the dangers, if not known, are all (i) fixed and (ii) capable of being known: like the rocks and coasts. No allowance is thus made for variables which cannot be plotted and categorized. The assumptions, and the kind of execution to which they give rise, are suspect for social problems having quantitative bases.

It might be asked what is the proportion of 'planners' having any kind of scientific training for giving them a perception of finding relations between variable concepts and quantities; alternatively or in addition: how many scientists would expect to fulfil a useful purpose (in the unlikely event of their being asked to do so) as associates of conventional 'planners'?

The British Broadcasting Corporation's attitude to science

It is noticeable that popular magazines nominally devoted to science tend to eschew abstract sciences such as mathematics and chemistry, and devote most of their space to what may be called 'gadgetry'—meaning the concrete (and photographable) achievements of technology, but including medical applications of chemistry (new drugs and so forth) and astronomy and similar visible applications of mathematical thought. In so doing these periodicals are, no doubt, accurately reflecting the tastes of their readers. Journalists are accordingly impelled (if they have a taste for science) to write on topics about which the public already has some idea—in short, what will 'sell'. After all, editors are expert opinion-tasters and are necessarily very good at their job: which is to produce a profit on their paper by keeping readers and advertisers content; it is not to present any particular image of science.

The social risk in drawing attention only or mainly to subjects which journalists hear being talked about in the train, or in a London club, is that some socially important scientific topics may become neglected, or may be discussed by the wrong 'authorities' (which comes to much the same thing). The B.B.C. not being under any commercial restriction, but being charged with an educative function, might be expected to escape blind spots about science; yet, being (it seems) in scientific matters almost wholly under the control of ex-journalists, it seems to me to have shown a curiously uneven treatment of science: sometimes magnificent, sometimes ignorant.

The praiseworthy productions—particularly outstanding on TV—have been distinguished by being given by scientists invited to talk about their own subject. The near-misses and failures include some in which a journalist has been asked to present a programme. In the latter class was presumably the radio talk on marvels to be expected from nuclear energy, offered as a serious contribution by a man whose sole announced qualification was that he was a former Member of Parliament. The general impression I have received from B.B.C. treatment of science for adults is that it has been sometimes stimulating, sometimes misleading, and on the whole so scrappy and aleatory as to suggest that the Corporation has had no overall policy in the matter. [M8]

There is no rubric of science criticism, either in broadcasting or newspapers, comparable to what exists for several sections of the arts. It is difficult to obtain correction of any mistake more weighty than something relating to the first performance of an opera or the name of a former variety performer.

The B.B.C. seems to draw its TV speakers from a narrow ambit which seldom extends beyond the London-Cambridge-Oxford triangle; and, for medical men, appears to be restricted to London. It almost looks as if the Corporation is afraid of ideas—as distinct from travel talks and the like—that have not originated in the Home Counties. In an excellent radio series on the way scientists do their thinking it extended its ambit considerably; but such catholicity is exceptional. A related TV enquiry into the way mathematicians think was restricted to three speakers from London and one just outside. In view of the fact that mathematicians occur all over the United Kingdom, and that the Corporation's studios are also well distributed, the apparent limitation is hard to understand. 'No articulate mathematicians occur outside London' sounds like the beginning of a parody of one of Lewis Carroll's exercises in logic: leading possibly to the conclusion that babies cannot manage crocodiles [M9], or that the B.B.C. is really the English Broadcasting Corporation. One of the mathematicians happened to be interested in clouds; and a B.B.C. recording team was sent all the way to Snowdonia to get some cloud photographs for inclusion in the programme; so questions of expense associated with distance can hardly have entered in.

To engage in a survey of B.B.C. trends about ecology might raise fears of prolixity; but in recent years there has been so little on that subject that all I have seen or heard can be reviewed in a paragraph or two. (About real beings, that is; a penetrating series of talks about biology in science fiction was given by Professor W. T. Williams and colleagues of the University of Southampton, and these were accorded the accolade of publication in *Listener*. A decisive influence of *letterati* may be suspected). Both the mentionable allusions to ecology of people were in 'unlikely' TV programmes. One was on the dependence of the human population of the Lofoten islands on the indigenous puffins; the other was in a talk by Sir Fitzroy Maclean on Mongolia, in which he mentioned that the well-being of Mongolians—traditionally dependent on horses—depended on the state of the pastures. I have not *selected* these examples, so minuscule on a world scale: they are all that have come my way. It seems relevant to ask why, if the B.B.C. can permit a more or less incidental allusion to what, before industrialization, kept Mongolians going, it cannot find interest in devoting attention to bases of food and population in Britain.

In 1953 I was allowed to give a volunteer radio talk entitled 'Food, Fuel, and the Future'. The B.B.C. thus became one of the pioneers in disseminating knowledge about the relationship between fossil fuels and the growth of human population. The talk was translated for the Italian Terzo Programma ('The University of the Air') but had no other traceable sequel. No other instance is known to me of the Corporation's departing from old-fashioned ecological treatments restricted to consideration of surface resources.

Choice and chance in journalism and broadcasting

Whereas there is much scope for extending the appreciation of science among adults, none of these remarks about what does obtain publication implies a need for more censorship than is normal in use of the editorial blue pencil in removing ordinary infelicities. What is implied—some latitude being granted for news items—is the need for having someone on call who can recognize and query scientific absurdities, especially in contributed articles.

Along with that should go enough scientific judgment to see when someone who has been rightly selected as an authority on one subject may be helped to stay within his brief so as not to venture into fields about which he is not qualified. Responsible scientists seldom do that; but there is always a risk that a sociologist will make a pronouncement about food, or an economist about prospects for energy, that requires qualification (to put it kindly).

A more positive aspect of avoidance is suggested by someone's doing a piece about science in its relations with society. By finding the toppest scientist whom the author can think of, and interviewing him, the canons of the best journalism will be satisfied. But, if the chosen authority is a physicist (say), his position may reflect no more than a Governmental concern with machines, including weapons: which are admittedly important for society. Food science is then unlikely to come into the picture except in mechanical matters such as refrigeration and other aspects of food preservation (technology again). To an intending author, not having enough knowledge of his own about a complex subject, the choice of a specialist in one branch as the official authority may seem the right one, because he is then relying on another kind of 'authority'. It will not be his fault if the article is lop-sided about the relations between Man and science; nevertheless, the intending author or commentator, as a well-read person enjoying access to the best authorities, will be expressing the imbalance of current education about Man, and without being aware that his article, so far from clarifying the existing fog, is contributing to its continuance.

There is a converse to the trust which relies on 'names' and personalities rather than on delving into a situation. However indubitable the facts and however simple the relationship between them, they can easily be dismissed as of no account if the messenger is not deemed to be an authority. Attention is then given solely to the insignificant person of the messenger and not to the message.

> Yet the first bringer of unwelcome news
> Hath but a losing office. . . .   [M10]

The best example of this is the (imaginary) science master [M4]: the individual facts were well known and their relationship, once the message may be supposed to have been brought to official notice, would be evident to everybody. If a pertinent communication had in fact been made, the course of history shows that it must have been, in Ernest Bramah's words, 'consigned by the merest official pencil-moistener to the eternal oblivion of the dove's retreat.' *Cf.* the example in Note M3.

What is needed in publishing circles—it being mostly lacking—is a degree of editorial responsibility and caution about technical and scientific subjects that is almost as good as that which infuses the majority of pages and talks on music, literature, and the arts generally—including science fiction, which is writing. In these subjects imagination is supreme; but imagination and belief should be allowed no place in attempting to keep the public informed about science: with the single exception of essays about the scientists' thought-processes, which might be interesting and possibly useful to explore. Some of the examples would resemble the solving of conundrums openly arrived at. That the puzzles have been set by Nature may or may not be germane; but their elucidation could resemble an art-form which seems particularly suited to televisual demonstration.

The United Kingdom Government's attitude to science to-day

In a B.B.C. Schools talk Mr Erskine Childers remarked that nowadays a nation's dynamism is reckoned by the attention it gives to science. In the teeth of speeches from high Government quarters saying how greatly the United Kingdom depends on its cultivation of science and technology at home and on encouraging the export of British 'know-how', there has been a refusal to issue special stamps to commemorate John Dalton (chemistry) in 1966 and Michael Faraday (electricity) in 1967. Her Majesty the Queen might have been expected to smile graciously beside some reminder of those two worthies. Poland and Russia between them have given three philatelic acknowledgments to the Russian chemist D. I. Mendeléef (1834-1907). For 1966, British official addiction to the ancient bygones of English history is typified by the circumstance that none of the constituent nations of the United Kingdom has failed to have the opportunity—whether they deem it appropriate or not—to celebrate, on stamps, the defeat of the English by the Normans nine hundred years ago.

The Postmaster-General at the time this issue was decided upon was, before he became Minister of the Crown, connected with a firm engaged in chemical and technical publishing; so, if dynamism were to triumph over mandarinism, a token of that modern victory could have been looked for in 1966, if only in respect of U.K. postage-stamps carrying the message at home and overseas. Towards the end of 1966 the British Post Office issued a series of stamps depicting significant stages in British technology, *e.g.*, a nuclear power station and several types of motor-cars. It cannot be said by an outsider whether the issue was intended to represent British science and whether there was confusion about science and technology in the minds of the Post Office officials; or whether, like good journalists and opinion-tasters, they judged that most of the recipients of the stamps would be equally unappreciative of an honourable distinction— somewhat like sending an enterprising ballet company on a provincial tour while expecting that it would be confined to a repertory of familiar items which the yokels would understand. If it was the latter which operated, the series was an opportunity of education missed.

Dalton and Faraday were workers in pure science who never invented any gadget or tangible piece of technology; and it may be presumed that for that reason their merits were not appreciated in Whitehall. Putting Dalton and Faraday aside, then: if it had been desired to display and honour British science on stamps devoted to energy and telecommunications, portraits of men like Soddy and Clerk Maxwell and Kelvin and Grove would have ably represented all parts of the United Kingdom, which can claim many such 'firsts'; but there has never been a British scientist honoured on a stamp of the country of his birth.

The peak time of British official recognition of what science could do for public affairs was at about the end of the last War. At that time 'public affairs' were almost exclusively those concerned with waging war. Professor Jones (*loc. cit.*) said: 'For if blood, toil, tears, and sweat were what Winston Churchill offered us in 1940, it was gallantry, humour, science and technology that had to be added to the mixture for us to survive. And it was clear [to scientists, I suppose Prof. Jones meant] that these latter ingredients were always in future going to be required, in either war or peace.'

An incidental but profound remark was made by Professor W. T. Williams, a botanist, in the course of a quiz-type

radio programme organized by Dr Archie Clow [MII].
Replying to a question from an amateur gardener, Prof.
Williams said something to the effect that 'once you start
interfering with Nature you have to go the whole way.'
[cf. page 51, Chapter 6]. That remark could have served
as the text for this book. I commend it as a text to the B.B.C.
or other educational institution in whatever it does to promote understanding of the conditions of life in a technically-
advanced society.

In an article dealing with political and military aspects of
the near future [MI2] Sir Solly Zuckerman (described as
the British Government's chief scientific adviser) mentioned
the accelerated growth of population throughout the world.
Having noted that the world shortage of food is already acute,
Sir Solly wrote: 'Whether the possibilities of synthetic food
production will be realized in time remains to be seen.'
Having also pointed out that national differences in population parameters [MI3] 'as well as in supplies of food and
other raw materials' are likely to be greater as we approach
the end of the century, Sir Solly might with advantage have
added something like: 'provided that fuel and raw materials
are reserved for production of that synthetic food.' It looks
as if he had not been aware that production of synthetic
food might exacerbate the conflict of resources.

If that were merely the *obiter dictum* of a biologist it
would not call for special comment. However, a person in
Sir Solly's position would be able to draw upon all the in-
formation-services of 'a modern technological society'. The
implication is either that the United Kingdom governmental
archives contain no information about the relations between
food, fossil fuel, and population, or that the facilities for
retrieval and use of the information that exists, about what
has for many years been a national, and indeed a world,
problem, leave much to be desired.

[MI] William Stanley Jevons, London: 1st edn. 1865, 2nd edn.
1866. A revised and edited edition was published in 1906 (London:
Macmillan).

[M2]   Much information, some of which I have used, about the Victorian attitudes to fuel was given in the late Mr L. S. Mumford's paper 'The loneliness of the long-range forecaster' in *Chemistry and Industry*, 9th Nov., 1963, 1788-96. Mr Mumford was mainly concerned with forecasting from economic and financial angles. In writing to him to congratulate him on his discussion, I pointed out that he had named four collaborators; whereas the members of what we jokingly called the Fuel-for-Food Club were even more lonely, one being in Edinburgh and the other in Glasgow.

[M3]   I have quoted this from Prof. Jones's Joseph Payne Memorial Lectures; reference at head of next Chapter.

Professor R. V. Jones, F.R.S., Professor of Natural Philosophy in the University of Aberdeen, was responsible for the development of Scientific Intelligence. About that he wrote an entertaining account (*Chemistry and Industry*, 1965, 530-4) in reviewing books about the *Vergeltungs* campaign with rocket weapons. It included a mention of some accurate information received in November 1939. An official then senior to him argued that it must be suspect 'because no man could possibly know about all the diverse fields covered.' Dr Jones could not prevail against this opinion; and his copy was the only one not to be thrown into a waste-paper basket. He added: 'There was much insensitivity regarding the importance of [scientific] Intelligence... While Intelligence could not by itself win the war, it could, single-handed, lose it.'

I would add: as the lack of it almost did in 1914. See M4.

[M4]   Until about 1913 practically the only raw material for making nitric acid for explosives was natural nitrate of soda imported from Chile, upon which the United Kingdom relied throughout the First World War. Its principal use in peacetime was as fertilizer. All uses of Chilean nitrate by the Germans were hampered by the British blockade; but large stocks of the material had by July, 1914, accumulated in Antwerp, which was the principal *entrepôt* for Western European countries. Germany had pioneered with the efficient Haber process for making synthetic nitric acid from air-nitrogen, and had a small 'Haber' factory in production at the outbreak of war: a much larger one under construction being several months short of completion.

While the Germans were making their drive on Antwerp no attempt was made to remove the stocks of nitrate into safe keeping or to dump them into the Scheldt. The nitrate seems to have been regarded by the Allies simply as fertilizer; and there were qualms about disposing of such a harmless commodity of which part was stored (awaiting the next spring) on behalf of neutral countries. As soon as Antwerp was captured, the Germans sent all the 'fertilizer' to Germany including what was already on rail for neutral countries. It was sufficient to supply the German munition factories with all the nitric acid they needed until the big Haber plant came into production. After that, Germany became wholly independent of imported nitrate.

Since Chilean nitrate was known to be the sole source of nitric acid for British manufacture of explosives, there was an extraordinary failure to connect facts that had crucial importance for the whole Allied war effort. There was no military secret about the existence of the Haber process or the unreadiness of the big German factory. The process was mentioned in the 1914 edition of J. W. Mellor's famous textbook of inorganic chemistry (London: Longmans Green); and its commercial progress had been reported in technical periodicals. I was a school-boy at the time; but I have often wondered what would have been the reception accorded to a letter sent by an informed adult (a science teacher, say) to the War Office or some other official agency able to pass it on to an appropriate quarter.

There seems to be only one account of print of this item of the history of Chile nitrate. The story remains generally unknown. Without having made a special search, and from such comments as I have happened to read, I think that no military commentator has discussed the Antwerp campaign of 1914 except as a limited strategic exercise, or has reached any conclusion except that the result may have been to delay by a couple of days the German advance to the North Sea ports. It is interesting to speculate how and when the First World War would have ended if the British and Belgian Governments—possibly jabbed by a suggestion from the French— had been able to co-ordinate action with facts which pointed so markedly in their favour.

[M5] Where the information exists at all. This book states several instances wherein relevant information about matters touching on food is not only lacking but is not being sought for.

[M6] 'The new optimism on energy in U.S.,' *The Times* (London), 20 and 21 May, 1965. The passage quoted is from the second article.

[M7] That the essence of experiment is comparison was known to Bacon in his 'Tryall of Apples'. The word is commonly used about trying a single expedient with the idea of 'seeing how we like it'. A test for its tautological use is to see whether a word like *innovation* can be substituted of it; if it can, 'experiment' is only a synonym without scientifically new meaning. The philosophic advance from mere comparison to the idea of carrying out what is called a control experiment (or 'witness' experiment, to translate the apt French term) was—if the 'Tryall of Apples' is excluded—apparently first made for both chemistry and biology by the Dutch microscopist Antoni van Leeuwenhoek in 1688. He made a control experiment in testing for common salt, using red blood cells as what would nowadays be called osmometers: 'Alle de Brieven (Collected Letters),' Vol. 7, Amsterdam: Swets & Zeitlinger. 1964 (an annotated edition in both Dutch and English). *See* especially pages 176-7, also 364-5.

The very first controlled trial seems to have been that made in 1648 at the instigation of Blaise Pascal by his brother-in-law Florin Périer on the Puy de Dôme, to test the principle of the Torricellian barometer. A good account of it has been given by L. T. C. Rolt in 'Thomas Newcomen: the prehistory of the steam engine,' David & Charles: Dawlish (England). 1963.

[M8]   General presentations, or discussions, about food-and-population assume the shapelessness of unenlightened factual journalism. A typical TV programme on the subject of 'What we must do to feed the remorselessly expanding population' goes something like this:

> Opening talk on increases of population; with graphs.
> The importance of protein; graphs of calories per head; shots of pot-bellied children; mention of protein shortages.
> 'Fertilizers from the air' (great advance); pictures of spreading of fertilizers *or* of fertilizer factory.
> Peasants planting paddy rice.
> Miserable Mesopotamian ploughing with a bullock.
> Wheat breeder demonstrating variety alleged to yield five times as much as unimproved varieties.
> Harvesting, or ploughing, by tractor—for mass-produced cereals.
> Extraction of grass protein.
> Talk by economist on marshalling 'science' and (money) resources to improve standards of living: 'The hope for the future'.

So this is science as she is spoke loudest! Well-meant claims that such talks are educational cannot be sustained in any adult sense. The first two items will be instructional for children by bringing home to them that a problem, or congeries of problems, exists; nevertheless, as a whole, such a clueless assembly can only perpetuate the already serious confusion between technology and science in the matter of food. Even a comic strip has a theme and connects with past and future episodes.

This is silent about quantitative science as the basis of every picture shown and as a reckoning for every hope indulged. The chief impression that it must leave is that the problem can be beaten by the wish-fulfilment of applying more 'intelligence' to technology and economics in the production and distribution of food—leaving out, that is, the terms of fundamental science as they have been revealed by the intelligence of scientists during the past hundred years.

Compilers of such pieces of folk-wit cannot have absorbed the dignified lesson that scientific progress comes, in part, from putting facts (pictorial or other) into significant relation with each other; and what could be one of the first primers for a post-Imperial country has not been even adumbrated.

[M9]   An example given in Weaver's book 'Lady Luck' (ref. in Note MI, Chapter 18) is

1. Babies are illogical.
2. Nobody is despised who can manage a crocodile.
3. Illogical persons are despised.
   therefore: Babies cannot manage crocodiles.

[M10]   William Shakespeare, 'King Henry IV. Part 11,' Act 1, sc. 1.

[M11] Dr Archie Clow was also responsible for securing the broadcasting of Prof. Jones's three Lectures (ref. at head of next Chapter).

[M12]   *Sunday Times* (London), 20th Feb., 1966.

[M13]   A *parameter* can be loosely 'defined' as 'a quantity defining, or expressing, a variable.'

24

Opinions and Suggestions

II. Some Suggestions

Only when people are in extremity, and realize that they are so, are they likely to act on fundamental advice for their salvation.
—Professor R. V. Jones: *The Advancement of Learning 1605-2005 A.D.*, Lecture III, Joseph Payne Memorial Lectures to the College of Preceptors, 1965

'Insert your chopstick in the solid meat, Tso Paik. What have we got to *do*?'
'Putting aside these gems of philosophical profundity, Benign, the nature of your submission is neither palatable nor light.'—Ernest Bramah: *Kai Lung unrolls his mat*, Richards Press: London. 1928 (also Penguin Books Ltd.)

The length of the time during which Man as a population can expect to live in relative comfort will depend on the extent to which the rates of fuel consumption, for all purposes, conform with the attitude of the other player, who 'never overlooks a mistake, or makes the smallest allowance for ignorance'.

The code of rules is not mine. These remarks are by way of dispassionate comment on the present degree of conformity with it; and giving some idea about what it might be found desirable to perform now, not *in*, but *for*, the future.

Sheer waste of natural gas

Where saving of fuel to buy an extension of time is most evidently possible is by stopping the waste of gas by 'flaring' the oil wells of the Middle East. This waste is regarded by oilmen as a normal concomitant of obtaining oil in certain countries remote from industrial centres able to use the gas. The waste serves no purpose, and is going on day and night. A little of the gas that would otherwise be wasted is being devoted to subsidiary local purposes such as distillation of sea water; and the magnitude of the waste is not widely known because the publicity given to those minor achievements is in the inverse ratio to their importance—the waste of gas being possibly about 95% of what is produced whereas nearly all the publicity has been given to engineering associated with the other fraction.

Export of liquefied methane from the Sahara is a welcome pointer to what can be done; but to conserve fuel by transport of gas over very long distances is customarily regarded as uneconomic. It is not necessarily the wicked capitalist who is to blame, since Governments of the oil-producing countries seem no less anxious to take short views by cashing-in money which can be obtained for their oil at whatever cost in irrecoverable burnt gas. Part of the remedy would be to pool production of oil and natural gas throughout the world. Economic ideas ruling at present seem to forbid anything so sensible. The burning-off of natural gas on an immense scale is a hurtful symptom of reliance on money-economics.

Costing in fuel terms

What would greatly contribute to Man's having a more prolonged relationship with fossil fuel than is at present in sight is a development of consciousness of costs in fuel— as an accompaniment to equally scrupulous regard to costs in money.

Those two things are not the same. There is already an acute consciousness about fuel costs in money terms. For example, it is an important part of the job of transport managers of large companies which operate many lorries, to reduce the costs per mile or per ton to the least possible; and that implies that the consumption of fuel by their firms is also kept to a minimum. Fuel economy of this sort (based on money costs in particular spheres) has a long history. It can be seen clearly in the increase in efficiency of marine boilers and engines throughout the coal age; substitution of oil for coal is a continuation of the same aspect. Also, there is little room for doubt that substitution of steam power by diesel power for railway traction has led to large savings in tonnage of fuel consumed per mile; perhaps to monetary savings on fuel as well.

However, instances like these represent fuel saved in particular narrow spheres. Taken as a whole in, say, national terms, they have not been accompanied by a lessening of total consumption of fuel. That has been constantly increasing: the saving of fuel in one department or a few sections having been exceeded by new consumption of fuel in related as well as unrelated departments of a nation's activity. Economies in fuel costs have been looked upon as money costs within particular undertakings and not as over-all prescience about drafts on fuel.

What has been gained on the swings has often been more than lost on the roundabouts. The net result has been to leave less fuel; and consequently to defer the grave problems which will be associated with a forced decline of population. A future generation will have to decide (supposing that the present generation does not make the decision) whether to cut down on amenity or population. That decision will have to be made not later than the time when the honeymoon with fuel is generally seen to be nearing its end.

The position is, and will remain, exactly comparable with that of a honeymoon couple not equipped with unbounded ordinary wealth. Any such couple will be aware that, though they choose deliberately to live extravagantly for a short while, they will someday have to settle down to the realities of everyday living within their means and to a managed economy in the literal sense of the word *economy*.

Fuel balance-sheets

These—costed in fuel terms—will be among the most desirable necessities. At present, almost no information is available; we are still in the stage of economics in which discounted cash flow and other less modern forms of money-costings are held to be decisive. Some information which could be biologically useful is kept as state secrets.

It can be expected that when fossil fuel threatens to be difficult to obtain, money costs will rise so greatly that fuel costs may, in some sectors, compel first attention; by then, it may be too late to avert the worst.

Actual shortage of fuel need not be imminent for a serious scare to be created. The analogy of ordinary financial credit will apply. A bank or other enterprise may be sound, judged by normal criteria; but to have its credit-worthiness put in question may be enough to start a run on it: the real crisis being of confidence.

Nevertheless, whereas additional resources may be brought in from outside to prop up a temporarily shaken financial condition (of a company or a nation), to counter an impending global shortage of fuel there are no outside resources. It therefore seems prudent to begin drawing up fuel balance-sheets, as a beginning of a practical form of insurance to ensure that a limited annuity of fuel can be drawn for as long as possible.

The most immediate contribution which enquiries on balance-sheet lines could make toward delaying the involution of population would be by establishing how far those methods of generating power which are found to be the most economical in fuel could be substituted for those which make heavy demands on fuel considered as raw material. As examples: supposing hydroelectricity and/or nuclear power were shown to be less expensive in total costs of combustible fuel than coal or oil for generating electricity, the product—which is simply energy—could be reserved for purely energy uses, like driving fixed machinery and heating of houses. The fuel saved would remain as raw material for producing substance—notably food and drugs.

There is no substitute for substance for production of other substance. At present, much substance is used for producing energy which might more economically (in fuel terms) be produced in ways involving smaller destruction of fuel.

The enquiries might extend to the comparative fuel costs of producing natural and synthetic fibres. At present there is little information about the fuel costs of wool and cotton produced by intensive methods of farming. Much vegetable and animal material (fibres and hides) employed in clothing the technically-advanced peoples is produced by people who live under almost subsistence conditions; therefore, an enquiry could have wide sociological implications.

Corresponding enquiries might be publicly made into the relative fuel costs of other alternatives and substitutes; *e.g.*, plastics *v.* metals.

An example in skeleton form

If there were any thought about giving serious attention to conservation of natural resources, the example of track costs of railway and road would be simple to work out, given the appropriate engineering data. Dealing only with track while leaving the form of traction out of account, and assuming (*a*) that a double-track railway would have a traffic capacity similar to that of a four-lane road; (*b*) that bridging and other accessory works are of similar magnitude for both:

If a steel rail weighs 110 pounds per yard (just over 50 kg. per metre) the weight of steel would be 440 pounds per yard; chairs and other metal fastenings might require an addition of 60%; a total of say, 700 lb. per yard (340 kg. per metre) of metal. The rest of the materials would be stones for the road-bed and timber for the sleepers; both would be renewable at a relatively small cost in fuel for procurement and transport.

The cost of stone and gravel for concrete for a highway would hardly be less than that of a railway road-bed. Would a main road be constructed more cheaply in terms of metals? Assuming a ferro-concrete road and concrete surfacing: would that involve less than 700 lb. of metal per yard, plus a large amount of fuel for cement and concrete? Not being an engineer, I can do no more than call attention to the problem. If we are seriously intending to prepare for the next couple of generations by looking to the future, these are the sorts of questions which need asking—and answering.

There is the matter of replacement values. The metal of the railway track suffers little annual loss by wear, but there will be some loss by corrosion. The metal of the road, being buried in concrete, suffers no such loss. Nearly all the rail metal can be remelted, with a small addition, every 20 years, say; but how recoverable is the metal and fuel used for building a road? If a concrete highway were to last 40 or 100 years before it had to be replaced, a road might be, per annum, cheaper in fuel costs than a railway; and, when built, might last for a couple of generations without incurring any further cost in fuel. On the other hand, the railway would require new sleepers every few years.

If the result of considerations like these were that a railway is the less demanding on capital resources, the effect of building fewer good roads and more good railways might be to approach or exceed the annual increment of timber growth; and that would have to be considered in conjunction with other demands on timber.

That example is an instance of what could be done by balancing income—as represented by renewable resources —against capital: of fuel.

A type of enquiry which suggests itself is the question whether it is more economical in fuel, for busy traffic routes over a relatively short distance, for passengers to be carried by aeroplane or surface transport. If we take the North Atlantic transit as an example, the question is whether it is better from the fuel point of view to undertake many fast journeys with small numbers of passengers in each flight lasting a few hours, or to have fewer journeys by ships carrying ten times the number of passengers on journeys lasting about ten times as long. Seen on conventional lines, it is a matter of rivalry between two forms of transport; and the time saved on the faster crossing will be stressed as a modern advantage. In fuel terms the advantage is not so obvious; where, then, does the advantage lie on the long view? A similar enquiry might be made into the relative fuel costs of aeroplane and train for journeys of several hundreds or thousands of miles in North America, within Britain, and across Europe.

The need for fuel accountancy

Several examples have been mentioned (pages 155, 199 et al.) of taking fuel for granted; that is, of disregarding fossil fuel entirely as a feature of sociological reckonings for the present and the future. Although engineers are among those who have daily concern with thermodynamics in designing machines, they are by no means free from assuming an infinite plenty of fuel with which to operate those machines.

An example and a contrast have been provided by C. R. Bennett, a specialist in the field of water desalination. He wrote (*Nature*, Vol. 213, 1967, 129-30): 'Not many people would be prepared to buy a solar distillation plant with a capacity of 100,000 gallons for $1 million when the same sized distillation plant [fuel-operated, understood] would cost nearer a fifth of this amount.'

Not only the running cost of the fuel, but its continuance, is taken for granted in that comparison. A solar distillation plant would incur an initial capital cost of fuel to make the metals or glass and plastics involved in its construction; but during its life it would demand little but renewable energy until its materials had to be renewed—probably some decades later. By that time of reappraisal, both the fuel- and the money-economics might have altered enough to make it a question whether a rebuilt solar distillation plant might not be the better buy in solid terms of investment—which is to say, deployment of scarce materials.

A humanitarian role for science

Whatever enquiry is undertaken, the balance sheets should be complete; that is to say, they should take account of all fuel costs, and not merely of the costs in fuel of energy needed for operating fixed and propulsive machinery. The code of rules is not esoteric: its basis is known to thousands of scientists in every technically-advanced country, and all that is lacking is the congruent information for measuring up against the code.

That some of the enquiries here suggested relate to questions about which data are hard to find must underline the need, in a scientific age, for establishing balances in fuel as well as in money. That some of the questions here outlined relate to transport is highly germane to food and population of the near future, for the reason that the extra fuel spent on the more fuel-expensive alternatives is making a contribution to little more than present convenience. It is possible that a difference in fuel costs, now being paid as a bonus for convenience, is something which could be saved for keeping people alive within a generation or two.

Such enquiries, conducted on a broad front into many aspects of exploitation of fuel in pursuing temporary technical 'progress', would be justified on humanitarian grounds.

An examination of the whole of society from a standpoint of cost-consciousness about renewable and irreplaceable resources is something to which the physical sciences might well address some of their effort.

Fossil fuel the main source of food

Whatever is done in the future cannot navigate outside the narrow channel set by the limitations of the remaining fossil fuel. That narrowing channel is bounded on the one side by the Scylla of depletion of fossil resources: on the other side by the Charybdis of making unreasonable, unregulated, demands on renewable resources of fuel.

That is true for purposes of machines and amenity considered by themselves; but any course of action that does not leave a prescient reserve of fuel, above and below ground, for production of food will be sacrificing population of the future (and it may be, a not very distant future) for machines of the present.

Since it is fossil fuel which is indicated as the prime source of food for keeping an increasing population above the level of numbers reached by the population of a hundred years ago, the alternatives reduce to two: namely

(i) maintaining a well-fed population at about the present level of numbers of all people, but not greatly exceeding that level;
     and

(ii) cutting down on use of machines requiring fossil fuel for their construction and operation.

Epilogue

There can be no second chance.
Man is the phoenix that can never rise again from the ashes of his predecessors' use of fossil fuel.

MORE QUOTATIONS

Naturam expellas furca, tamen usque recurret.
(Nature can be driven out with a fork, but she will always come back).—Horace, *Epistles*

De nihilo nihilum, in nihilum nil posse reverti.
(Nothing can come out of nothing, nothing can go back to nothing.)—Persius, 34-62 A.D.

Naturae enim non imperatur, nisi parendo.
(Nature cannot be commanded, except by obeying her).—Francis Bacon, 'Novum Organum'

I eat the air, promise-cramm'd. You cannot feed capons so.
—William Shakespeare, 'Hamlet', Act III, sc. ii

Let us all be happy, and live within our means, even if we have to borrer the money to do it with.—Artemus Ward, 'Science and Natural History'

In Nature there are neither rewards nor punishments—there are consequences.—Robert G. Ingersoll, 'Lectures and Essays'

> This is the way the world ends
> Not with a bang but a whimper.
> —T. S. Eliot, 'The Hollow Men'

There is a great technological explosion around us, generated by science. This explosion is already freeing vast numbers of people from their traditional bondage to Nature, and now at last we have it in our power to free mankind once and for all from the fear which is based on want.
—Sir Leon Bagrit, British Broadcasting Corporation Reith Lectures, 1964: 'I. The Age of Automation', *Listener*, 1964, Vol. 72, 743-6

The newspaper quotations which follow may be ephemeral and local: one refers to death and damage caused by the collapse of waste from a colliery, the other only to money economics; and both were written with only the United Kingdom in mind. It is coincidental to the theme of this book that one relates to a product of winning of fuel—

the other having been written about possible reform of the Parliament of the United Kingdom. Nevertheless, when read in the widest possible context and as apologues of what has been put forward in this book, the wording of these final quotations can stand; they harmonize strikingly with the quotations from very different sources given at the beginning.

The Aberfan tragedy is a reminder that there are large areas of Britain where the people still live with the legacy of neglect and shabby indifference to human needs left by the Industrial Revolution.—Editorial comment, *The Observer*, 23rd October, 1966

Britain's basic problem is a social problem of making existing knowledge available and of preparing the public for their involvement in economic policies.—Bernard Crick, Professor of Politics, University of Sheffield; same paper, same day

Index

For subjects (*e.g.*, protein, fuel, water, equilibrium) which form the warp and weft of the book the reader may be referred primarily to the Chapter headings in the Table of Contents, page *v;* only special aspects of general matters are here indexed by pages, along with some geographical entries, most books, and a complete list of authors and persons mentioned.

Bold figures indicate a whole Chapter. A bracket round a number signifies mention of the subject under another name.